Industrial and Applied Mathematics

Industrial and Applied Mathematics, a Scopus-indexed book series, publishes high-quality research-level monographs, lecture notes and contributed volumes focusing on areas where mathematics is used in a fundamental way, such as industrial mathematics, bio-mathematics, financial mathematics, applied statistics, operations research and computer science.

Santosh Kumar Upadhyay · Jay Singh Maurya

The Bessel Wavelet Transform

Springer

Santosh Kumar Upadhyay
Department of Mathematical Sciences
Indian Institute of Technology Varanasi
Varanasi, Uttar Pradesh, India

Jay Singh Maurya
Department of Mathematical Sciences
Indian Institute of Technology Varanasi
Varanasi, Uttar Pradesh, India

Chandigarh University
Unnao, Uttar Pradesh, India

ISSN 2364-6837 ISSN 2364-6845 (electronic)
Industrial and Applied Mathematics
ISBN 978-981-96-9937-7 ISBN 978-981-96-9938-4 (eBook)
https://doi.org/10.1007/978-981-96-9938-4

Mathematics Subject Classification: 46F12, 46F05, 46A30, 42C40, 65T60, 44A35, 45B05, 65R10, 47B38

This Springer imprint is published by the registered company Springer Nature Singapore Pte Ltd.
The registered company address is: 152 Beach Road, #21-01/04 Gateway East, Singapore 189721, Singapore

Preface

Wavelet transform has a considerable effect in the area of mathematical sciences and engineering and gives a brief description of time-frequency analysis. It is an efficient tool to analyze local as well as global information of a signal. Contents of this monograph include recent research works, most of which are not available in book form. The aforesaid book also contains the results of many other honourable researchers who have worked on the theory of Hankel transform and Bessel wavelet transform. This book will provide new dimensions in the theory and applications of the Bessel wavelet transform and will enrich the theory of the wavelet transform. This book is useful for graduate students, researchers in different fields, and other interested individuals in the areas of mathematics, physics, engineering, and applied sciences.

Throughout the book, the reader is assumed to have an understanding of the elements of analysis. Chapter 1 primarily covers the prerequisites for distribution theory and gives a brief idea about the Hankel transforms and its associated results.

Chapter 2 describes the continuous Bessel wavelet transformation and its inversion formula, and the Parseval relation using the theory of the Hankel convolution. A relation between the Bessel wavelet transformation and the Hankel-Hausdorff operator is established.

In Chap. 3, the Bessel wavelet transform on χ_μ and $\mathcal{Q}_\mu$ type spaces of exponential growth are investigated and their properties discussed by using the theory of the Hankel transform. Using this said theory, the integral equation of Fredholm type is defined and some examples associated with this integral equation are given.

In Chap. 4, the convolution product associated with the Bessel wavelet transformation is investigated. Certain norm inequalities for the convolution product are established.

In Chap. 5, the relation between Bessel wavelet convolution product and Hankel convolution product is discussed by using the Bessel wavelet transform and the Hankel transform. Approximation results of Bessel wavelet convolution product is investigated by exploiting the Hankel transformation tool. Motivated from the results of Pinsky [61], Heuristic treatment of Bessel wavelet transform is introduced and other properties of Bessel wavelet transform studied.

In Chap. 6, various properties and the sufficient condition for the integrability of the kernel of the inverse Bessel wavelet transform are obtained by using the theory of Hankel transform and Hankel convolution.

In Chap. 7, the continuous Bessel wavelet transform is extended to distributions in $H'_\mu(I)$ and obtained continuity results. Boundedness of continuous Bessel wavelet transform of distributions is investigated in a generalized Sobolev space.

In Chap. 8, the characterizations of the Besov and Triebel-Lizorkin type spaces are discussed by using the multiplier theorem.

In Chap. 9, the inversion formula of the continuous Bessel wavelet transform of distributions is investigated by exploiting the theory of the Hankel transform in $H'_\mu(I)$. Some auxiliary results related to the inversion formula are also obtained in this chapter. Using the theory of inversion formula of continuous Bessel wavelet transform of distributions, the Calderón reproducing formula is developed. The continuous Bessel wavelet transform of distributions through heat equation is discussed and its inversion formula is considered.

In Chap. 10, the inversion formula of the continuous Bessel wavelet transform of distributions in β'_μ-space and its associated results with the Bessel wavelet kernel containing non-vanishing moments of even orders weighted by $x^{\mu+\frac{1}{2}}$ are investigated by exploiting the theory of Hankel transform.

In Chap. 11, the inversion formula and the continuity of the continuous Bessel wavelet transform of distributions in $H'_{\mu,2}$ space are investigated. For the uniqueness of the inversion formula, the Bessel wavelet kernel of nonvanishing moments is considered.

Finally, the first author expresses gratitude to the Department of Mathematical Sciences, IIT (BHU) Varanasi, and SERB DST (MTR/2021/000266) for providing the facilities necessary to write this book. The authors also thank their coworkers—Ms. Sanchita Mal, Ms. Priyanka Balvant, Ms. Anusuiya Yadav, and Ms. Sonali Verma—for their invaluable support during the preparation of the entire book.

Varanasi, India
August 2022

Santosh Kumar Upadhyay
Jay Singh Maurya

Contents

Acronyms

$\mathbb{N}$	Set of natural numbers
$\mathbb{N}_0$	Set of nonnegative integers
I, $\mathbb{R}^+$	Open interval $(0, \infty)$
$\mathbb{R}$	Set of real numbers
$\mathbb{R}^n$	Usual Euclidean space of dimension n
$\mathbb{C}$	Set of complex numbers
$D(I)$	Set of all complex valued smooth function with compact support
$E(x)$ or $[x]$	Integer part of x
$\|x\|$	Norm of x
$D_x \equiv \frac{\partial}{\partial x}$	Partial derivative with respect to variable x
a.e.	Almost everywhere
R.H.S.	Right-hand side
L.H.S.	Left-hand side

Chapter 1
An Overview

1.1 Introduction

A Fourier transform is a mathematical technique that converts a function of time, $f(t)$, into a frequency function, $\hat{f}(\omega)$. The Fourier series is closely related to it. One of the main disadvantages of Fourier series is that they can only be applied to periodic signals. Several naturally occurring signals cannot be represented by Fourier series due to their non-periodicity or aperiodicity. Fourier developed a mathematical model to solve this problem called 'Fourier transform', which transforms signals from the time (or spatial) domain to the frequency domain. The Fourier transform is widely used in physics and engineering, for example in LTI systems, RADAR systems, astronomy, and signal processing.

Fourier transform gives only global information of the signal. To overcome this difficulty, wavelet transform was introduced. It was the theory of Fourier transform that led to the development of wavelet transform. As a result, wavelet transforms provide both local and global information about a signal at the same time. Fourier transformation encompasses the entire wavelet theory. Many authors have developed continuous and discrete wavelet transforms in various functional spaces and explored their properties. This theory is applicable in problems of image processing, signal processing, and other areas of mathematics and engineering.

The Hankel transformation played an important role to solve many problems of physics, engineering, and mathematical sciences. It is an useful and efficient tool for finding solution of cylindrical boundary value problem. Hermann Hankel (1839-1873) developed the Hankel transform and its kernel is a Bessel function of the first kind. The conventional Hankel transformation was introduced by Zemanian [1] and discussed its various properties on the Zemanian space H_μ. Zemanian [1–4], Koh [5, 6], Pathak et al. [7–10], Lee [11], Dube and Pandey [12] explored the theory of Hankel transform on various function spaces and characterized many results.

Hankel convolution is an important tool which is used to study many properties of function spaces and exploiting this theory many applications were done by many

S. K. Upadhyay and J. S. Maurya, *The Bessel Wavelet Transform*,
Industrial and Applied Mathematics,
https://doi.org/10.1007/978-981-96-9938-4_1

authors. Particularly, Betancor and others [13–24] had found many interesting results by utilizing the theory of the Hankel convolution and Hankel transform. In the present chapter, our main concerns are to study various properties of the Hankel transform and Hankel convolution on Zemanian space H_μ and its dual.

1.2 Fourier Transform

Suppose f is a Lebesgue integrable function on $\mathbb{R}$. Since e^{-ist} is continuous and bounded, the product $e^{-ist} f$ is locally integrable for any $s \in \mathbb{R}$. Also $|e^{-ist}| \leq 1$ for all s and t on $\mathbb{R}$. Consider the integral

$$\langle f, e^{ist} \rangle = \int_{-\infty}^{\infty} f(t) e^{-ist} dt, \ s \in \mathbb{R}. \tag{1.1}$$

Clearly,

$$\left| \int_{-\infty}^{\infty} f(t) e^{-ist} dt \right| \leq \int_{-\infty}^{\infty} |f(t)| dt = \|f\|_1 < \infty. \tag{1.2}$$

This means that the integral in (1.1) exists for all $s \in \mathbb{R}$. Thus, the Fourier transform is given as follows (Figs. 1.1 and 1.2):

Definition 1.1 Let $f \in L^1(\mathbb{R})$. The Fourier transform of $f(t)$ is denoted by $\hat{f}(s)$ and defined by

$$\hat{f}(s) = \mathscr{F}\{f(t)\} = \int_{-\infty}^{\infty} f(t) e^{-ist} dt, \ s \in \mathbb{R}. \tag{1.3}$$

Example 1.1
Let $f(x) = exp(-c^2x^2)$, then its Fourier transform is given by

$$\hat{f}(s) = \mathscr{F}\{exp(-c^2x^2)\} = \frac{\sqrt{\pi}}{c} exp\Big(- \frac{s^2}{4c^2}\Big), \ c > 0.$$

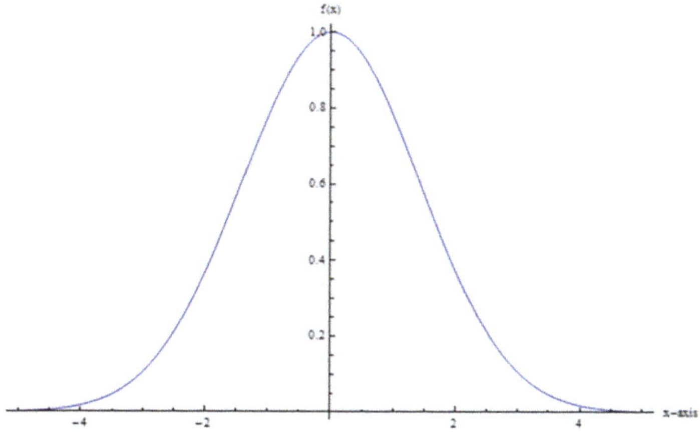

Fig. 1.1 $f(x)$ at $c = \frac{1}{2}$

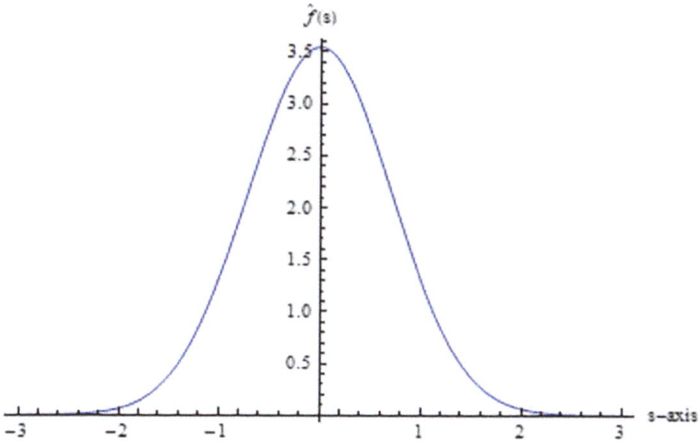

Fig. 1.2 $\hat{f}(s)$ at $c = \frac{1}{2}$

Example 1.2
Characteristic function is defined by

$$\chi_\tau(x) = \begin{cases} 1, & -\tau < x < \tau \\ 0, & \text{otherwise.} \end{cases} \tag{1.4}$$

This function is often called a rectangular pulse or gate function. Its Fourier transform is

$$\hat{\chi}_\tau(s) = \left(\frac{2}{s}\right) sin(s\tau). \tag{1.5}$$

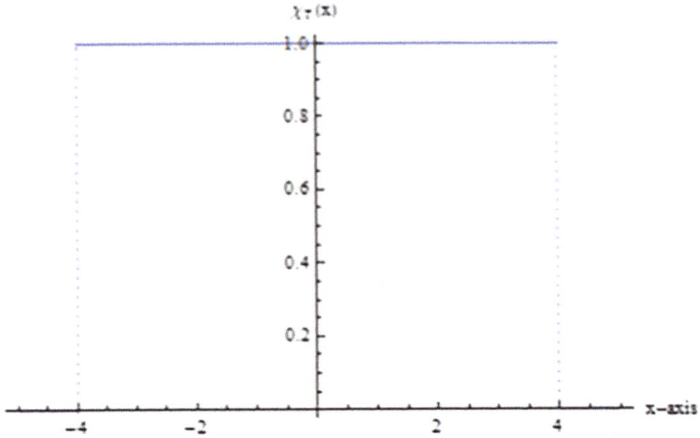

Fig. 1.3 $\chi_\tau(x)$ for $\tau = 4$

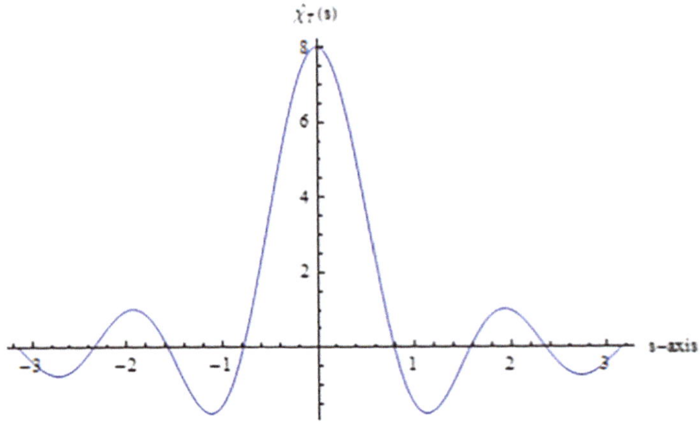

Fig. 1.4 $\hat{\chi}_\tau(s)$ for $\tau = 4$

Remarks:

- It is important to note that the constant function c, $sin(s_0 t)$, and $cos(s_0 t)$, do not belong to $L^1(\mathbb{R})$ and hence they do not have Fourier transforms. However, when these functions are multiplied by the characteristic function $\chi_\tau(t)$, the resulting functions belong to $L^1(\mathbb{R})$ and have Fourier transforms.
- In general, the Fourier transform $\hat{f}(s)$ is a complex function of a real variable s. From a physical point of view, the polar representation of the Fourier transform is often convenient. The Fourier transform $\hat{f}(s)$ can be expressed in the polar form

$$\hat{f}(s) = R(s) + iX(s) = A(s)exp\{i\theta(s)\}, \tag{1.6}$$

where $A(s) = |\hat{f}(s)|$ is called the amplitude spectrum of the signal $f(t)$, and $\theta(s) = arg\{\hat{f}(s)\}$ is called the phase spectrum of $f(t)$.

The nature of $A(s)$ can be explained by using Example 1.2 which shows $A(s) = |\hat{\chi_\tau}(s)| \leq \frac{2}{s}$. This means that the amplitude spectrum is very low at high frequencies when τ is very large, $A(s) = \frac{2}{s} sin(s\tau)$ is very high at low frequencies (Figs. 1.3 and 1.4).

Basic Properties of Fourier Transforms

Theorem 1.1 (Linearity) *If $f(t), g(t) \in L^1(\mathbb{R})$ and α, β are any two complex constants, then*

$$\mathscr{F}\{\alpha f(t) + \beta g(t)\} = \alpha \mathscr{F}\{f(t)\} + \beta \mathscr{F}\{g(t)\}. \tag{1.7}$$

Proof From (1.3), we have

$$\begin{aligned} \mathscr{F}\{\alpha f(t) + \beta g(t)\} &= \int_{-\infty}^{\infty} \{\alpha f(t) + \beta g(t)\} e^{-ist} dt \\ &= \int_{-\infty}^{\infty} \{\alpha f(t) e^{-ist} + \beta g(t) e^{-ist}\} dt. \end{aligned}$$

By the linearity property of integration, we can write

$$\begin{aligned} \mathscr{F}\{\alpha f(t) + \beta g(t)\} &= \alpha \int_{-\infty}^{\infty} f(t) e^{-ist} dt + \beta \int_{-\infty}^{\infty} g(t) e^{-ist} dt \\ &= \alpha \mathscr{F}\{f(t)\} + \beta \mathscr{F}\{g(t)\}. \end{aligned}$$

Note: For $a, b, c \in \mathbb{R}$ and $c \neq 0$, the translation, modulation, and dilation operators are defined by

$$\begin{aligned} T_a f(x) &= f(x-a) \quad \text{(Translation)}, \\ M_b f(x) &= e^{ibx} f(x) \quad \text{(Modulation)}, \\ D_c f(x) &= \frac{1}{\sqrt{|c|}} f\left(\frac{x}{c}\right) \quad \text{(Dilation)}. \end{aligned}$$

Theorem 1.2 *If $f(x) \in L^1(\mathbb{R})$, then the following results hold:*

(a) **(Shifting)**

$$\mathscr{F}\{T_a f(x)\} = M_{(-a)} \hat{f}(s). \tag{1.8}$$

Proof Using the definition of translation and (1.3), for $s \in \mathbb{R}$ we find

$$\mathscr{F}\{T_a f(x)\} = \int_{-\infty}^{\infty} (T_a f(x)) e^{-isx} dx = \int_{-\infty}^{\infty} f(x-a) e^{-isx} dx.$$

On substituting $x - a = t$, we get

$$\begin{aligned}\mathscr{F}\{T_a f(x)\} &= \int_{-\infty}^{\infty} f(t) e^{-is(t+a)} dt \\ &= e^{-ias} \int_{-\infty}^{\infty} f(t) e^{-ist} dt = e^{-ias} \hat{f}(s) = M_{(-a)} \hat{f}(s).\end{aligned}$$

□

(b) ***(Scaling)***

$$\mathscr{F}\{D_{\frac{1}{a}} f(x)\} = Sgn(a)\ D_a \hat{f}(s), \tag{1.9}$$

where $Sgn(a)$ is a signum function.

Proof Applying the definition of dilation and (1.3), for $a \neq 0,\ s \in \mathbb{R}$ we obtain

$$\mathscr{F}\{D_{\frac{1}{a}} f(x)\} = \int_{-\infty}^{\infty} \big(D_{\frac{1}{a}} f(x)\big) e^{-isx} dx = \int_{-\infty}^{\infty} \sqrt{|a|} f(ax) e^{-isx} dx.$$

On substituting $ax = t$, yields

$$\begin{aligned}\mathscr{F}\{D_{\frac{1}{a}} f(x)\} &= \sqrt{|a|} \int_{-\infty}^{\infty} f(t) e^{-is\frac{t}{a}} \frac{dt}{a} \\ &= \frac{Sgn(a)}{\sqrt{|a|}} \int_{-\infty}^{\infty} f(t) e^{-i\frac{s}{a}t} dt = \frac{Sgn(a)}{\sqrt{|a|}} \hat{f}\Big(\frac{s}{a}\Big) = Sgn(a)\ D_a \hat{f}(s).\end{aligned}$$

□

(c) ***(Conjugation)***

$$\mathscr{F}\{\overline{D_{-1} f(x)}\} = \overline{\hat{f}(s)}. \tag{1.10}$$

Proof From the definition of dilation and (1.3), $s \in \mathbb{R}$ we obtain

$$\mathscr{F}\{\overline{D_{-1} f(x)}\} = \int_{-\infty}^{\infty} (\overline{D_{-1} f(x)}) e^{-isx} dx = \int_{-\infty}^{\infty} \overline{\frac{1}{\sqrt{|(-1)|}} f\Big(\frac{x}{(-1)}\Big)} e^{-isx} dx$$

On substituting $-x = t$, yields

$$\begin{aligned}\mathscr{F}\{D_{-1}f(x)\} &= \int_{-\infty}^{\infty} \overline{f(t)}e^{ist}dt \\ &= \overline{\int_{-\infty}^{\infty} f(t)e^{-ist}dt} = \overline{\hat{f}(s)}.\end{aligned}$$

(d) ***(Modulation)***

$$\mathscr{F}\{M_a f(t)\} = T_a \hat{f}(s). \tag{1.11}$$

Proof By the definition of modulation and 1.3, for $s \in \mathbb{R}$ we write

$$\begin{aligned}\mathscr{F}\{M_a f(x)\} &= \int_{-\infty}^{\infty} (M_a f(x))e^{-isx}dx \\ &= \int_{-\infty}^{\infty} e^{iax} f(x)e^{-isx}dx \\ &= \int_{-\infty}^{\infty} f(x)e^{-i(s-a)x}dx \\ &= \hat{f}(s-a) = T_a \hat{f}(s).\end{aligned}$$

Theorem 1.3 **(Continuity)** *If $f(t) \in L^1(\mathbb{R})$, then $\hat{f}(s)$ is continuous on $\mathbb{R}$.*

Proof For any $s, h \in \mathbb{R}$, we have

$$\begin{aligned}|\hat{f}(s+h) - \hat{f}(s)| &= \left| \int_{-\infty}^{\infty} e^{-ist}(e^{-iht} - 1) f(t)dt \right| \\ &\leq \int_{-\infty}^{\infty} |(e^{-iht} - 1)||f(t)|dt.\end{aligned} \tag{1.12}$$

Since

$$|(e^{-iht} - 1)||f(t)| \leq 2|f(t)| \text{ and } \lim_{h\to 0} |(e^{-iht} - 1)| = 0 \tag{1.13}$$

for all $t \in \mathbb{R}$, we conclude that as $h \to 0$

$$|\hat{f}(s+h) - \hat{f}(s)|, \tag{1.14}$$

is independent of s. Then by the Lebesgue dominated convergence theorem $\hat{f}(s)$ is continuous in $\mathbb{R}$. Since (1.12) is independent of s; $\hat{f}(s)$ is, in fact, uniformly continuous on $\mathbb{R}$. □

Theorem 1.4 (Derivatives of Fourier Transforms) *If both $f(t)$ and $tf(t)$ belong to $L^1(\mathbb{R})$, then $\frac{d}{ds}\hat{f}(s)$ exists and is given by*

$$\frac{d}{ds}\hat{f}(s) = (-i)\mathscr{F}\{tf(t)\}. \tag{1.15}$$

Proof We have

$$\begin{aligned}\frac{d\hat{f}(s)}{ds} &= \lim_{h\to 0}\frac{1}{h}\left[\hat{f}(s+h) - \hat{f}(s)\right]\\ &= \lim_{h\to 0}\left[\int_{-\infty}^{\infty} e^{-ist} f(t)\Big(\frac{e^{-iht}-1}{h}\Big)dt\right].\end{aligned} \tag{1.16}$$

Note that

$$\left|\frac{e^{-iht}-1}{h}\right| = \frac{1}{|h|}\left|e^{-\frac{iht}{2}}(e^{\frac{iht}{2}} - e^{-\frac{iht}{2}})\right| = 2\left|\frac{sin(ht/2)}{h}\right| \leq |t|.$$

Also,

$$\lim_{h\to 0}\left(\frac{e^{-iht}-1}{h}\right) = -it.$$

Thus result (1.16) becomes

$$\begin{aligned}\frac{d\hat{f}(s)}{ds} &= \int_{-\infty}^{\infty} e^{-ist} f(t)\lim_{h\to 0}\left(\frac{e^{-iht}-1}{h}\right)dt\\ &= (-i)\int_{-\infty}^{\infty} tf(t)e^{-ist}dt\\ &= (-i)\mathscr{F}\{tf(t)\}.\end{aligned}$$

Corollary 1.1 (The nth Derivative of $\hat{f}(s)$) *If $f \in L^1(\mathbb{R})$ and $t^n f(t) \in L^1(\mathbb{R})$ for finite $n \in \mathbb{N}$, then the nth derivative of $\hat{f}(s)$ exists and is given by*

$$\frac{d^n}{ds^n}\hat{f}(s) = (-i)^n\mathscr{F}\{t^n f(t)\}. \tag{1.17}$$

Proof From Theorem 1.4 and the mathematical induction principle, (1.17) can be proved. Setting $s = 0$, we can find

$$\left[\frac{d^n}{ds^n}\hat{f}(s)\right]_{s=0} = (-i)^n\int_{-\infty}^{\infty} t^n f(t)dt = (-i)^n m_n, \tag{1.18}$$

where m_n represents the nth moment of $f(t)$. Thus, the moments $m_1, m_2, m_3, \ldots, m_n$ can be calculated from (1.18). □

Theorem 1.5 (The Riemann-Lebesgue Lemma) *If* $f \in L^1(\mathbb{R})$, *then*

$$\lim_{|s|\to\infty} |\hat{f}(s)| = 0. \tag{1.19}$$

Proof Since $e^{-ist} = -exp\{-is(t+\frac{\pi}{s})\}$, we have

$$\begin{aligned}\hat{f}(s) &= -\int_{-\infty}^{\infty} exp\{-is(t+\frac{\pi}{s})\}\, f(t)dt\\ &= -\int_{-\infty}^{\infty} e^{-isx} f(x-\frac{\pi}{s})dx.\end{aligned}$$

Thus,

$$\begin{aligned}\hat{f}(s) &= \frac{1}{2}\Big[\int_{-\infty}^{\infty} e^{-ist} f(t)dt - \int_{-\infty}^{\infty} e^{-ist} f(t-\frac{\pi}{s})dt\Big]\\ &= \frac{1}{2}\int_{-\infty}^{\infty} e^{-ist}\Big[f(t) - f(t-\frac{\pi}{s})\Big]dt.\end{aligned}$$

Clearly,

$$\lim_{|s|\to\infty} |\hat{f}(s)| \le \frac{1}{2}\lim_{|s|\to\infty}\int_{-\infty}^{\infty}\Big[f(t) - f(t-\frac{\pi}{s})\Big]dt = 0.$$

Theorem 1.6 *(a) If* $f(t)$ *is a continuously differentiable function,* $\lim_{|t|\to\infty} f(t) = 0$ *and both* $f,\ f' \in L^1(\mathbb{R})$, *then*

$$\mathscr{F}\{f'(t)\} = (is)\mathscr{F}\{f(t)\} = (is)\hat{f}(s). \tag{1.20}$$

(b) If $f(t)$ *is continuously n-times differentiable,* $f, f', \ldots, f^{(n)} \in L^1(\mathbb{R})$ *and*

$$\lim_{|t|\to\infty} f^{(r)}(t) = 0 \quad for\ r = 1, 2, \ldots, n-1, \tag{1.21}$$

then

$$\mathscr{F}\{f^{(n)}(t)\} = (is)^n\mathscr{F}\{f(t)\} = (is)^n\hat{f}(s). \tag{1.22}$$

Proof By definition of the Fourier transform, we get

$$\mathscr{F}\{f'(t)\} = \int_{-\infty}^{\infty} e^{-ist} f'(t)dt.$$

Integrating by parts, above yields

$$\begin{aligned}\mathscr{F}\{f'(t)\} &= \left[e^{-ist}\right]_{-\infty}^{\infty} + (is)\int_{-\infty}^{\infty} e^{-ist} f(t)dt \\ &= (is)\hat{f}(s).\end{aligned}$$

Definition 1.2 (Inverse Fourier Transform) If $f \in L^1(\mathbb{R})$ and its Fourier transform $\hat{f} \in L^1(\mathbb{R})$, then the inverse Fourier transform of $\hat{f}(s)$ is defined by

$$f(t) = \mathscr{F}^{-1}\{\hat{f}(s)\} = \frac{1}{2\pi}\int_{-\infty}^{\infty} e^{ist}\hat{f}(s)ds \tag{1.23}$$

for almost every $t \in \mathbb{R}$. If f is continuous, then (1.23) holds for every t. In general, f can be reconstructed from $\hat{f}$ at each point $t \in \mathbb{R}$, where f is continuous.

Using the polar form (1.6) of the Fourier spectrum $\hat{f}(s)$, the function (or signal) $f(t)$ is defined by

$$f(t) = \frac{1}{2\pi}\int_{-\infty}^{\infty} A(s)exp[i\{st + \theta(s)\}]ds, \tag{1.24}$$

where $A(s)$ is the amplitude spectrum and $\theta(s)$ is the phase spectrum of the signal $f(t)$.

This integral shows that the signal $f(t)$ is represented as a superposition of the infinite number of sinusoidal oscillations of infinitesimal amplitude $A(s)$ and of phase $\theta(s)$.

Physically, (1.23) implies that any signal $f(t)$ can be regarded as a superposition of an infinite number of sinusoidal oscillations with different frequencies $s = 2\pi\nu$ so that

$$f(t) = \frac{1}{2\pi}\int_{-\infty}^{\infty} e^{2\pi i\nu t}\hat{f}(s)ds. \tag{1.25}$$

Equation (1.23) or (1.25) is called the **spectral resolution** of the signal f, and $\hat{f}$ is called the **spectral density** represented by

$$\hat{f}(s) = \frac{1}{2\pi}\int_{\infty}^{\infty} e^{2\pi i\nu t} f(t)dt. \tag{1.26}$$

Definition 1.3 The convolution of two functions $f, g \in L^1(\mathbb{R})$ is defined by

$$(f * g)(t) = \int_{-\infty}^{\infty} f(t-\tau)g(\tau)d\tau. \tag{1.27}$$

Theorem 1.7 (Convolution Theorem) *If $f, g \in L^1(\mathbb{R})$, then*

$$\mathscr{F}\{(f * g)(t)\} = \mathscr{F}\{f(t)\}\mathscr{F}\{g(t)\} = \hat{f}(s)\hat{g}(s). \tag{1.28}$$

Or, equivalently

$$\int_{-\infty}^{\infty} f(t-\tau)g(\tau)d\tau = \frac{1}{2\pi}\int_{-\infty}^{\infty} e^{ist}\hat{f}(s)\hat{g}(s)ds. \tag{1.29}$$

Proof Since $f * g \in L^1(\mathbb{R})$, applying the definition of the Fourier transform, we get

$$\begin{aligned}
\mathscr{F}\{(f * g)(t)\} &= \int_{-\infty}^{\infty} e^{-ist}dt \int_{-\infty}^{\infty} f(t-\tau)g(\tau)d\tau \\
&= \int_{-\infty}^{\infty} g(\tau)\int_{-\infty}^{\infty} e^{-ist}f(t-\tau)dtd\tau \\
&= \int_{-\infty}^{\infty} e^{-is\tau}g(\tau)d\tau \int_{-\infty}^{\infty} e^{-isu}f(u)du, \ (t-\tau=u) \\
&= \hat{f}(s)\hat{g}(s),
\end{aligned}$$

after utilizing Fubini's theorem. □

Theorem 1.8 (General Modulation) *If $\mathscr{F}\{f(t)\} = \hat{f}(s)$ and $\mathscr{F}\{g(t)\} = \hat{g}(s)$, where $\hat{f}$ and $\hat{g}$ belong to $L^1(\mathbb{R})$, then*

$$\mathscr{F}\{f(t)g(t)\} = \frac{1}{2\pi}(\hat{f} * \hat{g})(s). \tag{1.30}$$

Or, equivalently

$$\int_{-\infty}^{\infty} e^{-ist}f(t)g(t)dt = \frac{1}{2\pi}\int_{-\infty}^{\infty} \hat{f}(x)\hat{g}(s-x)dx. \tag{1.31}$$

Proof Using (1.23), the L.H.S of (1.30) is

$$\begin{aligned}
\mathscr{F}\{f(t)g(t)\} &= \int_{-\infty}^{\infty} e^{-ist}f(t)g(t)dt \\
&= \frac{1}{2\pi}\int_{-\infty}^{\infty} e^{-ist}g(t)dt \int_{-\infty}^{\infty} e^{ixt}\hat{f}(x)dx \\
&= \frac{1}{2\pi}\int_{-\infty}^{\infty} \hat{f}(x)dx \int_{-\infty}^{\infty} e^{-it(s-x)}g(t)dt \\
&= \frac{1}{2\pi}\int_{-\infty}^{\infty} \hat{f}(x)\hat{g}(s-x)dx \\
&= (\hat{f} * \hat{g})(s).
\end{aligned}$$

Definition 1.4 We denote the norm in $L^2(\mathbb{R})$ by $\|.\|_2$ and this norm is defined by

$$\|f\|_2 = \left(\int_{-\infty}^{\infty} |f(t)|^2 dt\right)^{\frac{1}{2}}, \tag{1.32}$$

where $f \in L^2(\mathbb{R})$.

Definition 1.5 (Fourier Transform in $L^2(\mathbb{R})$) If $f \in L^2(\mathbb{R})$ and $\{\phi_n\}$ is a sequence of continuous functions with compact support convergent to f in $L^2(\mathbb{R})$, that is, $\|f - \phi_n\|_2 \to 0$ as $n \to \infty$, then the Fourier transform of f is defined by

$$\hat{f} = \lim_{n\to\infty} \hat{\phi_n}, \tag{1.33}$$

where the limit is taken with respect to the norm in $L^2(\mathbb{R})$.

It is important to note that the convergence in $L^2(\mathbb{R})$ does not imply pointwise convergence, and therefore the Fourier transform of a square integrable function is not defined at a point, unlike the Fourier transform of an integrable function.

Theorem 1.9 (Parseval's Relation)
If $f \in L^2(\mathbb{R})$, then

$$\|f\|_2 = \|\hat{f}\|_2. \tag{1.34}$$

In physical problems, the quantity $\|f\|_2$ is a measure of energy, and $\|\hat{f}\|_2$ represents the power spectrum of a signal f. More precisely, the total energy of a signal (or waveform) is defined by

$$E = \|f\|_2^2 = \int_{-\infty}^{\infty} |f(t)|^2 dt. \tag{1.35}$$

Theorem 1.10 *If $f \in L^2(\mathbb{R})$, then*

$$\hat{f}(s) = \lim_{n\to\infty} \frac{1}{\sqrt{2\pi}} \int_{-n}^{n} e^{-ist} f(t)dt, \tag{1.36}$$

where the convergence is with respect to the L^2-norm.

Proof For $n = 1, 2, 3, \ldots$ we define

$$f_n(t) = \begin{cases} f(t), & for\ |t| < n \\ 0, & for\ |t| \geq n. \end{cases} \tag{1.37}$$

Clearly, $\|f - f_n\|_2 \to 0$ and hence, $\|\hat{f} - \hat{f_n}\|_2 \to 0$ as $n \to \infty$. □

Theorem 1.11 *If $f, g \in L^2(\mathbb{R})$, then*

$$\langle f, \overline{\hat{g}} \rangle = \int_{-\infty}^{\infty} f(t)\hat{g}(t)dt = \int_{-\infty}^{\infty} \hat{f}(t)g(t)dt = \langle \hat{f}, \overline{g} \rangle. \tag{1.38}$$

Proof From (1.37), we define both $f_n(t)$ and $g_n(t)$ for $n = 1, 2, 3, \ldots$. Since

$$\hat{f}_m(t) = \frac{1}{\sqrt{2\pi}} \int_{-\infty}^{\infty} e^{-ixt} f_m(x)dx,$$

we obtain

$$\int_{-\infty}^{\infty} \hat{f}_m(t)g_n(t)dt = \frac{1}{\sqrt{2\pi}} \int_{-\infty}^{\infty} g_n(t) \int_{-\infty}^{\infty} e^{-ixt} f_m(x)dxdt. \tag{1.39}$$

The function $e^{-ixt}g_n(t)f_m(x)$ is integrable over $\mathbb{R}^2$, and hence by Fubini Theorem, (1.39) can be written in the following form:

$$\begin{aligned}\int_{-\infty}^{\infty} \hat{f}_m(t)g_n(t)dt &= \frac{1}{\sqrt{2\pi}} \int_{-\infty}^{\infty} f_m(x) \int_{-\infty}^{\infty} e^{-ixt} g_n(t)dtdx \\ &= \int_{-\infty}^{\infty} f_m(x)\hat{g}_n(x)dx.\end{aligned}$$

Since $\|g - g_n\| \to 0$ and $\|\hat{g} - \hat{g}_n\| \to 0$, as $n \to \infty$ with the continuity of the inner product yields

$$\int_{-\infty}^{\infty} \hat{f}_m(t)g_n(t)dt = \int_{-\infty}^{\infty} f_m(t)\hat{g}_n(t)dt.$$

Similarly, letting $m \to \infty$ gives the desired result (1.38). □

Lemma 1.1 *If $f \in L^2(\mathbb{R})$ and $g = \overline{\hat{f}}$, then $f = \overline{\hat{g}}$.*

Proof From Theorems 1.9 and 1.11 and $g = \overline{\hat{f}}$, we can find

$$\langle f, \overline{\hat{g}} \rangle = \langle \hat{f}, \overline{g} \rangle = \langle \hat{f}, \hat{f} \rangle = \|\hat{f}\|_2^2 = \|f\|_2^2. \tag{1.40}$$

Also, we have

$$\overline{\langle f, \overline{\hat{g}} \rangle} = \overline{\langle \hat{f}, \hat{f} \rangle} = \|f\|_2^2. \tag{1.41}$$

Finally, by Parseval's relation we have

$$\|\hat{g}\|_2^2 = \|g\|_2^2 = \|\hat{f}\|_2^2 = \|f\|_2^2. \tag{1.42}$$

Using (1.40)-(1.42 gives the following

$$\|f-\overline{\hat{g}}\|_2^2=\langle f-\overline{\hat{g}}, f-\overline{\hat{g}}\rangle=\|\hat{f}\|_2^2-\langle f,\overline{\hat{g}}\rangle-\overline{\langle f,\overline{\hat{g}}\rangle}+\|\hat{g}\|_2^2=0.$$

This implies that

$$f=\overline{\hat{g}}. \tag{1.43}$$

Theorem 1.12 (Inversion of Fourier Transforms in) $L^2(\mathbb{R})$ *If* $f \in L^2(\mathbb{R})$, *then*

$$f(t)=\lim_{n\to\infty}\frac{1}{2\pi}\int_{-n}^{n} e^{ist}\hat{f}(s)ds, \tag{1.44}$$

where the convergence is with respect to the $L^2(\mathbb{R})$*-norm.*

Proof If $f \in L^2(\mathbb{R})$, and $g=\overline{\hat{f}}$, then, by Lemma 1.1

$$\begin{aligned} f=\overline{\hat{g}} &= \lim_{n\to\infty}\frac{1}{2\pi}\overline{\int_{-n}^{n} e^{-ist}g(s)ds} \\ &= \lim_{n\to\infty}\frac{1}{2\pi}\int_{-n}^{n}\overline{e^{-ist}g(s)}ds \\ &= \lim_{n\to\infty}\frac{1}{2\pi}\int_{-n}^{n} e^{ist}\overline{g(s)}ds \\ &= \lim_{n\to\infty}\frac{1}{2\pi}\int_{-n}^{n} e^{ist}\hat{f}(s)ds. \end{aligned}$$

Corollary 1.2 *If* $f \in L^1(\mathbb{R}) \cap L^2(\mathbb{R})$, *then the following formula*

$$f(t)=\lim_{n\to\infty}\frac{1}{2\pi}\int_{-n}^{n} e^{ist}\hat{f}(s)ds, \tag{1.45}$$

holds almost everywhere in $\mathbb{R}$.

Theorem 1.13 (General Parseval's Relation) *If* $f, g \in L^2(\mathbb{R})$, *then*

$$\langle f, g\rangle=\int_{-\infty}^{\infty} f(x)\overline{g(x)}dx=\int_{-\infty}^{\infty}\hat{f}(s)\overline{\hat{g}(s)}ds=\langle\hat{f},\hat{g}\rangle. \tag{1.46}$$

Proof It follows from (1.40) that

$$\|f+tg\|_2^2=\|\hat{f}+t\hat{g}\|_2^2,\quad t\in\mathbb{C}.$$

Or, equivalently,

$$\int_{-\infty}^{\infty} |f + tg|^2 dx = \int_{-\infty}^{\infty} |\hat{f} + t\hat{g}|^2 ds,$$
$$\int_{-\infty}^{\infty} (f + tg)(\bar{f} + \overline{tg}) dx = \int_{-\infty}^{\infty} (\hat{f} + t\hat{g})(\overline{\hat{f}} + \overline{t\hat{g}}) ds.$$

Simplifying both sides gives

$$\int_{-\infty}^{\infty} |f|^2 dx + \int_{-\infty}^{\infty} \{\bar{t}(f\bar{g}) + t(g\bar{f})\} dx + \int_{-\infty}^{\infty} |t|^2 |g|^2 dx$$
$$= \int_{-\infty}^{\infty} |\hat{f}|^2 ds + \int_{-\infty}^{\infty} \{\bar{t}(\hat{f}\overline{\hat{g}}) + t(\hat{g}\overline{\hat{f}})\} ds + \int_{-\infty}^{\infty} |t|^2 |\hat{g}|^2 ds.$$

On comparing the powers of t, we get

$$\int_{-\infty}^{\infty} f(x)\overline{g(x)} dx = \int_{-\infty}^{\infty} \hat{f}(s)\overline{\hat{g}(s)} ds. \tag{1.47}$$

Theorem 1.14 (Plancherel's Theorem) *For every $f \in L^2(\mathbb{R})$, there exists $\hat{f} \in L^2(\mathbb{R})$ such that*

(i) *If $f \in L^1(\mathbb{R}) \cap L^2(\mathbb{R})$, then $\hat{f}(s) = \frac{1}{\sqrt{2\pi}} \int_{-\infty}^{\infty} e^{-ist} f(t) dt$.*

(ii) $\left\| \hat{f}(s) - \frac{1}{\sqrt{2\pi}} \int_{-n}^{n} e^{-ist} f(t) dt \right\|_2 \to 0$ *as* $n \to \infty$, *and* $\left\| f(t) - \frac{1}{\sqrt{2\pi}} \int_{-n}^{n} e^{ist} \hat{f}(s) ds \right\|_2 \to 0$ *as* $n \to \infty$.

(iii) $\langle f, g \rangle = \langle \hat{f}, \hat{g} \rangle$.

(iv) $\| f \|_2 = \| \hat{f} \|_2$.

(v) *The mapping $f \to \hat{f}$ is a Hilbert space isomorphism of $L^2(\mathbb{R})$ onto $L^2(\mathbb{R})$.*

Theorem 1.15 *The Fourier transform is a unitary operator on $L^2(\mathbb{R})$.*

Proof We first observe that

$$\hat{\bar{g}}(s) = \frac{1}{\sqrt{2\pi}} \int_{-\infty}^{\infty} e^{-ist} \overline{g(t)} dt = \overline{\frac{1}{\sqrt{2\pi}} \int_{-\infty}^{\infty} e^{-ist} g(t) dt} = \overline{\mathscr{F}^{-1}\{g(t)\}(s)}.$$

Using Theorem 1.19, we obtain

$$\langle \mathscr{F}\{f(t)\}, g \rangle = \frac{1}{\sqrt{2\pi}} \int_{-\infty}^{\infty} \hat{f}(s)\overline{g(s)} ds = \frac{1}{\sqrt{2\pi}} \int_{-\infty}^{\infty} f(s)\hat{\bar{g}}(s) ds$$
$$= \frac{1}{\sqrt{2\pi}} \int_{-\infty}^{\infty} f(s)\overline{\mathscr{F}^{-1}\{g(t)\}(s)} ds = \langle f, \mathscr{F}^{-1} g \rangle.$$

This implies that $\mathscr{F}^{-1} = \mathscr{F}$, and hence the Fourier transform operator is unitary. □

Theorem 1.16 (Duality) *If* $\hat{f}(s) = \mathscr{F}\{f(t)\}$, *then*

$$\mathscr{F}\{\hat{f}(s)\} = f(-s). \tag{1.48}$$

Proof By definition Fourier transform, we have

$$\begin{aligned}\mathscr{F}\{\hat{f}(s)\} &= \frac{1}{\sqrt{2\pi}}\int_{-\infty}^{\infty} e^{-ist}\hat{f}(s)ds \\ &= \frac{1}{\sqrt{2\pi}}\int_{-\infty}^{\infty} e^{-ist}\hat{f}(t)dt \\ &= f(-s),\end{aligned}$$

by the inversion formula of Fourier transform. □

1.3 Wavelet Transforms

Wavelet transform is an efficient and effective time-frequency representation algorithm. Based on the idea of wavelets as a family of functions constructed from translation and dilation of a single function ψ, called the mother wavelet (or affine coherent states), we define wavelets by

$$\psi_{a,b}(t) = \frac{1}{\sqrt{|a|}}\psi\left(\frac{t-b}{a}\right), \; a, b \in \mathbb{R}, \; a \neq 0, \tag{1.49}$$

where a is called a scaling parameter which measures the degree of compression or scale, and b is a translation parameter which determines the time location of the wavelet. If $|a| < 1$, the wavelet (1.49) is the compressed version (smaller support in time-domain) of the mother wavelet and corresponds mainly to higher frequencies. Thus, wavelets have time-widths adapted to their frequencies. It may be noted that the resolution of wavelets at different scales varies in the time and frequency domains as governed by the Heisenberg uncertainty principle. At large scale, the solution is coarse in the time domain and fine in the frequency domain. On the other hand, as the scale a decreases, the resolution in the time domain decreases (the time resolution becomes finer), while that in the frequency domain increases (the frequency resolution becomes coarser). Different values of the parameter b represent the time localization center, and each $\psi_{a,b}(t)$ is localized around the center $t = b$. As scale parameter a varies, wavelet $\psi_{a,b}(t)$ covers different frequency ranges. Small values of $|a|(0 < |a| \ll 1)$ result in very narrow windows and correspond to high frequencies or very fine scales $\psi_{a,b}$, whereas very large values of $|a|(|a| \gg 1)$ result in very wide windows and correspond to small frequencies or very coarse scales $\psi_{a,b}(t)$. The wavelet transform gives a time-frequency description of a signal f.

The continuous wavelet transform is similar to the Fourier transform in the sense that it is based on a single function ψ and this function is scaled. But, unlike the Fourier transform, we also shift the function, thus generating a two-parameter family of functions $\psi_{a,b}(t)$ defined by (1.49).

We next give formal definitions of a wavelet and a continuous wavelet transform of a function.

Definition 1.6 (Wavelet) A wavelet is a function $\psi \in L^2(\mathbb{R})$ which satisfies the admissibility condition

$$C_\psi = \int_{-\infty}^{\infty} \frac{|\hat{\psi}(s)|}{|s|} ds < \infty, \tag{1.50}$$

where $\hat{\psi}(s)$ is the Fourier transform of $\psi(t)$.

- If $\psi \in L^2(\mathbb{R})$, then $\psi_{a,b}(t) \in L^2(\mathbb{R})$ for all a, b. We have

$$\|\psi_{a,b}(t)\|^2 = |a|^{-1} \int_{-\infty}^{\infty} \left|\psi\left(\frac{t-b}{a}\right)\right|^2 dt = \int_{-\infty}^{\infty} |\psi(x)|^2 dt = \|\psi\|^2. \tag{1.51}$$

- The Fourier transform of $\psi_{a,b}(t)$ is given by

$$\hat{\psi}_{a,b}(s) = |a|^{-\frac{1}{2}} \int_{-\infty}^{\infty} e^{-ist} \psi\left(\frac{t-b}{a}\right) dt = |a|^{\frac{1}{2}} e^{-ibs} \hat{\psi}(as). \tag{1.52}$$

Definition 1.7 (Continuous Wavelet Transform) If $\psi \in L^2(\mathbb{R})$, and $\psi_{a,b}(t)$ is given by (1.49), then

$$\mathscr{W}_\psi[f](a,b) = \langle f, \psi_{a,b} \rangle = \int_{-\infty}^{\infty} f(t)\overline{\psi_{a,b}(t)} dt \tag{1.53}$$

is called a continuous wavelet transform of $f(t) \in L^2(\mathbb{R})$.

The kernel $\psi_{a,b}(t)$ in (1.53) plays the same role as the kernel e^{-ist} in the Fourier transform. The continuous wavelet transformation is linear. A function of b for a fixed scaling parameter a, $\mathscr{W}_\psi[f](a,b)$ represents the detailed information contained in the signal $f(t)$ at the scale a.

Using the Parseval relation of the Fourier transform, from (1.52), (1.53) can be written as

$$\mathscr{W}_\psi[f](a,b) = \langle f, \psi_{a,b} \rangle = \langle \hat{f}, \hat{\psi}_{a,b} \rangle = \int_{-\infty}^{\infty} \{|a|^{\frac{1}{2}} \hat{f}(s)\bar{\hat{\psi}}(as)\} e^{ibs} ds. \tag{1.54}$$

From (1.54), we have

$$\mathscr{F}\{\mathscr{W}_\psi[f](a,b)\} = \int_{-\infty}^{\infty} e^{-ibs} \mathscr{W}_\psi[f](a,b) db = \sqrt{|a|}\, \hat{f}(s)\, \bar{\hat{\psi}}(as). \tag{1.55}$$

Some Examples:

Example 1.3
The Haar wavelet is defined by

$$\psi(x) = \begin{cases} 1, & 0 \le x < \frac{1}{2} \\ -1, & \frac{1}{2} \le x < 1 \\ 0, & otherwise \end{cases} \tag{1.56}$$

and its Fourier transform is given by

$$\hat{\psi}(s) = \frac{ie^{-(\frac{is}{2})} sin^2(\frac{s}{4})}{(\frac{s}{4})}. \tag{1.57}$$

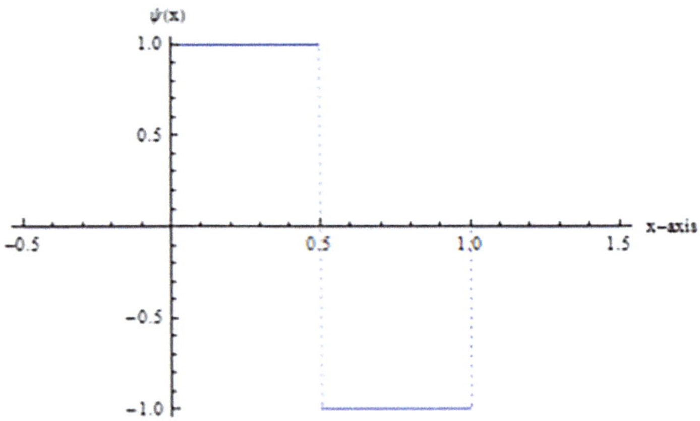

Fig. 1.5 $\psi(x)$

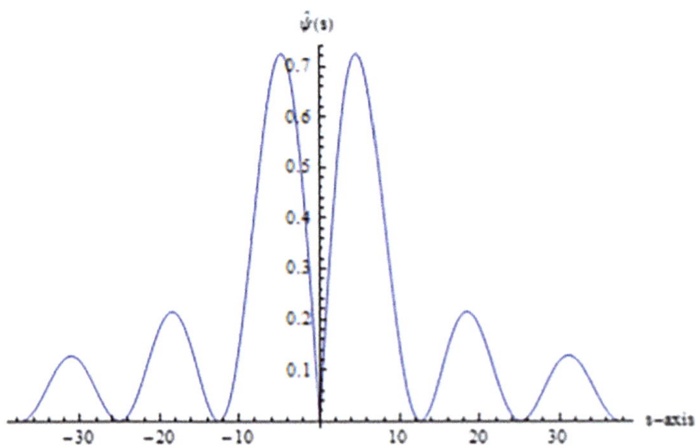

Fig. 1.6 $\hat{\psi}(s)$

The Haar wavelet has good time localization but poor frequency localization. Indeed, the discontinuity of ψ causes a slow decay of $\hat{\psi}$ as $s \to \infty$. Its discontinuous nature is a serious weakness in many applications. However, the Haar wavelet is one of the most fundamental examples that illustrate major features of the general wavelet theory (Figs. 1.5 and 1.6).

Theorem 1.17 *If ψ is a wavelet and ϕ is a bounded integrable function, then the convolution function $\psi * \phi$ is a wavelet.*

Proof We have

$$\begin{aligned}
\int_{-\infty}^{\infty} |\psi * \phi|^2 dx &= \int_{-\infty}^{\infty} \left| \int_{-\infty}^{\infty} \psi(x-u)\phi(u)du \right|^2 dx \\
&\leq \int_{-\infty}^{\infty} \left(\int_{-\infty}^{\infty} |\psi(x-u)||\phi(u)|du \right)^2 dx \\
&= \int_{-\infty}^{\infty} \left(\int_{-\infty}^{\infty} |\psi(x-u)||\phi(u)|^{\frac{1}{2}} |\phi(u)|^{\frac{1}{2}} du \right)^2 dx \\
&\leq \int_{-\infty}^{\infty} \left(\int_{-\infty}^{\infty} |\psi(x-u)|^2 |\phi(u)|du \int_{-\infty}^{\infty} |\phi(u)|du \right) dx \\
&\leq \int_{-\infty}^{\infty} |\phi(u)|du \int_{-\infty}^{\infty} \int_{-\infty}^{\infty} |\psi(x-u)|^2 |\phi(u)| dx du \\
&= \left(\int_{-\infty}^{\infty} |\phi(u)|du \right)^2 \int_{-\infty}^{\infty} |\psi(x)|^2 dx < \infty.
\end{aligned}$$

The above shows that $\psi * \phi \in L^2(\mathbb{R})$. Moreover,

$$\begin{aligned}
\int_{-\infty}^{\infty} \frac{|\mathcal{F}\{\psi * \phi\}|^2}{|s|} ds &= \int_{-\infty}^{\infty} \frac{|\hat{\psi}(s)\hat{\phi}(s)|^2}{|s|} ds \\
&\leq \int_{-\infty}^{\infty} \frac{|\hat{\psi}(s)|^2}{|s|} ds \sup |\hat{\phi}(s)|^2 < \infty.
\end{aligned}$$

Thus, the convolution function $\psi * \phi$ is a wavelet. □

Example 1.4
If we take the Haar wavelet and convolute it with the following function

$$\phi(t) = \begin{cases} 1, & 0 \leq t \leq 1 \\ 0, & otherwise \end{cases} \tag{1.58}$$

forms a simple wavelet $\psi * \phi$.

Example 1.5
The convolution of the Haar wavelet with $\phi(t) = e^{-t^2}$ generates a smooth wavelet $\psi * \phi$.

In order for the wavelets to be useful analyzing functions, the mother wavelet must have certain properties. One such property is defined by (1.49) which guarantees the existence of the inversion formula for the continuous wavelet transform. Condition (1.49) is referred as the admissibility condition for the mother wavelet. If $\psi \in L^1(\mathbb{R})$, then its Fourier transform $\hat{\psi}$ is continuous. Since $\hat{\psi}$ is continuous, C_ψ can be finite only if $\hat{\psi}(0) = 0$ or, equivalently, $\int_{-\infty}^{\infty} \psi(t)dt = 0$. This indicates that ψ must be an oscillatory function with zero mean. (1.50) imposes a restriction on the rate of decay of $|\hat{\psi}(s)|^2$ and is required in finding the inverse of the continuous wavelet transform.

Basic Properties of Wavelet Transforms

Theorem 1.18 *If ψ and ϕ are wavelets and f, g are functions which belong to $L^2(\mathbb{R})$, then*

(i) (Linearity)

$$\mathscr{W}_\psi(\alpha f + \beta g)(a, b) = \alpha(\mathscr{W}_\psi f)(a, b) + \beta(\mathscr{W}_\psi g)(a, b), \tag{1.59}$$

where α and β are any two scalars.

(ii) (Translation)

$$(\mathscr{W}_\psi(T_c f))(a, b) = (\mathscr{W}_\psi f)(a, b - c), \tag{1.60}$$

where T_c is the translation operator defined by $T_c f(t) = f(t - c)$.

(iii) *(Dilation)*

$$(\mathscr{W}_\psi(D_c f))(a,b) = \frac{1}{\sqrt{c}}(\mathscr{W}_\psi f)\left(\frac{a}{c}, \frac{b}{c}\right), \quad c > 0, \tag{1.61}$$

where D_c *is the dilation operator defined by* $D_c f(t) = \frac{1}{c} f\left(\frac{t}{c}\right)$.

(iv) *(Symmetry)*

$$(\mathscr{W}_\psi f)(a,b) = \overline{(\mathscr{W}_f \psi)\left(\frac{1}{a}, \frac{-b}{a}\right)}, \quad a \neq 0. \tag{1.62}$$

(v) *(Parity)*

$$(\mathscr{W}_{P\psi} Pf)(a,b) = (\mathscr{W}_\psi f)(a,-b), \tag{1.63}$$

where P *is the parity operator defined by* $Pf(t) = f(-t)$.

(vi) *(Antilinearity)*

$$(\mathscr{W}_{\alpha\psi+\beta\phi} f)(a,b) = \bar{\alpha}(\mathscr{W}_\psi f)(a,b) + \bar{\beta}(\mathscr{W}_\phi f)(a,b), \tag{1.64}$$

for any scalars α, β.

(vii)

$$(\mathscr{W}_{T_c\psi} f)(a,b) = (\mathscr{W}_\psi f)(a, b+ca). \tag{1.65}$$

(viii)

$$(\mathscr{W}_{D_c\psi} f)(a,b) = \frac{1}{\sqrt{c}}(\mathscr{W}_\psi f)(ac, b), \quad c > 0. \tag{1.66}$$

Theorem 1.19 (Parseval's Formula for Wavelet Transforms)
If $\psi \in L^2(\mathbb{R})$ *and* $(\mathscr{W}_\psi f)(a,b)$ *is the wavelet transform of* f *defined by (1.53), then, for any functions* f, $g \in L^2(\mathbb{R})$, *we obtain*

$$\int_{-\infty}^{\infty}\int_{-\infty}^{\infty} (\mathscr{W}_\psi f)(a,b)\overline{(\mathscr{W}_\psi g)(a,b)}\frac{dbda}{a^2} = C_\psi \langle f, g\rangle, \tag{1.67}$$

where

$$C_\psi = \int_{-\infty}^{\infty} \frac{|\hat{\psi}(s)|^2}{|s|} ds < \infty. \tag{1.68}$$

Proof By Parseval's relation (1.46) for the Fourier transforms, we have

$$
\begin{aligned}
(\mathscr{W}_\psi f)(a,b) &= \int_{-\infty}^{\infty} f(t)|a|^{-\frac{1}{2}}\overline{\psi\Big(\frac{t-b}{a}\Big)}dt \\
&= \langle f, \psi_{a,b}\rangle \\
&= \frac{1}{2\pi}\langle \hat{f}, \hat{\psi}_{a,b}\rangle \\
&= \frac{1}{2\pi}\int_{-\infty}^{\infty} \hat{f}(s)|a|^{\frac{1}{2}}e^{ibs}\overline{\hat{\psi}(as)}ds \ \text{ by (1.54).}
\end{aligned} \tag{1.69}
$$

Similarily,

$$
\begin{aligned}
\overline{(\mathscr{W}_\psi f)(a,b)} &= \int_{-\infty}^{\infty} \overline{\hat{g}(t)}\ |a|^{-\frac{1}{2}}\psi\Big(\frac{t-b}{a}\Big)dt \\
&= \frac{1}{2\pi}\int_{-\infty}^{\infty} \overline{\hat{g}(\sigma)}\ |a|^{\frac{1}{2}}e^{-ib\sigma}\hat{\psi}(a\sigma)d\sigma.
\end{aligned} \tag{1.70}
$$

From (1.69) and (1.70), (1.67) gives

$$
\begin{aligned}
&\int_{-\infty}^{\infty}\int_{-\infty}^{\infty}(\mathscr{W}_\psi f)(a,b)\overline{(\mathscr{W}_\psi g)(a,b)}\frac{dbda}{a^2} \\
&= \frac{1}{(2\pi)^2}\int_{-\infty}^{\infty}\int_{-\infty}^{\infty}\frac{dbda}{a^2}\int_{-\infty}^{\infty}\int_{-\infty}^{\infty}|a|\hat{f}(s)\overline{\hat{g}}(\sigma)\overline{\hat{\psi}}(as)\hat{\psi}(a\sigma)e^{ib(s-\sigma)}dsd\sigma,
\end{aligned} \tag{1.71}
$$

which is, by interchanging the order of integration,

$$
\begin{aligned}
&= \frac{1}{(2\pi)}\int_{-\infty}^{\infty}\frac{da}{|a|}\int_{-\infty}^{\infty}\int_{-\infty}^{\infty}\hat{f}(s)\overline{\hat{g}}(\sigma)\overline{\hat{\psi}}(as)\hat{\psi}(a\sigma)dsd\sigma\frac{1}{(2\pi)}\int_{-\infty}^{\infty}e^{ib(s-\sigma)}db \\
&= \frac{1}{(2\pi)}\int_{-\infty}^{\infty}\frac{da}{|a|}\int_{-\infty}^{\infty}\int_{-\infty}^{\infty}\hat{f}(s)\overline{\hat{g}}(\sigma)\overline{\hat{\psi}}(as)\hat{\psi}(a\sigma)\delta(\sigma-s)dsd\sigma \\
&= \frac{1}{(2\pi)}\int_{-\infty}^{\infty}\frac{da}{|a|}\int_{-\infty}^{\infty}\hat{f}(s)\overline{\hat{g}}(s)|\hat{\psi}(as)|^2ds
\end{aligned}
$$

which is, again interchanging the order of integration and putting $as = x$,

$$\begin{aligned}
&\int_{-\infty}^{\infty}\int_{-\infty}^{\infty}(\mathscr{W}_\psi f)(a,b)\overline{(\mathscr{W}_\psi g)(a,b)}\frac{dbda}{a^2}\\
&= \frac{1}{(2\pi)}\int_{-\infty}^{\infty}\hat{f}(s)\overline{\hat{g}}(s)ds\int_{-\infty}^{\infty}\frac{|\hat{\psi}(x)|^2}{|x|}dx\\
&= C_\psi\frac{1}{(2\pi)}\langle\hat{f}(s),\hat{g}(s)\rangle\\
&= C_\psi\langle f,g\rangle.
\end{aligned}$$

Theorem 1.20 (Inversion Formula) *If $f \in L^2(\mathbb{R})$, then f can be reconstructed by the formula*

$$f(t) = \frac{1}{C_\psi}\int_{-\infty}^{\infty}\int_{-\infty}^{\infty}(\mathscr{W}_\psi f)(a,b)\psi_{a,b}(t)\frac{dbda}{a^2}, \tag{1.72}$$

where the equality holds almost everywhere.

Proof For any $g \in L^2(\mathbb{R})$ and from Theorem 1.19

$$\begin{aligned}
C_\psi\langle f,g\rangle &= \langle\mathscr{W}_\psi f,\mathscr{W}_\psi g\rangle\\
&= \int_{-\infty}^{\infty}\int_{-\infty}^{\infty}(\mathscr{W}_\psi f)(a,b)\overline{(\mathscr{W}_\psi g)(a,b)}\frac{dbda}{a^2}\\
&= \int_{-\infty}^{\infty}\int_{-\infty}^{\infty}(\mathscr{W}_\psi f)(a,b)\overline{\int_{-\infty}^{\infty}g(t)\overline{\psi_{a,b}(t)}dt}\frac{dbda}{a^2}\\
&= \int_{-\infty}^{\infty}\int_{-\infty}^{\infty}\int_{-\infty}^{\infty}(\mathscr{W}_\psi f)(a,b)\psi_{a,b}(t)\frac{dbda}{a^2}\overline{g(t)}dt
\end{aligned}$$

$$= \left\langle\int_{-\infty}^{\infty}\int_{-\infty}^{\infty}(\mathscr{W}_\psi f)(a,b)\psi_{a,b}(t)\frac{dbda}{a^2}, g(t)\right\rangle. \tag{1.73}$$

Since g is an arbitrary element of $L^2(\mathbb{R})$, the inversion formula (1.72) follows. □

If $f = g$ in (1.67), then

$$\int_{-\infty}^{\infty}\int_{-\infty}^{\infty}|(\mathscr{W}_\psi f)(a,b)|^2\frac{dbda}{a^2} = C_\psi\|f\|^2 = C_\psi\int_{-\infty}^{\infty}|f(t)|^2dt. \tag{1.74}$$

This shows that, except for the factor C_ψ, the wavelet transform is an isometry from $L^2(\mathbb{R})$ to $L^2(\mathbb{R}^2)$.

1.4 Hankel Transform

From Zemanian [1], Betancor and Marrero [21], Pathak [25] and Macaulay-Owen [26] and others, the conventional Hankel transformation of function $f \in L^1(I)$ is defined by

$$F(y) = (h_\mu f)(y) = \int_0^\infty (xy)^{\frac{1}{2}} J_\mu(xy) f(x) dx, \quad \mu \geq -\frac{1}{2} \tag{1.75}$$

where $y \in I$, μ is a real number, and J_μ is the Bessel function of first kind and order μ.

From (Watson [27]; p. 456), the inversion formula of (1.75) is given below:

Theorem 1.21 *If $f(x) \in L^1(I)$, if $f(x)$ is of bounded variation in a neighborhood of the point $x = x_0 > 0$, if $\mu \geq -\frac{1}{2}$, and if $F(y)$ is defined by (1.75), then*

$$\frac{1}{2}[f(x_0+0) + f(x_0-0)] = h_\mu^{-1} F = \int_0^\infty F(y)(x_0 y)^{\frac{1}{2}} J_\mu(x_0 y) dy. \tag{1.76}$$

Note: When $\mu \geq -\frac{1}{2}$, this conventional inverse Hankel transformation h_μ^{-1} is defined by precisely the same formula as is the direct Hankel transformation h_μ; in symbols, $h_\mu = h_\mu^{-1}$.

Theorem 1.22 *If $f(x)$ and $G(y)$ are in $L^1(I)$, if $\mu \geq -\frac{1}{2}$, if $F(y) = h_\mu[f(x)]$, and if $g(x) = h_\mu^{-1}[G(y)]$, then*

$$\int_0^\infty f(x)g(x)dx = \int_0^\infty F(y)G(y)dy. \tag{1.77}$$

In particular, for $f \in L^2(I)$

$$\int_0^\infty |(h_\mu f)(y)|^2 dy = \int_0^\infty |f(x)|^2 dx. \tag{1.78}$$

The proof of other cases of Parseval formula (1.77) can be seen in Macauley-Owen [26].

Definition 1.8 Let $x^{\mu+\frac{1}{2}} f(x) \in L^1(I)$ and $x^{\mu+\frac{1}{2}} g(x) \in L^1(I)$. The Hankel convolution $f\#g$ of f and g is defined by

$$(f\#g)(x) = \int_0^\infty f(y)(\tau_x g)(y)dy = \int_0^\infty (\tau_x f)(y)g(y)dy, \tag{1.79}$$

where

$$(\tau_x g)(y) = g(x, y) = \int_0^\infty g(z) D_\mu(x, y, z) dz \tag{1.80}$$

is the Hankel translation, and $D_\mu(x, y, z)$ is a basic function which is defined by

$$D_\mu(x, y, z) = \int_0^\infty t^{-\mu-\frac{1}{2}}(xt)^{\frac{1}{2}} J_\mu(xt)(yt)^{\frac{1}{2}} J_\mu(yt)(zt)^{\frac{1}{2}} J_\mu(zt)dt, \tag{1.81}$$

for all $x, y, z \in I$ and holds the following properties:

(i)

$$D_\mu(x, y, z) \geq 0, \ x, y, z \in I. \tag{1.82}$$

(ii)

$$\int_0^\infty t^{-\mu-\frac{1}{2}}(zt)^{\frac{1}{2}} J_\mu(zt) D_\mu(x, y, z)dz = (xt)^{\frac{1}{2}} J_\mu(xt)(yt)^{\frac{1}{2}} J_\mu(yt), \ t \in I. \tag{1.83}$$

(iii)

$$\int_0^\infty D_\mu(x, y, z) z^{\mu+\frac{1}{2}} dz = \frac{(xy)^{\mu+\frac{1}{2}}}{2^\mu \Gamma(\mu+1)}. \tag{1.84}$$

Theorem 1.23 *If $x^{\mu+\frac{1}{2}} f(x) \in L^1(I)$ and $x^{\mu+\frac{1}{2}} g(x) \in L^1(I)$, then*

$$h_\mu(f\#g)(y) = y^{-\mu-\frac{1}{2}} h_\mu f(y) h_\mu g(y). \tag{1.85}$$

Definition 1.9 From Wing [28] and Kerr [29], for $\mu \geq -\frac{1}{2}$, the Hankel transformation of a function $f \in L^2(I)$ is defined by

$$(h_\mu f)(y) = \underset{N\to\infty}{l.i.m.} \int_0^N (xy)^{\frac{1}{2}} J_\mu(xy) f(x)dx, \tag{1.86}$$

and the corresponding inverse Hankel transform is

$$f(x) = \underset{N\to\infty}{l.i.m.} \int_0^N (xy)^{\frac{1}{2}} J_\mu(xy) h_\mu f(y)dy, \tag{1.87}$$

where $l.i.m.$(limit in mean) denote convergence in $L^2(I)$.

1.5 The Testing-Function Space H_μ and Its Dual

For each real number μ we define a countably multinormed space H_μ, as follows. A function $\phi(x)$ is in H_μ,if and only if it is defined on $0 < x < \infty$, it is complex-valued and smooth, and, for each pair of nonnegative integers m and k,

$$\gamma_{m,k}^{\mu}(\phi) \triangleq \sup_{x\in I}\left|x^m\left(x^{-1}D_x\right)^k[x^{-\mu-\frac{1}{2}}\phi(x)]\right| < \infty. \tag{1.88}$$

H_μ is a linear space. Also, each $\gamma_{m,k}^{\mu}$ is a seminorm on H_μ, and the collection $\{\gamma_{m,k}^{\mu}\}_{m,k=0}^{\infty}$ is a multinorm because the $\gamma_{m,0}^{\mu}$ are norms. The topology of H_μ is that generated by $\{\gamma_{m,k}^{\mu}\}_{m,k=0}^{\infty}$.

Lemma 1.2 *$\phi(x)$ is a member of H_μ if and only if it satisfies the following three conditions:*

(i) *$\phi(x)$ is a smooth complex-valued function on $0 < x < \infty$.*
(ii) *For each nonnegative integer k,*

$$\phi(x) = x^{\mu+\frac{1}{2}}[a_0 + a_2x^2 + \cdots + a_{2k}x^{2k} + R_{2k}(x)] \tag{1.89}$$

where the a's are constants given by

$$a_{2k} = \frac{1}{k!2^k}\lim_{x\to 0+}(x^{-1}D)^k x^{-\mu-\frac{1}{2}}\phi(x) \tag{1.90}$$

and the remainder term $R_{2k}(x)$ satisfies

$$(x^{-1}D)^k R_{2k}(x) = o(1) \qquad x \to 0+ \tag{1.91}$$

(iii) *For each nonnegative integer k, $D^k\phi(x)$ is of rapid descent as $x \to \infty$ [i.e., $D^k\phi(x)$ tends to zero faster than any power of $\frac{1}{x}$ as $x \to \infty$].*

Proof See Zemanian [2, pp. 130-131]. □

Note: For any fixed $y \in I$, $\sqrt{xy}J_\mu(xy)$ as a function of x satisfies conditions (i) and (ii) of Lemma 1.2. However, it does not satisfy condition (iii) since

$$\sqrt{xy}J_\mu(xy) \sim \sqrt{\frac{2}{\pi}}cos(xy - \frac{\mu\pi}{2} - \frac{\pi}{4}) \qquad x \to \infty \tag{1.92}$$

(See Jahnke, Emde, and Losch [30], p. 134 and p. 147). Hence, $\sqrt{xy}J_\mu(xy)$ is not a member of H_μ.

For every nonnegative integer ν, we have the identity

$$(x^{-1}D_x)^\nu[x^{-\mu-\frac{1}{2}}\sqrt{xy}J_\mu(xy)] = (-1)^\nu y^{\mu+\frac{1}{2}+2\nu}(xy)^{-\mu-\nu}J_{\mu+\nu}(xy). \tag{1.93}$$

Lemma 1.3 *H_μ is complete and therefore a Fréchet space.*

Proof Let $\{\phi_\nu\}_{\nu=1}^{\infty}$ be a Cauchy sequence in H_μ,. In view of (1.93) and the seminorms $\gamma_{0,k}^{\mu}$, it follows by induction on k that, for each k, $\{D^k\phi_\nu\}_{\nu=1}^{\infty}$ converges uniformly on every compact subset of I. Therefore, there exists a smooth function $\phi(x)$ defined on I such that, for each k and x, $D^k\phi_\nu(x) \to D^k\phi(x)$ as $\nu \to \infty$.

Moreover, again by the fact that $\{\phi_\nu\}_{\nu=1}^{\infty}$ is a Cauchy sequence, for each m and k and a given $\epsilon > 0$ there exists a real number $N_{m,k}$ such that, for every $\nu, \eta > N_{m,k}$, $\gamma_{m,k}^{\mu}(\phi_\nu - \phi_\eta) < \epsilon$. Taking the limit as $\eta \to \infty$, we obtain

$$\gamma_{m,k}^{\mu}(\phi_\nu - \phi) \leq \epsilon \tag{1.94}$$

for all $\nu > N_{m,k}$, which shows that $\gamma_{m,k}^{\mu}(\phi_\nu - \phi) \to 0$ as $\nu \to \infty$.

Finally, there exists a constant $C_{m,k}$ not depending on ν such that $\gamma_{m,k}^{\mu}(\phi_\nu) < C_{m,k}$. Therefore, from (1.94) and [1, Sec. 1.5, Eq. (1)] we obtain

$$\gamma_{m,k}^{\mu}(\phi) < C_{m,k} + \epsilon. \tag{1.95}$$

We have shown therefore that $\phi \in H_\mu$, and that $\{\phi_\nu\}$ converges in H_μ, to ϕ, as was required. □

H'_μ denotes the dual of H_μ. According to [2, Theorem 1.8-3], H'_μ is also complete. The members of H'_μ are the generalized functions on which our Hankel transformation will be defined. We now list some other properties of H_μ and H'_μ that we shall have need of subsequently.

I. $D(I)$ is a subspace of H_μ for every choice of μ, and that convergence in $D(I)$ implies convergence in H_μ. Consequently, the restriction of any $f \in H'_\mu$ to $D(I)$ is a member of $D'(I)$. However, $D(I)$ is not dense in H_μ.
II. If q is an even positive integer, then $H_{\mu+q} \subset H_\mu$, and the topology of $H_{\mu+q}$ is stronger than that induced on it by H_μ.
III. For each μ, H_μ is clearly a subspace of $\mathscr{E}(I)$. Moreover, it is dense in $\mathscr{E}(I)$ because H_μ, contains $D(I)$ and $D(I)$ is dense in $\mathscr{E}(I)$.
IV. For each choice of the nonnegative integer r, set

$$\rho_r^{\mu}(\phi) = \max_{\substack{0 \leq m \leq r \\ 0 \leq k \leq r}} \gamma_{m,k}^{\mu}(\phi). \tag{1.96}$$

By [2, Theorem 1.8-1], for each $f \in H'_\mu$ there exist a positive constant C and a nonnegative integer r such that

$$|\langle f, \phi \rangle| \leq C\rho_r^{\mu}(\phi) \tag{1.97}$$

for every $\phi \in H_\mu$. Here, C and r depend on f but not on ϕ.
V. Let $f(x)$ be a locally integrable function on $0 < x < \infty$ such that $f(x)$ is of slow growth as $x \to \infty$ and $x^{\mu+\frac{1}{2}} f(x)$ is absolutely integrable on $0 < x < 1$. Then, $f(x)$ generates a regular generalized function f in H'_μ by

$$\langle f, \phi \rangle \triangleq \int_0^{\infty} f(x)\phi(x)dx. \tag{1.98}$$

1.6 Some Operations on H_μ and H'_μ

Multipliers in H_μ : Let $\mathcal{O}$ denote the linear space of all smooth functions $\theta(x)$ defined on $0 < x < \infty$ such that, for each nonnegative integer ν, there is an integer n_ν for which

$$\frac{(x^{-1}D)^\nu \theta(x)}{1 + x^{n_\nu}}$$

is bounded on $0 < x < \infty$. The product of any two members of $\mathcal{O}$ is also in $\mathcal{O}$. Any $\theta \in \mathcal{O}$ is a multiplier for H_μ for every μ [2, p. 134].

Theorem 1.24 *If $\theta \in \mathcal{O}$ and $\phi \in H_\mu(I)$, then $\theta\phi \in H_\mu(I)$ and θ is a multiplier for H_μ, for every μ.*

Proof For $\theta \in \mathcal{O}$ and $\phi \in H_\mu$, by Leibnitz formula, we have

$$(x^{-1}D_x)^k x^{-\mu-\frac{1}{2}}(\theta\phi) = \sum_{\nu=0}^{k} \binom{k}{\nu} \frac{(x^{-1}D_x)^\nu \theta}{1 + x^{n_\nu}} (1 + x^{n_\nu})(x^{-1}D_x)^{k-\nu} x^{-\mu-\frac{1}{2}} \phi,$$

so that

$$\begin{aligned}
\left| x^m (x^{-1}D_x)^k x^{-\mu-\frac{1}{2}}(\theta\phi) \right| &= \left| \sum_{\nu=0}^{k} \binom{k}{\nu} \frac{(x^{-1}D_x)^\nu \theta}{1 + x^{n_\nu}} (1 + x^{n_\nu})(x^{-1}D_x)^{k-\nu} x^{-\mu-\frac{1}{2}} \phi \right| \\
&\leq \sum_{\nu=0}^{k} \binom{k}{\nu} \left| \frac{(x^{-1}D_x)^\nu \theta}{1 + x^{n_\nu}} \right| \left| x^m (1 + x^{n_\nu})(x^{-1}D_x)^{k-\nu} x^{-\mu-\frac{1}{2}} \phi \right| \\
&\leq \sum_{\nu=0}^{k} \binom{k}{\nu} \left| \frac{(x^{-1}D_x)^\nu \theta}{1 + x^{n_\nu}} \right| \left| (x^m + x^{m+n_\nu})(x^{-1}D_x)^{k-\nu} x^{-\mu-\frac{1}{2}} \phi \right|.
\end{aligned}$$

Using (1.88) and that $\theta \in \mathcal{O}$, we get

$$\gamma^\mu_{m,k}(\theta\phi) \leq \sum_{\nu=0}^{k} \binom{k}{\nu} B_\nu [\gamma^\mu_{m,k-\nu}(\phi) + \gamma^\mu_{m+n_\nu,k-\nu}(\phi)]$$

where the B_ν are constants. This shows that the linear operator $\phi \to \theta\phi$ is a continuous mapping of H_μ, into itself. □

By [2, Sec. 2.5], the adjoint operator $f \mapsto \theta f$ is defined on H'_μ by

$$\langle \theta f, \phi \rangle \triangleq \langle f, \theta\phi \rangle \qquad f \in H'_\mu,\ \phi \in H_\mu,\ \theta \in \mathcal{O} \tag{1.99}$$

is a continuous linear mapping of H'_μ into itself. We emphasize that the space $\mathcal{O}$ does not depend upon μ; it is a space of multipliers for H_μ no matter what real value μ assumes.

Lemma 1.4 *If $P(x)$ and $Q(x)$ are polynomials and $Q(x)$ has no zeros on $0 \le x < \infty$, then $\frac{P(x^2)}{Q(x^2)}$ is a member of $\mathcal{O}$.*

Proof See the proof in [2, pp. 134-135]. □

Lemma 1.5 *For any positive or negative integer n and for any μ, the mapping $\phi(x) \mapsto x^n\phi(x)$ is an isomorphism from H_μ onto $H_{\mu+n}$. Consequently, the operator $f(x) \mapsto x^n f(x)$, which is defined by*

$$\langle x^n f(x), \phi(x)\rangle \triangleq \langle f(x), x^n\phi(x)\rangle \tag{1.100}$$

is an isomorphism from $H'_{\mu+n}$ onto H'_μ.

Some differential and integral operators: Two linear differential operators N_μ and M_μ and a linear integral operator N_μ^{-1} are defined by

$$N_\mu\phi(x) \triangleq x^{\mu+\frac{1}{2}} D x^{-\mu-\frac{1}{2}}\phi(x) \tag{1.101}$$

$$M_\mu\phi(x) \triangleq x^{-\mu-\frac{1}{2}} D x^{\mu+\frac{1}{2}}\phi(x) \tag{1.102}$$

$$N_\mu^{-1}\phi(x) \triangleq x^{\mu+\frac{1}{2}} \int_\infty^x D t^{-\mu-\frac{1}{2}}\phi(t)dt. \tag{1.103}$$

In the dual spaces we follow the notational convention described in [2, Sec. 2.5] and define N_μ when it is acting on certain generalized functions, as the adjoint of $-M_\mu$, and M_μ, in similar circumstances, as the adjoint of $-N_\mu$. More specifically, N_μ is defined as a generalized differential operator on H'_μ by

$$\langle N_\mu f, \phi\rangle \triangleq \langle f, -M_\mu\phi\rangle \qquad f \in H'_\mu,\ \phi \in H_{\mu+1}. \tag{1.104}$$

On the other hand, M_μ is defined as a generalized differential operator on $H'_{\mu+1}$ by

$$\langle M_\mu f, \phi\rangle \triangleq \langle f, -N_\mu\phi\rangle \qquad f \in H'_{\mu+1},\ \phi \in H_\mu. \tag{1.105}$$

We give some results regarding above operators as

Lemma 1.6 *(i) The conventional differential operator N_μ, defined by (1.101), is an isomorphism from H_μ onto $H_{\mu+1}$, the inverse mapping being N_μ^{-1}.*

(ii) The conventional differential operator M_μ, defined by (1.102), is a continuous linear mapping of $H_{\mu+1}$ into H_μ.

(iii) The generalized differential operator N_μ defined by (1.104) is a continuous linear mapping of H'_μ into $H'_{\mu+1}$.

(iv) The generalized differential operator M_μ defined by (1.105) is an isomorphism from $H'_{\mu+1}$ onto H'_μ.

(i) and (ii) of Lemma 1.6 imply that the conventional differential operator:

$$M_\mu N_\mu = D^2 - \frac{4\mu^2 - 1}{4x^2} \tag{1.106}$$

is a continuous linear mapping of H_μ into H_μ. Taking the concept of (1.104) and (1.105) we define the generalized differential operator $M_\mu N_\mu$ by

$$\langle M_\mu N_\mu f, \phi\rangle \triangleq \langle f, M_\mu N_\mu \phi\rangle \qquad f \in H'_\mu,\ \phi \in H_\mu \tag{1.107}$$

and obtain there by a continuous linear mapping of H'_μ into H'_μ.

1.7 The Conventional Hankel Transformation on H_μ

If $\phi \in H_\mu \subset L^1(I)$, then the conventional Hankel transform

$$\Phi(y) = (h_\mu \phi)(y) = \int_0^\infty \phi(x)\sqrt{xy}\,J_\mu(xy)dx \qquad 0 < y < \infty,\ \mu \geq -\frac{1}{2} \tag{1.108}$$

exists, by virtue of Lemma 1.2 and the facts that

$$\sqrt{xy}\,J_\mu(xy) = O(x^{\mu+\frac{1}{2}}) \text{ as } x \to 0+ \tag{1.109}$$

and

$$\sqrt{xy}\,J_\mu(xy) = O(1) \text{ as } x \to \infty \tag{1.110}$$

(see Jahnke, Emde, and Losch [30], p. 134 and p. 147).

Lemma 1.7 *Let* $\mu \geq -\frac{1}{2}$. *If* $\phi \in H_\mu$, *then*

$$h_{\mu+1}(-x\phi) = N_\mu h_\mu \phi \tag{1.111}$$
$$h_{\mu+1}(N_\mu \phi) = -y h_\mu \phi \tag{1.112}$$
$$h_\mu(-x^2\phi) = M_\mu N_\mu h_\mu \phi \tag{1.113}$$
$$h_\mu(M_\mu N_\mu \phi) = -y^2 h_\mu \phi. \tag{1.114}$$

If $\phi \in H_{\mu+1}$, *then*

$$h_\mu(x\phi) = M_\mu h_{\mu+1}\phi \tag{1.115}$$
$$h_\mu(M_\mu \phi) = y h_{\mu+1}\phi. \tag{1.116}$$

Proof To prove (1.111), for $\Phi = h_\mu\phi$, we use the formula (Jahnke, Emde, and Losch [30], p. 154):

$$D_y y^{-\mu} J_\mu(xy) = -xy^{-\mu} J_{\mu+1}(xy) \tag{1.117}$$

and take the differentiation under an integral sign as follows.

$$\begin{aligned} D_y y^{-\mu-\frac{1}{2}} \Phi(y) &= D_y y^{-\mu-\frac{1}{2}} \int_0^\infty \phi(x)\sqrt{xy} J_\mu(xy)dx \\ &= \int_0^\infty \phi(x)\sqrt{x} D_y[y^{-\mu} J_\mu(xy)]dx \\ &= -\int_0^\infty \phi(x) x^{\frac{3}{2}} y^{-\mu} J_{\mu+1}(xy)dx. \end{aligned} \tag{1.118}$$

This is possible, because for $\mu \geq -\frac{1}{2}$, $J_{\mu+1}(xy)$ is a smooth bounded function on $0 < xy < \infty$, and $\phi(x)x^{\frac{3}{2}}$ is a member of $L^1(I)$ when $\phi \in H_\mu$ according to Lemma 1.2. Consequently, the R.H.S of (1.118) is a uniformly convergent integral on any compact subset of $0 < y < \infty$.

On multiplying (1.118) by $y^{\mu+\frac{1}{2}}$, we obtain

$$N_\mu h_\mu \phi = h_{\mu+1}(-x\phi). \tag{1.119}$$

Now, we derive (1.112). From (Jahnke, Emde, and Losch [30], p. 154), we have

$$D_x x^{\mu+1} J_{\mu+1}(xy) = yx^{\mu+1} J_\mu(xy). \tag{1.120}$$

According to Lemma 1.6-(i), $N_\mu\phi$ is in $H_{\mu+1}$, so that we may take its $(\mu+1)th$-order Hankel transform. An integration by parts and the use of (1.120) yields

$$\begin{aligned} h_{\mu+1}(N_\mu\phi) &= \int_0^\infty [x^{\mu+\frac{1}{2}} D_x x^{-\mu-\frac{1}{2}} \phi(x)]\sqrt{xy} J_{\mu+1}(xy)dx \\ &= \sqrt{y} \int_0^\infty [D_x x^{-\mu-\frac{1}{2}} \phi(x)] x^{\mu+1} J_{\mu+1}(xy)dx \\ &= \phi(x)\sqrt{xy} J_{\mu+1}(xy)\Big|_{x\to 0+}^{x\to\infty} - y\int_0^\infty \phi(x)\sqrt{xy} J_\mu(xy)dx. \end{aligned}$$

The limit terms are equal to zero since $\phi(x)$ is of rapid descent as $x \to \infty$ and, as $x \to 0+$, $\sqrt{xy} J_{\mu+1}(xy) = O(x)$ and $\phi(x) = O(1)$ when $\mu \geq -\frac{1}{2}$. This verifies (1.112).

Next, we have to prove (1.115). Now, assume that $\phi \in H_{\mu+1}$ and set $\Phi(y) = h_{\mu+1}[\phi(x)]$. By differentiating under the integral sign and using formula (1.120) with x and y interchanged, we get

$$
\begin{aligned}
D_y y^{\mu+\frac{1}{2}}\Phi(y) &= D_y y^{\mu+\frac{1}{2}}\int_0^\infty \phi(x)\sqrt{xy}J_{\mu+1}(xy)dx \\
&= \int_0^\infty \phi(x)\sqrt{x}D_y[y^{\mu+1}J_{\mu+1}(xy)]dx \\
&= \int_0^\infty \phi(x)x^{\frac{3}{2}}y^{\mu+1}J_\mu(xy)dx.
\end{aligned} \tag{1.121}
$$

This procedure is valid because, for $\mu \geq -\frac{1}{2}$, $\sqrt{xy}J_\mu(xy)$ is smooth and bounded for $0 < xy < \infty$ and $x\phi(x) \in L^1(I)$ by virtue of Lemma 1.2; consequently, the R.H.S of (1.121) converges uniformly on every compact subset of $0 < y < \infty$. The multiplication of (1.121) by $y^{-\mu-\frac{1}{2}}$ yields

$$
h_\mu(x\phi) = M_\mu h_{\mu+1}\phi. \tag{1.122}
$$

To get (1.116), using Lemma 1.6(ii) and applying h_μ, we have

$$
\begin{aligned}
h_\mu(M_\mu\phi) &= \int_0^\infty [x^{-\mu-\frac{1}{2}}D_x x^{\mu+\frac{1}{2}}\phi(x)]\sqrt{xy}J_\mu(xy)dx \\
&= \sqrt{y}\int_0^\infty [D_x x^{\mu+\frac{1}{2}}\phi(x)]x^{-\mu}J_\mu(xy)dx.
\end{aligned}
$$

Taking integration by parts and the use of (1.117), above yields

$$
h_\mu(M_\mu\phi) = \phi(x)\sqrt{xy}J_\mu(xy)\Big|_{x\to 0+}^{x\to\infty} + y\int_0^\infty \phi(x)\sqrt{xy}J_{\mu+1}(xy)dx. \tag{1.123}
$$

By Lemma 1.2 and the fact that $\mu \geq -\frac{1}{2}$, $\phi(x) = O(x)$ as $x \to 0+$, and $\phi(x)$ is of rapid descent as $x \to \infty$. Moreover, $\sqrt{xy}J_\mu(xy)$ is bounded for $0 < xy < \infty$. Hence, the limit terms are equal to zero, and we have obtained (1.116).

Formula (1.113) is obtained by combining (1.111) and (1.115), and formula (1.114) by combining (1.112) and (1.116). □

Moreover, the Bessel differential operator of order n be

$$
S_{\mu,x}^n f(x) = \sum_{j=0}^n A_j x^{2j+\mu+\frac{1}{2}}\left(x^{-1}D_x\right)^{n+j}x^{-\mu-\frac{1}{2}}f(x), \tag{1.124}
$$

where $S_{\mu,x} = x^{-\mu-\frac{1}{2}}D_x x^{2\mu+1}D_x x^{-\mu-\frac{1}{2}}$ and A_j are constants depending on j and μ. We now turn to our fundamental theorem.

Theorem 1.25 *For $\mu \geq -\frac{1}{2}$, the conventional Hankel transformation h_μ is an automorphism on H_μ.*

Proof Let $\Phi(y) = h_\mu[\phi(x)]$, where $\phi \in H_\mu$ and m and k are any pair of nonnegative integers. By applying (1.111) k times and (1.112) m times and noting that

$$N_{\mu+k+m-1}\dots N_{\mu+k+1}N_{\mu+k}x^k\phi(x) = x^k N_{\mu+m-1}\dots N_{\mu+1}N_\mu\phi(x),$$

then, we obtain

$$(-y)^m N_{\mu+k-1}\dots N_\mu\Phi(y) = \int_0^\infty (-x)^k[N_{\mu+m-1}\dots N_\mu\phi(x)]\sqrt{xy}J_{\mu+k+m}(xy)dx.$$

Above yields

$$\begin{aligned}&(-1)^{m+k}y^m(y^{-1}D_y)^k y^{-\mu-\frac{1}{2}}\Phi(y)\\&=\int_0^\infty x^{2\mu+2k+m+1}[(x^{-1}D_x)^m x^{-\mu-\frac{1}{2}}\phi(x)]\frac{J_{\mu+k+m}(xy)}{(xy)^{\mu+k}}dx.\end{aligned} \tag{1.125}$$

Furthermore, since $\mu \geq -\frac{1}{2}$, $J_{\mu+k+m}(xy)/(xy)^{\mu+k}$ is bounded on $0 < xy < \infty$ and it is equal to constant $B_{k,m}$. It follows that the last integral converges uniformly on $0 < y < \infty$ so that the L.H.S of (1.125) is a continuous function for every m and k. By an inductive argument based upon [1, Sec. 5.2, Eq. (6)], we can conclude that $\Phi(y)$ is a smooth function on $0 < y < \infty$.

Now, assume that n is an integer no less than $\mu + k + \frac{1}{2}(m+1)$. Then, $x^{2\mu+2k+m+1} < (1+x^2)^n$ for $x > 0$. Hence, from (1.125) we obtain

$$\begin{aligned}\gamma_{m,k}^\mu(\Phi) &\leq \int_0^\infty (1+x^2)^{n+1}|(x^{-1}D_x)^m x^{-\mu-\frac{1}{2}}\phi(x)|\frac{B_{k,m}}{1+x^2}dx\\&\leq \frac{\pi}{2}B_{k,m}\sum_{\nu=0}^{n+1}\binom{n+1}{\nu}\gamma_{2\nu,m}^\mu(\phi).\end{aligned}$$

Above inequality proves that Φ is also in H_μ and that the linear mapping h_μ is also continuous from H_μ into H_μ.

Since, $H_\mu \subset L^1(0,\infty)$, $\mu \geq -\frac{1}{2}$ and by the classical inversion Theorem 1.21, we have $h_\mu = h_\mu^{-1}$. These show that h_μ is a one-to-one mapping of H_μ onto H_μ and it is an automorphism on H_μ. □

1.8 The Generalized Hankel Transformation

In this section, we consider that $\mu \geq -\frac{1}{2}$ and the generalized Hankel transformation h'_μ on H'_μ as the adjoint of h_μ on H_μ is defined by

$$\langle F, \Phi\rangle \triangleq \langle f, \phi\rangle \tag{1.126}$$

for arbitrary $\Phi \in H_\mu$ and $\phi = h_\mu \Phi$ and for arbitrary $f \in H'_\mu$, $F = h'_\mu f$.
Also, we can write

$$\langle h'_\mu f, \Phi \rangle \triangleq \langle f, h_\mu \Phi \rangle. \tag{1.127}$$

Theorem 1.26 *For $\mu \geq -\frac{1}{2}$, the generalized Hankel transformation h'_μ is an automorphism on H'_μ.*

Theorem 1.27 *Let $\mu \geq -\frac{1}{2}$. If $f \in H'_\mu$, then*

$$h_{\mu+1}(-xf) = N_\mu h_\mu f \tag{1.128}$$

$$h_{\mu+1}(N_\mu f) = -y h_\mu f \tag{1.129}$$

$$h_\mu(-x^2 f) = M_\mu N_\mu h_\mu f \tag{1.130}$$

$$h_\mu(M_\mu N_\mu f) = -y^2 h_\mu f. \tag{1.131}$$

If $f \in H'_{\mu+1}$, then

$$h_\mu(xf) = M_\mu h_{\mu+1} f \tag{1.132}$$

$$h_\mu(M_\mu f) = y h_{\mu+1} f. \tag{1.133}$$

Note: Here, (1.128) and (1.129) are understood in the sense of equality in $H'_{\mu+1}$, and (1.130) through (1.133) in the sense of equality in H'_μ.

1.9 The Hankel Transformation on $\mathscr{E}'(I)$

From Zemanian[1, p.36], the following descriptions regarding $\mathscr{E}'(I)$-space are given below:
$\mathscr{E}(I)$ is the space of all complex-valued smooth functions on I. There is no restriction imposed on the rate of growth of any function $\phi(t) \in \mathscr{E}(I)$ as $t \in I$ approaches the boundary of I. $\mathscr{E}(I)$ is a linear space under the usual definitions. Moreover, $D(I)$ is contained in $\mathscr{E}(I)$. $\mathscr{E}(I)$ is always taken to be a multinormed space by assigning to it the following topology: For each compact subset K of I and each nonnegative integer k, let $\gamma_{K,k}$ be the seminorm on $\mathscr{E}(I)$ defined by

$$\gamma_{K,k} \triangleq \sup_{t \in K} |D_t^k \phi(t)|, \quad \phi \in \mathscr{E}(I). \tag{1.134}$$

For every $\phi \in \mathscr{E}(I)$ other than the identically zero function on I there is at least one $\gamma_{K,0}$ such that $\gamma_{K,0}(\phi) \neq 0$. Consequently, the collection R of all $\gamma_{K,k}$ is separating and therefore is a multinorm on $\mathscr{E}(I)$, even though no single $\gamma_{K,k}$ is a norm. The topology of $\mathscr{E}(I)$ is that generated by R. $\mathscr{E}(I)$ is also complete.

$\mathscr{E}'(I)$ is the dual of $\mathscr{E}(I)$. According to [1, Theorem 1.8-3], $\mathscr{E}'(I)$ is complete.

The Hankel transform of $f \in \mathscr{E}'(I)$ is given by

$$F(y) = \langle f(x), \sqrt{xy} J_\mu(xy) \rangle, \quad \mu \geq -\frac{1}{2} \tag{1.135}$$

which we shall prove.

We shall first prove that, when $f \in \mathscr{E}'(I)$, $F(y)$ is a smooth function on $0 < y < \infty$. Above can be extended into an analytic function on the complex plane whose only singularities at the origin and at infinity. Let η be a complex variable, then set

$$F(\eta) = \langle f(x), \sqrt{x\eta} J_\mu(x\eta) \rangle. \tag{1.136}$$

For any fixed $x > 0$, $\sqrt{x\eta} J_\mu(x\eta)$ is a multivalued function of η except when $1 + 2\mu$ is an even integer. Now,

$$\sqrt{x\eta e^{i2n\pi}} J_\mu(x\eta e^{i2n\pi}) = e^{in\pi(1+2\mu)} \sqrt{x\eta} J_\mu(x\eta)$$

where $\eta \neq 0$ and n is any integer, (See Jahnke, Emde, and Losch [30], p. 134). Then, $F(\eta)$ also satisfies

$$F(\eta e^{i2n\pi}) = e^{in\pi(1+2\mu)} F(\eta), \quad \eta \neq 0$$

thus being multivalued when $1 + 2\mu$ is not an even integer.

Theorem 1.28 *Let f be a member of $\mathscr{E}'(I)$, μ any real number and η a complex variable. Then, $F(\eta)$ is defined by (1.136), an analytic function on the finite η plane except for a branch point at $\eta = 0$. Moreover,*

$$D_\eta F(\eta) = \langle f(x), D_\eta \sqrt{x\eta} J_\mu(x\eta) \rangle, \quad \eta \neq 0. \tag{1.137}$$

Proof See the detailed proof in Zemanian [1, Theorem 5.6-1, p. 146]. □

Theorem 1.29 *Let f be a member of $\mathscr{E}'(I)$, $\mu \geq -\frac{1}{2}$ and $F(y)$ is defined by (1.135). Then, $F(y)$ satisfies the inequality:*

$$|F(y)| \leq \begin{cases} K y^{\mu+1/2}, & 0 < y < 1 \\ K y^p, & 1 < y < \infty \end{cases} \tag{1.138}$$

where K and p are sufficiently large real numbers.

Proof For the proof, see Zemanian [1, Theorem 5.6-2, p. 147]. □

Theorem 1.30 *If $f \in \mathscr{E}'(I)$ and $\mu \geq -\frac{1}{2}$, the generalized Hankel transform of f, as defined by Sec. 1.6, Eq. (1.127), is the regular generalized function in H'_μ that is generated by the smooth function $F(y)$ defined by (1.135).*

Note that $F(y)$ truly does generate a regular member of H'_μ in view of Sec. 1.5, note V, Theorems 1.28 and 1.29, and the condition $\mu \geq -\frac{1}{2}$. The proof of Theorem 1.30 proceeds by the way of two lemmas.

Lemma 1.8 *If $\mu \geq -\frac{1}{2}$ and Φ is a member of H_μ, then*

$$\psi_Y(x) \triangleq \int_Y^\infty \Phi(y)\sqrt{xy}J_\mu(xy)dy$$

converges in $\mathscr{E}(I)$ to zero as $Y \to \infty$.

Proof The above lemma can be proved from Zemanian [1, Lemma 5.6-1, pp. 147-148]. □

Lemma 1.9 *If $\mu \geq -\frac{1}{2}$, $\Phi \in H_\mu$, $f \in \mathscr{E}'(I)$, and Y is a fixed (finite) positive number, then*

$$\int_0^Y \Phi(y)\langle f(x), \sqrt{xy}J_\mu(xy)\rangle dy = \langle f(x), \int_0^Y \Phi(y)\sqrt{xy}J_\mu(xy)dy\rangle. \quad (1.139)$$

Proof See the proof in Zemanian [1, Lemma 5.6-2, pp. 148-149]. □

Proof (**Proof of Theorem** 1.30) We have to show that, for any $\Phi \in H_\mu$,

$$\langle\langle f(x), \sqrt{xy}J_\mu(xy)\rangle, \Phi(y)\rangle = \langle f, h_\mu\Phi\rangle. \quad (1.140)$$

Using Lemma 1.2, Theorems 1.28 and 1.29, we have

$$\begin{aligned}&\langle\langle f(x), \sqrt{xy}J_\mu(xy)\rangle, \Phi(y)\rangle \\ &= \int_0^Y \langle f(x), \sqrt{xy}J_\mu(xy)\rangle\Phi(y)dy + \int_Y^\infty \langle f(x), \sqrt{xy}J_\mu(xy)\rangle\Phi(y)dy. \quad (1.141)\end{aligned}$$

Moreover, given any $\epsilon > 0$, there exists a Y_1 such that, for all $Y > Y_1$, the second term in (1.141) is bounded in magnitude by ϵ. We again write the R.H.S of (1.140) by

$$\langle f, h_\mu\Phi\rangle = \langle f(x), \int_0^Y \Phi(y)\sqrt{xy}J_\mu(xy)dy\rangle + \langle f(x), \int_Y^\infty \Phi(y)\sqrt{xy}J_\mu(xy)dy\rangle. \quad (1.142)$$

From Lemma 1.8, there is a Y_2 such that the second term in (1.142) is bounded in magnitude by ϵ whenever $Y > Y_2$. Finally, the first terms in (1.141) and (1.142) are equal to each other by Lemma 1.9. Thus, the difference between the two sides of (1.140) is less than 2ϵ. Since $\epsilon > 0$ can be chosen arbitrarily small, the proof of Theorem 1.30 is complete. □

Relation between Fourier transform and Hankel transform
In view of [31], the volume in n dimensions is

$$\text{vol} = d^n x = dx_1 dx_2 \ldots dx_n = r^{n-1} dr d^{n-1}\omega, \tag{1.143}$$

where $r = |x|$ is the radius, and $\omega = \frac{x}{r}$ is a radial unit vector. Also $d^{n-1}\omega$ represents the angular integral. For instance, when $n = 2$ it is $d\theta$ for $0 \le \theta \le 2\pi$, and for $n = 3$ it is $sin(\theta)d\theta d\phi$ for $0 \le \theta \le \pi$ and $0 \le \phi \le 2\pi$. The radial component of the volume gives the area of the sphere. The area of the unit sphere $S_{n-1} \subseteq \mathbb{R}^n$ is $\omega_{n-1} = \frac{2\pi^{\frac{n}{2}}}{\Gamma(\frac{n}{2})}$. Now, we discuss the relation between Fourier transform and Hankel transform.

Theorem 1.31 *The n-dimensional Fourier transform can be expressed in terms of the Hankel transform as*

$$(\mathscr{F} f)(s) = \tau^{-(\frac{n-1}{2})} h_{\frac{n-2}{2}}\{r^{\frac{n-1}{2}} F(r)\}(\tau),$$

where $f(x) = F(r)$, r and τ are radial parameter and

$$h_{\frac{n-2}{2}}\{r^{\frac{n-1}{2}} F(r)\}(\tau) = \int_0^\infty (\tau r)^{\frac{1}{2}} J_{(\frac{n-2}{2})}(\tau r) r^{\frac{n-1}{2}} F(r) dr,$$

for $r = \sqrt{x_1^2 + x_2^2}$ and $\tau = \sqrt{s_1^2 + s_2^2}$.

Proof From the definition of n-dimensional Fourier transform, we have

$$(\mathscr{F} f)(s) = \frac{1}{(2\pi)^{\frac{n}{2}}} \int_{\mathbb{R}^n} e^{-is.x} f(x) d^n x. \tag{1.144}$$

Let $r = |x|$ and $\tau = |s|$. Taking the polar coordinates with the z axis along s, so that $s.x = \tau r cos(\theta)$. Since function is radial, i.e., $f(x) = F(r)$, we have

$$\begin{aligned}(\mathscr{F} f)(s) &= \frac{1}{(2\pi)^{\frac{n}{2}}} \int_0^\infty \int_0^\pi e^{-i\tau r cos\theta} F(r)\omega_{n-2} sin(\theta)^{n-2} d\theta r^{n-1} dr \\ &= \frac{1}{(2\pi)^{\frac{n}{2}}} \int_0^\infty r^{n-1} F(r) dr \ \omega_{n-2} \int_0^\pi e^{-i\tau r cos\theta} sin(\theta)^{n-2} d\theta.\end{aligned}$$

From [31], using the result

$$(\tau r)^{-(\frac{n-2}{2})} J_{(\frac{n-2}{2})}(\tau r) = \frac{\omega_{n-2}}{(2\pi)^{\frac{n}{2}}} \int_0^\pi e^{-i\tau r cos\theta} sin(\theta)^{n-2} d\theta,$$

we find

$$
\begin{aligned}
(\mathscr{F} f)(s) &= \int_0^\infty r^{n-1} F(r)(\tau r)^{-(\frac{n-2}{2})} J_{(\frac{n-2}{2})}(\tau r)dr \\
&= \tau^{-(\frac{n-1}{2})} \int_0^\infty (\tau r)^{\frac{1}{2}} J_{(\frac{n-2}{2})}(\tau r) r^{\frac{n-1}{2}} F(r)dr \\
&= \tau^{-(\frac{n-1}{2})} h_{\frac{n-2}{2}} \{r^{\frac{n-1}{2}} F(r)\}(\tau).
\end{aligned}
$$

□

References

1. Zemanian, A.H.: Generalized integral transformations. Pure and applied mathematics XVIII. Interscience Publishers, New York (1968)
2. Zemanian, A.H.: A distributional Hankel transformation, SIAM J. Appl. Math. **14**(3, 561–576 (1966)
3. Zemanian, A.H.: The Hankel transformation of certain distributions of rapid growth. SIAM J. Appl. Math. **14**(4), 678–690 (1966)
4. Zemanian, A.H.: Hankel transforms of arbitrary order. Duke Math. J. **34**(4), 761–769 (1967)
5. Koh, E.L.: The Hankel transformation of negative order for distributions of rapid growth. SIAM J. Math. Anal. **1**(3), 322–327 (1970)
6. Koh, E.L.: The n-dimensional distributional Hankel transformation. Canad. J. Math. **27**(2), 423–433 (1975)
7. Pathak, R.S.: On Hankel transformable spaces and a Cauchy problem. Canad. J. Math. **37**(1), 84–106 (1985)
8. Pathak, R.S.: Integral transforms of generalized functions and their applications. Gordon and Breach Science Publishers, Amsterdam (1997)
9. Pathak, R.S., Pandey, A.B.: On Hankel transforms of ultradistributions. Appl. Anal. **20**(3–4), 245–268 (1985)
10. Pathak, R.S., Pandey, P.K.: Sobolev type spaces associated with Bessel operators. J. Math. Anal. Appl. **215**(1), 95–111 (1997)
11. Lee, K.W.Y.: On spaces of type H_μ and their Hankel transformations. SIAM J. Math. Anal. **5**(2), 336–348 (1974)
12. Dube, L.S., Pandey, J.N.: On the Hankel transform of distributions. Tohoku Math. J. **27**(3), 337–354 (1975)
13. Betancor, J.J.: A new characterization of the bounded operators commuting with Hankel translation. Arch. Math. **69**(5), 403–408 (1997)
14. Betancor, J.J.: On Hankel transformable distribution spaces, Publ. Inst. Math. (Beograd)(N.S.) **65**(79), 123–141 (1999)
15. Betancor, J.J.: A generalized Hankel convolution on Zemanian spaces. Int. J. Math. Math. Sci. **23**(2), 131–140 (2000)
16. Betancor, J.J., Gonz, B.J.: A convolution operation for a distributional Hankel transformation. Studia Math. **117**(1), 57–72 (1995)
17. Betancor, J.J., Jerez, C.: Convolution Hankel transforms on the Zemanian spaces. Acta Math. Hungar. **80**(3), 225–235 (1998)
18. Betancor, J.J., Marrero, I.: Some properties of Hankel convolution operators. Canad. Math. Bull. **36**(4), 398–406 (1993)
19. Betancor, J.J., Marrero, I.: Structure and convergence in certain spaces of distributions and the generalized Hankel convolution. Math. Japon. **38**(6), 1141–1155 (1993)

20. Betancor, J.J., Marrero, I.: The Hankel convolution and the Zemanian spaces β_μ and β'_μ. Math. Nachr. **160**, 277–298 (1993)
21. Betancor, J.J., Marrero, I.: Algebraic characterization of convolution and multiplication operators on Hankel-transformable function and distribution spaces. Rocky Mountain J. Math. **25**, 1189–1204 (1995)
22. Betancor, J.J., Rodríguez-Mesa, L.: Hankel convolution on distribution spaces with exponential growth. Studia Math. **121**(1), 35–52 (1996)
23. Betancor, J.J., Rodríguez-Mesa, L.: On Hankel convolution equations in distribution spaces. Rocky Mountain J. Math. **29**(1), 93–114 (1999)
24. Marrero, I., Betancor, J.J.: Hankel convolution of generalized functions. Rend. Mat. Appl. **15**(3), 351–380 (1995)
25. Pathak, R.S.: The Wavelet Transform. Atlantic Press/World Scientific, Paris, France (2009)
26. Macaulay-Owen, P.: Parseval's theorem for Hankel transforms. Proc. London Math. Soc. **2**(1), 458–474 (1939)
27. Watson, G.N.: Theory of Bessel Functions, 2nd edn. Cambridge University Press, Cambridge (1958)
28. Wing, G.: On the L^p- theory of Hankel transforms. Pacific J. Math. **1**(2), 313–319 (1951)
29. Kerr, F.H.: A fractional power theory for Hankel transforms in $L^2(\mathbb{R}^+)$. J. Math. Anal. Appl. **158**(1), 114–123 (1991)
30. Jahnke, E., Lösch, F.: Tables of higher functions. McGraw-Hill (1960)
31. Faris, W.G.: Radial functions and the Fourier transform: Notes for Math 583A, Fall 2008. University of Arizona, Department of Mathematics (2008)

Chapter 2
The Continuous Bessel Wavelet Transformation Associated with the Hankel-Hausdorff Operator

2.1 Introduction

The continuous and discrete Bessel wavelet transformations were introduced by Pathak and Dixit [1], and analyzed their properties through the Hankel convolution approach developed by Haimo [2] and Hirschman [3]. However, many researchers have applied the Hankel transformation of type (1.75), and the Hankel convolution (1.79), to various function spaces, leading to numerous significant results. Liflyland and Moricz [4] considered the Hausdorff operator on the real Hardy space $H^1(\mathbb{R})$ and proved the boundedness property of this operator by exploiting the Fourier and Hilbert transformations.

Exploiting the theory of the Hankel transformation (1.75) and the Hankel convolution (1.79), this chapter provides the continuous Bessel wavelet transformation and explore its inversion formula, Parseval relation, and other fundamental properties using Hankel convolution theory and the connection between the Bessel wavelet transformation and the Hankel-Hausdorff operator are established.

Some results are given in detail which are helpful for this chapter:

The Stieltjes transformation of a function $f \in L^1(0, \infty)$ is defined as

$$(S_p f)(y) = \int_0^\infty \frac{f(t)}{(y+t)^p} dt, \qquad p > 1 \text{ and } y > 0 \tag{2.1}$$

provided the integral involved is convergent.
The Hardy space $H^1(0, \infty)$ is defined to be :

$$H^1(0, \infty) = \{f \in L^1(0, \infty) : (S_p f)(x) \in L^1(0, \infty)\}, \tag{2.2}$$

with the norm

$$\|f\|_{H^1(0,\infty)} = \|f\|_{L^1(0,\infty)} + \|S_p f\|_{L^1(0,\infty)}, \tag{2.3}$$

S. K. Upadhyay and J. S. Maurya, *The Bessel Wavelet Transform*,
Industrial and Applied Mathematics,
https://doi.org/10.1007/978-981-96-9938-4_2

and

$$\|f\|_{L^1(0,\infty)} = \int_0^\infty |f(x)|\, dx. \tag{2.4}$$

Let $\phi \in L^1(0,\infty)$. In Hankel setting we state the definition of the Hausdorff operator H_ϕ acting on $L^1(0,\infty)$ generated by a function ϕ belonging to $L^1(0,\infty)$. Given any function $f \in L^1(0,\infty)$, $H_\phi f$ is that function in $L^1(0,\infty)$ given by

$$h_\mu(H_\phi f)(t) = \int_0^\infty (h_\mu f)(xt)\phi(x)\, dx \text{ and } t \in (0,\infty), \tag{2.5}$$

provided $(H_\phi f)(x) = \int_0^\infty f(x/\xi)\phi(\xi)d\xi < \infty$.

Further, we define the space $L^2(0,\infty)$ as the space of square integrable functions f on $(0,\infty)$, for which

$$\|f\|_{L^2(0,\infty)} = \left(\int_0^\infty |f(x)|^2 dx\right)^{\frac{1}{2}} < \infty. \tag{2.6}$$

Then $L^1_\mu(0,\infty)$-estimates of the Hankel convolution of f and g is given by the following relation:

$$\|f\#g\|_{L^1_\mu(0,\infty)} \leq \|f\|_{L^1_\mu(0,\infty)}\|g\|_{L^1_\mu(0,\infty)}\,, \tag{2.7}$$

where

$$\|f\|_{L^1_\mu(0,\infty)} = \int_0^\infty |f(x)|x^{\mu+\frac{1}{2}}dx. \tag{2.8}$$

2.2 Continuous Bessel Wavelet Transformation

In this section (see [5]), we define the Bessel wavelet transform and studied some properties using the theory of Hankel convolution (1.79). A Bessel wavelet is a function $\psi \in L^2(0,\infty)$ which satisfies the condition

$$C_{\mu,\psi} = \int_0^\infty x^{-2\mu-2}|(h_\mu\psi)(x)|^2 dx < \infty, \qquad \mu \geq -\frac{1}{2} \tag{2.9}$$

where $(h_\mu\psi)(x)$ is the Hankel transform of $\psi(t)$. $C_{\mu,\psi}$ is called the admissibility condition of the Bessel wavelet. Admissibility condition also imposes a restriction on the rate of decay of $|h_\mu\psi|^2$ and is useful to find the continuous inverse Bessel wavelet transform.

Let $\psi \in L^2(0,\infty)$. For $b \geq 0$ and $a > 0$, we define the Bessel wavelet transformation of a function $f \in L^2(0,\infty)$ by

$$(B_\psi f)(b,a) = a^{\mu-\frac{1}{2}} \int_0^\infty f(t)\psi\left(\frac{t}{a},\frac{b}{a}\right)dt, \tag{2.10}$$

where ψ is a wavelet which satisfies (2.9) and $\psi(x,y)$ has the same meaning as given by (1.80).

Theorem 2.1 *Let $\psi \in L^2(0,\infty)$ and $f \in L^2(0,\infty)$. Then*

$$(B_\psi f)(b,a) = \int_0^\infty (bx)^{\frac{1}{2}} J_\mu(bx)(h_\mu f)(x)x^{-\mu-\frac{1}{2}}(h_\mu\psi)(ax)dx. \tag{2.11}$$

Proof It follows from (2.10) that

$$(B_\psi f)(b,a) = a^{\mu-\frac{1}{2}} \int_0^\infty f(t)\psi\left(\frac{t}{a},\frac{b}{a}\right)dt.$$

Now, consider $\psi(\frac{t}{a},\frac{b}{a}) = \psi(x,y)$ for putting $\frac{t}{a} = x$ and $\frac{b}{a} = y$. Then,

$$\begin{aligned}
\psi(x,y) &= \int_0^\infty \psi(z)D_\mu(x,y,z)dz \\
&= \int_0^\infty \psi(z)\left(\int_0^\infty \xi^{-\mu-\frac{1}{2}}(x\xi)^{\frac{1}{2}}J_\mu(x\xi)(y\xi)^{\frac{1}{2}}J_\mu(y\xi)(z\xi)^{\frac{1}{2}}J_\mu(z\xi)d\xi\right)dz \\
&= \int_0^\infty \left(\int_0^\infty (z\xi)^{\frac{1}{2}}J_\mu(z\xi)\psi(z)dz\right)\xi^{-\mu-\frac{1}{2}}(x\xi)^{\frac{1}{2}}J_\mu(x\xi)(y\xi)^{\frac{1}{2}}J_\mu(y\xi)d\xi \\
&= \int_0^\infty (x\xi)^{\frac{1}{2}}J_\mu(x\xi)(y\xi)^{\frac{1}{2}}J_\mu(y\xi)\xi^{-\mu-\frac{1}{2}}(h_\mu\psi)(\xi)d\xi.
\end{aligned}$$

Therefore,

$$\begin{aligned}
&(B_\psi f)(b,a) \\
&= a^{\mu-\frac{1}{2}} \int_0^\infty \left(\int_0^\infty \xi^{-\mu-\frac{1}{2}}\left(\frac{t\xi}{a}\right)^{\frac{1}{2}} J_\mu\left(\frac{t\xi}{a}\right)a^{-\frac{1}{2}}\left(\frac{b\xi}{a}\right)^{\frac{1}{2}} J_\mu\left(\frac{b\xi}{a}\right)(h_\mu\psi)(\xi)d\xi\right)f(t)\,dt \\
&= a^{\mu-\frac{1}{2}} \int_0^\infty \left(\int_0^\infty \left(\frac{t\xi}{a}\right)^{\frac{1}{2}} J_\mu\left(\frac{t\xi}{a}\right)f(t)dt\right)\left(\frac{b\xi}{a}\right)^{\frac{1}{2}} J_\mu\left(\frac{b\xi}{a}\right)\xi^{-\mu-\frac{1}{2}}(h_\mu\psi)(\xi)d\xi \\
&= a^{\mu-\frac{1}{2}} \int_0^\infty (h_\mu f)\left(\frac{\xi}{a}\right)\left(\frac{b\xi}{a}\right)^{\frac{1}{2}} J_\mu\left(\frac{b\xi}{a}\right)\xi^{-\mu-\frac{1}{2}}(h_\mu\psi)(\xi)d\xi.
\end{aligned}$$

By putting $\frac{\xi}{a} = x$, $d\xi = a\,dx$, the continuous Bessel wavelet transform is

$$(B_\psi f)(b,a) = \int_0^\infty (bx)^{\frac{1}{2}} J_\mu(bx)(h_\mu f)(x) x^{-\mu-\frac{1}{2}} (h_\mu \psi)(ax)dx.$$

□

Theorem 2.2 *Let $\psi \in L^2(0,\infty)$ and $b \geq 0$, $a > 0$ then Bessel wavelet transformation of a function $f \in L^2(0,\infty)$ is*

$$(B_\psi f)(b,a) = a^{\mu-\frac{1}{2}} \int_0^\infty f\left(t, \frac{b}{a}\right) \psi\left(\frac{t}{a}\right) dt.$$

Proof From (2.10), we have

$$(B_\psi f)(b,a) = a^{\mu-\frac{1}{2}} \int_0^\infty f(t)\, \psi\left(\frac{t}{a}, \frac{b}{a}\right) dt.$$

Putting $\frac{t}{a} = x$ then R.H.S of the above expression can be written as

$$(B_\psi f)(b,a) = a^{\mu-\frac{1}{2}} \int_0^\infty f(ax)\, \psi\left(x, \frac{b}{a}\right) a\, dx.$$

Finally, from (1.80) we have

$$\begin{aligned}(B_\psi f)(b,a) &= a^{\mu-\frac{1}{2}} \int_0^\infty (\tau_{\frac{b}{a}} f)(ax)\psi(x) a\, dx \\ &= a^{\mu-\frac{1}{2}} \int_0^\infty (\tau_{\frac{b}{a}} f)(t)\psi\left(\frac{t}{a}\right) dt \\ &= a^{\mu-\frac{1}{2}} \int_0^\infty f\left(t, \frac{b}{a}\right)\psi\left(\frac{t}{a}\right) dt.\end{aligned}$$

□

Theorem 2.3 *If $\psi \in L^2(0,\infty)$ and $(B_\psi f)(b,a)$ is the Bessel wavelet transformation of a function f defined by (2.10), then, for any two functions $f, g \in L^2(0,\infty)$, we obtain*

$$\int_0^\infty \int_0^\infty (B_\psi f)(b,a)(B_\psi g)(b,a)\, \frac{db\, da}{a^2} = C_{\mu,\psi}\langle f, g\rangle, \tag{2.12}$$

where $C_{\mu,\psi} = \int_0^\infty x^{-2\mu-2}(h_\mu \psi)(x)dx$.

Proof Since

$$(B_\psi f)(b,a) = a^{\mu-\frac{1}{2}} \int_0^\infty \psi\left(\frac{t}{a}, \frac{b}{a}\right) f(t)dt,$$

using (2.11), we have

$$\begin{aligned}
&\int_0^\infty \int_0^\infty (B_\psi f)(b,a)(B_\psi g)(b,a)\frac{da\,db}{a^{2\mu+2}}\\
&= \int_0^\infty \left(\int_0^\infty \left((B_\psi f)(b,a)(B_\psi g)(b,a)db\right)\frac{da}{a^{2\mu+2}}\right)\\
&= \left(\int_0^\infty \left(\int_0^\infty \left(\int_0^\infty (bx)^{\frac{1}{2}} J_\mu(bx)(h_\mu f)(x)x^{-\mu-\frac{1}{2}}(h_\mu \psi)(ax)dx\right)\right.\right.\\
&\times \left.\left.\left(\int_0^\infty (by)^{\frac{1}{2}} J_\mu(by)(h_\mu g)(y)y^{-\mu-\frac{1}{2}}(h_\mu \psi)(ay)dy\right)db\right)\frac{da}{a^{2\mu+2}}\right)\\
&= \left(\int_0^\infty \left(\int_0^\infty (h_\mu F)(b)(h_\mu G)(b)db\right)a^{-2\mu-2}da\right),
\end{aligned}$$

where $F(x) = (h_\mu f)(x)(h_\mu \psi)(ax)x^{-\mu-\frac{1}{2}}$ and $G(y) = (h_\mu g)(y)(h_\mu \psi)(ay)y^{-\mu-\frac{1}{2}}$.

Therefore, by Parseval formula (1.77)

$$\begin{aligned}
&\int_0^\infty \int_0^\infty (B_\psi f)(b,a)(B_\psi g)(b,a)\frac{da\,db}{a^{2\mu+2}}\\
&= \left(\int_0^\infty \left(\int_0^\infty F(x)G(x)dx\right)a^{-2\mu-2}da\right)\\
&= \left(\int_0^\infty \left(\int_0^\infty (h_\mu f)(x)x^{-\mu-\frac{1}{2}}(h_\mu \psi)(ax)(h_\mu g)(x)x^{-\mu-\frac{1}{2}}(h_\mu \psi)(ax)dx\right)a^{-2\mu-2}da\right).
\end{aligned}$$

Therefore, we get

$$\begin{aligned}
&\int_0^\infty \int_0^\infty (B_\psi f)(b,a)(B_\psi, g)(b,a)\frac{db\,da}{a^{2\mu+2}}\\
&= \int_0^\infty \left(\int_0^\infty |(h_\mu \psi)(ax)|^2\, x^{-2\mu-1} a^{-2\mu-2}da\right)(h_\mu f)(x)(h_\mu g)(x)dx\\
&= C_{\mu,\psi}\int_0^\infty (h_\mu f)(x)(h_\mu g)(x)dx\\
&= C_{\mu,\psi}\langle h_\mu f, h_\mu g\rangle.
\end{aligned}$$

Using Parseval relation (1.77) of the Hankel transformation, we find that

$$\int_0^\infty \int_0^\infty (B_\psi f)(b,a)(B_\psi g)(b,a)\frac{db\,da}{a^{2\mu+2}} = C_{\mu,\psi}\langle f, g\rangle.$$

This formula is called the Parseval relation for Bessel wavelet transformation. □

Theorem 2.4 *If $f \in L^2(0,\infty)$, then f can be reconstructed by the formula*

$$f(t) = \frac{1}{C_{\mu,\psi}} \int_0^\infty \int_0^\infty (B_\psi f)(a,b)\psi\left(\frac{t}{a},\frac{b}{a}\right)\frac{db\,da}{a^{\mu+5/2}}$$

for $a > 0$.

Proof Let $g \in L^2(0,\infty)$. Then, by Parseval's formula for the Bessel wavelet transformation, we have

$$\begin{aligned}
C_{\mu,\psi}\langle f, g\rangle &= \langle B_\psi f, B_\psi g\rangle \\
&= \int_0^\infty \int_0^\infty (B_\psi f)(b,a)(B_\psi g)(b,a)\frac{db\,da}{a^{2\mu+2}} \\
&= \left(\int_0^\infty \left(\int_0^\infty (B_\psi f)(b,a)\left(\int_0^\infty g(t)\psi\left(\frac{t}{a},\frac{b}{a}\right)a^{\mu-\frac{1}{2}}dt\right)\frac{db\,da}{a^{2\mu+2}}\right)\right) \\
&= \left(\int_0^\infty \left(\int_0^\infty \int_0^\infty (B_\psi f)(b,a)\psi\left(\frac{t}{a},\frac{b}{a}\right)\frac{db\,da}{a^{\mu+5/2}}\right)g(t)dt\right) \\
&= \left\langle\left(\int_0^\infty \int_0^\infty (B_\psi f)(b,a)\psi\left(\frac{t}{a},\frac{b}{a}\right)\frac{db\,da}{a^{\mu+5/2}}, g(t)\right\rangle.
\end{aligned}$$

If $f = g$, then

$$\begin{aligned}
C_{\mu,\psi}\langle f, f\rangle &= \left\langle\left(\int_0^\infty \int_0^\infty (B_\psi f)(b,a)\psi\left(\frac{t}{a},\frac{b}{a}\right)\frac{db\,da}{a^{\mu+5/2}}, f(t)\right\rangle \\
&= \left(\int_0^\infty \int_0^\infty (B_\psi f)(b,a)(B_\psi f)(b,a)\frac{db\,da}{a^{2\mu+2}}\right).
\end{aligned}$$

Therefore,

$$C_{\mu,\psi}\|f\|^2 = \int_0^\infty \int_0^\infty |(B_\psi f)(b,a)|^2\frac{db\,da}{a^{2\mu+2}}.$$

This implies that the Bessel wavelet transformation is isometrical from $L^2(I)$ to $L^2(I\times I)$, where $I = (0,\infty)$.

Theorem 2.5 *If $\psi \in L^2(0,\infty)$ is a Bessel wavelet and f is a bounded integrable function, then the convolution $\psi\# f$ is a Bessel wavelet.*

Proof It follows from (1.79) that

$$(\psi\#f)(x)=\int_0^\infty \psi(x,y)f(y)dy,\quad \text{for } x>0.$$

It follows from (1.80) that

$$\psi(x,y)=\int_0^\infty \psi(z)D_\mu(x,y,z)dz.$$

Then

$$\begin{aligned}|\psi(x,y)| &\le \int_0^\infty |\psi(z)|D_\mu(x,y,z)dz\\ &= \int_0^\infty |\psi(z)|z^{-\frac{1}{2}(\mu+\frac{1}{2})}D_\mu^{\frac{1}{2}}(x,y,z)z^{\frac{1}{2}(\mu+\frac{1}{2})}D_\mu^{\frac{1}{2}}(x,y,z)dz\\ &\le \left(\int_0^\infty |\psi(z)|^2 z^{-\mu-\frac{1}{2}}D_\mu(x,y,z)dz\right)^{\frac{1}{2}}\left(\int_0^\infty z^{\mu+\frac{1}{2}}D_\mu(x,y,z)dz\right)^{\frac{1}{2}},\end{aligned}$$

so that

$$|\psi(x,y)|^2\le\left(\int_0^\infty |\psi(z)|^2 z^{-\mu-\frac{1}{2}}D_\mu(x,y,z)dz\right)\left(\frac{(xy)^{\mu+\frac{1}{2}}}{2^\mu\Gamma(\mu+1)}\right).$$

Hence,

$$\begin{aligned}\int|\psi(x,y)|^2dx &\le \frac{1}{2^\mu\Gamma(\mu+1)}\int_0^\infty\left(\int_0^\infty |\psi(z)|^2z^{-\mu-\frac{1}{2}}D_\mu(x,y,z)dz\right)(xy)^{\mu+\frac{1}{2}}dx\\ &\le \frac{1}{2^\mu\Gamma(\mu+1)}\int_0^\infty |\psi(z)|^2z^{-\mu-\frac{1}{2}}y^{\mu+\frac{1}{2}}\left(\int_0^\infty x^{\mu+\frac{1}{2}}D_\mu(x,y,z)dx\right)dz\\ &\le \frac{1}{2^\mu\Gamma(\mu+1)}\int_0^\infty |\psi(z)|^2z^{-\mu-\frac{1}{2}}y^{\mu+\frac{1}{2}}\frac{(yz)^{\mu+\frac{1}{2}}}{2^\mu\Gamma(\mu+1)}dz\\ &\le \frac{y^{2\mu+1}}{(2^\mu\Gamma(\mu+1))^2}\int_0^\infty |\psi(z)|^2dz. \qquad (2.13)\end{aligned}$$

Now,

$$\begin{aligned}
\int_0^\infty |(\psi\# f)(x)|^2\,dx &= \int_0^\infty \left(\left|\int_0^\infty \psi(x,y)f(y)dy\right|\right)^2 dx\\
&\le \int_0^\infty \left(\int_0^\infty |\psi(x,y)|\,|f(y)|dy\right)^2 dx\\
&= \int_0^\infty \left(\int_0^\infty |\psi(x,y)|\,y^{-\frac{1}{2}(\mu+\frac{1}{2})}|f^{\frac{1}{2}}(y)|\,y^{\frac{1}{2}(\mu+\frac{1}{2})}|f^{\frac{1}{2}}(y)|dy\right)^2 dx\\
&\le \int_0^\infty \left[\left(\int_0^\infty |\psi(x,y)|^2\,y^{-\mu-\frac{1}{2}}|f(y)|dy\right)^{\frac{1}{2}}\left(\int_0^\infty y^{\mu+\frac{1}{2}}|f(y)|dy\right)^{\frac{1}{2}}\right]^2 dx\\
&\le \int_0^\infty \left(\int_0^\infty |\psi(x,y)|^2\,y^{-\mu-\frac{1}{2}}|f(y)|dy\right) dx\,\|y^{\mu+\frac{1}{2}}f(y)\|_{L^1(0,\infty)}\\
&\le \int_0^\infty y^{-\mu-\frac{1}{2}}|f(y)|\left(\int_0^\infty |\psi(x,y)|^2\,dx\right) dy\,\|y^{\mu+\frac{1}{2}}f(y)\|_{L^1(0,\infty)}\\
&\le \int_0^\infty y^{-\mu-\frac{1}{2}}|f(y)|\left(\frac{y^{2\mu+1}}{(2^\mu\Gamma(\mu+1))^2}\int_0^\infty |\psi(z)|^2dz\right) dy\,\|y^{\mu+\frac{1}{2}}f(y)\|_{L^1(0,\infty)}\\
&\le \frac{1}{(2^\mu\Gamma(\mu+1))^2}\int_0^\infty y^{\mu+\frac{1}{2}}|f(y)|dy\int_0^\infty |\psi(z)|^2dz\,\|y^{\mu+\frac{1}{2}}f(y)\|_{L^1(0,\infty)}.
\end{aligned}$$

We obtain from (2.13),

$$\int_0^\infty |(\psi\# f)(x)|^2dx \le \frac{1}{(2^\mu\Gamma(\mu+1))^2}\int_0^\infty y^{\mu+\frac{1}{2}}|f(y)|dy\int_0^\infty |\psi(z)|^2dz\,\|y^{\mu+\frac{1}{2}}f(y)\|_{L^1}.$$

This implies that

$$\|\psi\# f\|_{L^2(0,\infty)} \le \frac{1}{2^\mu\Gamma(\mu+1)}\|y^{\mu+\frac{1}{2}}f(y)\|_{L^1(0,\infty)}\|\psi\|_{L^2(0,\infty)}.$$

Thus,

$$\psi\# f \in L^2(0,\infty).$$

Next, we have to show that

$$\int_0^\infty \frac{|h_\mu(\psi\# f)(x)|^2}{x^{2\mu+2}}\,dx < \infty, \quad \text{for } x > 0.$$

From (2.3), we get

$$\begin{aligned}
&\int_0^\infty \frac{|h_\mu(\psi\# f)(x)|^2}{x^{2\mu+2}}\,dx \qquad x \neq 0\\
&= \int_0^\infty \frac{|x^{-\mu-\frac{1}{2}}(h_\mu\psi)(x)(h_\mu f)(x)|^2}{x^{2\mu+2}}dx\\
&\leq \sup_x |x^{-\mu-\frac{1}{2}}(h_\mu f)(x)|^2 \left(\int_0^\infty x^{-2\mu-2}|(h_\mu\psi)(x)|^2\,dx\right)\\
&= C_{\mu,\psi}\sup_x |x^{-\mu-\frac{1}{2}}(h_\mu f)(x)|^2 < \infty.
\end{aligned}$$

If $\psi \in L^2(0,\infty)$, then its Hankel transformation $h_\mu\psi$ is continuous. Since $h_\mu\psi$ is continuous, the admissibility condition (2.9) can be finite only if $(h_\mu\psi(0)) = 0$ or, equivalently $\int_0^\infty \psi(t)dt = 0$. Like $\psi \in L^2(0,\infty)$, the Hankel convolution $\psi\# f \in L^2(0,\infty)$ satisfies (2.9) and the above arguments.

This shows that $\psi\# f$ is a wavelet.

Theorem 2.6 *Let $f \in L^1(0,\infty)$ and $\phi \in L^1(0,\infty)$, be such that the Bessel wavelet transformation of a Hankel-Hausdorff operator, with respect to wavelet ψ, can be expressed in the following form*

$$B_\psi(H_\phi f)(b,a) = \int_0^\infty (B_\psi f)\Big(\frac{b}{t},a\Big)t^{\mu-\frac{1}{2}}\phi(t)dt, \qquad t>0.$$

Proof From (2.10) and (2.11) and [1], we have

$$\begin{aligned}
B_\psi(H_\phi f)(b,a) &= \int_0^\infty (bx)^{\frac{1}{2}}J_\mu(bx)h_\mu(H_\phi f)(x)x^{-\mu-\frac{1}{2}}(h_\mu\psi)(ax)dx\\
&= \int_0^\infty (bx)^{\frac{1}{2}}J_\mu(bx)h_\mu(H_\phi f)(x)x^{-\mu-\frac{1}{2}}(h_\mu\psi)(ax)dx\\
&= \int_0^\infty (bx)^{\frac{1}{2}}J_\mu(bx)\left(\int_0^\infty (h_\mu f)(xt)\phi(t)dt\right)x^{-\mu-\frac{1}{2}}(h_\mu\psi)(ax)dx.
\end{aligned}$$

Putting $xt = u$, $tdx = du$, we obtain

$$\begin{aligned}
&B_\psi(H_\phi f)(b,a)\\
&= \int_0^\infty\left(\int_0^\infty \left(\frac{bu}{t}\right)^{\frac{1}{2}} J_\mu\left(\frac{bu}{t}\right)(h_\mu\psi)\left(\frac{au}{t}\right)u^{-\mu-\frac{1}{2}}(h_\mu f)(u)du\right)t^{\mu-\frac{1}{2}}\phi(t)dt.
\end{aligned}$$

It then follows from (2.10) that

$$B_\psi(H_\phi f)(b,a) = \int_0^\infty (B_\psi f)\left(\frac{b}{t},a\right)t^{\mu-\frac{1}{2}}\phi(t)dt.$$

This is the desired result. □

Theorem 2.7 *The Hausdorff operator of Hankel convolution is bounded for* $\mu \geq -\frac{1}{2}$ *and satisfies the following estimate*

$$\|H_\phi(f\#\psi)(x)\|_{L^1_\mu(0,\infty)} \leq \|\phi\|_{L^1_\mu(0,\infty)}\|f\|_{L^1_\mu(0,\infty)}\|\psi\|_{L^1_\mu(0,\infty)}.$$

Proof Now, we have

$$\big(H_\phi(f\#\psi)(x)\big) = \int_0^\infty \frac{(f\#\psi)(\xi)}{\xi}\,\phi\left(\frac{x}{\xi}\right)\,d\xi.$$

Then

$$\int_0^\infty |H_\phi(f\#\psi)(x)|x^{\mu+\frac{1}{2}}dx \leq \left(\int_0^\infty \left(\int_0^\infty \frac{|(f\#\psi)(\xi)|}{\xi}\left|\phi\left(\frac{x}{\xi}\right)\right|d\xi\right)x^{\mu+\frac{1}{2}}dx\right).$$

Let $\frac{x}{\xi} = u$, $dx = \xi\,du$. Then

$$\begin{aligned}
&\int_0^\infty |H_\phi(f\#\psi)(x)|x^{\mu+\frac{1}{2}}dx \\
&\leq \left(\int_0^\infty |(f\#\psi)(\xi)|\xi^{\mu+\frac{1}{2}}d\xi\right)\left(\int_0^\infty |\phi(u)|du\right) \\
&\leq \|f\|_{L^1_\mu(0,\infty)}\|\psi\|_{L^1_\mu(0,\infty)}\|\phi\|_{L^1_\mu(0,\infty)}.
\end{aligned}$$

□

References

1. Pathak, R.S., Dixit, M.M.: Continuous and discrete Bessel wavelet transforms. J. Comput. Appl. Math. **160**(1–2), 241–250 (2003)
2. Haimo, D.T.: Integral equations associated with Hankel convolutions. Trans. Amer. Math. Soc. **116**, 330–375 (1965)
3. Hirschman, I.: Variation diminishing Hankel transforms. J. Analyse Math. **8**(1), 307–336 (1960–61)
4. Liflyand, E., Moricz, F.: The Hausdorff operator is bounded on the real Hardy space $H^1(\mathbb{R})$. Proc. Amer. Math. Soc. **128**(5), 1291–1396 (1999)
5. Debnath, L.: Wavelet transforms and their applications. Birkhäuser, Boston, MA (2002)

Chapter 3
The Bessel Wavelet Transform and the Spaces with Exponential Growth

3.1 Introduction

J.J.Betancor and Mesa [1] defined the space χ_μ which consists of all smooth complex-valued function $\phi(x)$, $x \in (0,\infty)$ satisfies the following norm

$$\gamma_{k,m}^{\mu}(\phi) = \sup_{x\in(0,\infty)} \left| e^{kx}(x^{-1}\frac{d}{dx})^m (x^{-\mu-\frac{1}{2}}\phi(x)) \right| < \infty \tag{3.1}$$

for every $k, m \in \mathbb{N}_0$.
The semi norm for $\phi \in \chi_\mu$ is given by

$$\eta_{k,m}^{\mu}(\phi) = \sup_{x\in(0,\infty)} \left| e^{kx} x^{-\mu-\frac{1}{2}} S_\mu^m \phi(x) \right|, \qquad k, m \in \mathbb{N}_0, \tag{3.2}$$

where $S_\mu = x^{-\mu-\frac{1}{2}}\frac{d}{dx}x^{2\mu+1}\frac{d}{dx}x^{-\mu-\frac{1}{2}}$, induces on χ_μ the same topology as defined by $\left\{\gamma_{k,m}^{\mu}\right\}_{k,m\in\mathbb{N}_0}$.

From [1], Q_μ as the space of all complex-valued functions Φ which satisfy the following two conditions

1. $z^{-\mu-\frac{1}{2}}\Phi(z)$ is an even entire function.
2. For every $k, m \in \mathbb{N}_0$, the following norm is given by

$$\omega_{k,m}^{\mu}(\Phi) = \sup_{|Imz|\le k} (1+|z|^2)^m |z^{-\mu-\frac{1}{2}}\Phi(z)| < \infty. \tag{3.3}$$

S. K. Upadhyay and J. S. Maurya, *The Bessel Wavelet Transform*,
Industrial and Applied Mathematics,
https://doi.org/10.1007/978-981-96-9938-4_3

The boundedness properties of Bessel function are given below

$$\text{(i)}\ \left|z^{-\mu} J_\mu(z)\right| \le Ce^{|Imz|}, \quad z \in \mathbb{C} \tag{3.4}$$

$$\text{(ii)}\ |z^{1/2} H_\mu^{(1)}(z)| \le Ce^{-Imz}, \quad z \in \mathbb{C}, |z| \ge 1 \tag{3.5}$$

where $H_\mu^{(1)}$ denotes the Hankel function of the first kind of order μ and C is a positive constant depending on μ in (3.4) and (3.5).

From [2], we recall the Bessel wavelet transform of a function $f \in L^2(0, \infty)$ with respect to a Bessel wavelet $\psi \in L^2(0, \infty)$ is

$$(B_\psi f)(b, a) = \int_0^\infty f(t)\psi_{a,b}(t)dt, \tag{3.6}$$

where

$$\psi_{a,b}(t) = a^{\mu-\frac{1}{2}}\psi\left(\frac{t}{a}, \frac{b}{a}\right) = a^{\mu-\frac{1}{2}}\int_0^\infty \psi(z)D_\mu\left(\frac{t}{a}, \frac{b}{a}, z\right)dz. \tag{3.7}$$

In this chapter, the Bessel wavelet transform on $\chi_\mu(I)$ and $Q_\mu(I)$ spaces are investigated and it is shown that Bessel wavelet transform $B_\mu : \chi_\mu(I) \longrightarrow \chi_\mu(I \times I)$, $B_\mu : Q_\mu(I) \longrightarrow Q_\mu(I \times I)$ are linear and continuous. Applying the continuity property of the Bessel wavelet transform, some properties of Hankel convolution are studied. Various examples of Fredholm integral equation associated with Hankel convolution and the Bessel wavelet transform are discussed.

3.2 The Bessel Wavelet Transform on the Spaces χ_μ and Q_μ

In this section the properties of Bessel wavelet transform on χ_μ and Q_μ type spaces are studied.

Lemma 3.1 *If $\psi \in \chi_\mu(I)$, $I = (0, \infty)$ then we have the following estimate*

$$\left|(a^{-1}\frac{d}{da})^q\,(h_\mu\psi)(a(\xi + i(k+1))\right| \le \sum_{r=0}^{q}\binom{q}{r}C_\mu a^{\mu+\frac{1}{2}-2r}\ |\xi + i(k+1)|^{\mu-2r+2q+\frac{1}{2}} \times \gamma_{0,k}^{\mu}(\phi)\Gamma(2\mu - 2r + 2q + 1),$$

where $\mu > r - q - \frac{1}{2}$ and $C_\mu = C \times A_{\mu,r}$ with arbitrary constant C and $A_{\mu,r} = (\mu + \frac{1}{2})(\mu + \frac{1}{2} - 2)...(\mu + \frac{1}{2} - 2(r-1))$.

Proof We have

$$\left(v^{-1}\frac{d}{dv}\right)^q (h_\mu\psi)(v) = \left(v^{-1}\frac{d}{dv}\right)^q \int_0^\infty (vy)^{1/2} J_\mu(vy)\psi(y)dy$$
$$= \int_0^\infty \left(v^{-1}\frac{d}{dv}\right)^q (vy)^{-\mu} J_\mu(vy)(vy)^{\mu+1/2}\psi(y)dy$$
$$= \int_0^\infty \left(v^{-1}\frac{d}{dv}\right)^q \left(v^{-\mu} J_\mu(vy)v^{\mu+1/2}\right) y^{-\mu} y^{\mu+1/2}\psi(y)dy$$

$$= \int_0^\infty \sum_{r=0}^q \binom{q}{r} \left(v^{-1}\frac{d}{dv}\right)^{q-r} \left(v^{-\mu} J_\mu(vy)\right) \left(v^{-1}\frac{d}{dv}\right)^r v^{\mu+1/2}$$
$$\times\, y^{-\mu} y^{\mu+1/2}\psi(y)dy. \tag{3.8}$$

Since

$$\left(v^{-1}\frac{d}{dv}\right)^{q-r} \left(v^{-\mu} J_\mu(vy)\right) = (-1)^{q-r} v^{-(\mu+q-r)}\, y^{q-r}\, J_{\mu+q-r}(vy) \tag{3.9}$$

and

$$\left(v^{-1}\frac{d}{dv}\right)^r v^{\mu+1/2} = (\mu+\frac{1}{2})(\mu+\frac{1}{2}-2)....(\mu+\frac{1}{2}-2(r-1))v^{\mu+\frac{1}{2}-2r}. \tag{3.10}$$

Now, putting values of (3.9) and (3.10) in (3.8), we get

$$\left(v^{-1}\frac{d}{dv}\right)^q (h_\mu\psi)(v)$$
$$= \int_0^\infty \sum_{r=0}^q \binom{q}{r} \Big\{(-1)^{q-r} v^{-(\mu+q-r)} y^{q-r}\, J_{\mu+q-r}(vy)$$
$$\times\, (\mu+\frac{1}{2})(\mu+\frac{1}{2}-2)...(\mu+\frac{1}{2}-2(r-1))v^{\mu+\frac{1}{2}-2r}\Big\}\, y^{-\mu} y^{\mu+1/2}\psi(y)dy$$
$$= \sum_{r=0}^q \int_0^\infty \binom{q}{r} (-1)^{q-r} (vy)^{-(\mu+q-r)} J_{\mu+q-r}(vy)\, y^{\mu+2q-2r+\frac{1}{2}}\, A_{\mu,r}\, v^{\mu+\frac{1}{2}-2r}\, \psi(y)dy$$
$$= \sum_{r=0}^q \binom{q}{r} (-1)^{q-r} A_{\mu,r}\, v^{\mu+\frac{1}{2}-2r} \int_0^\infty (vy)^{-(\mu+q-r)} J_{\mu+q-r}(vy)\, y^{\mu+2q-2r+\frac{1}{2}}\, \psi(y)dy.$$

Taking the absolute value of the above equation, we have

$$\left|\left(v^{-1}\frac{d}{dv}\right)^q (h_\mu\psi)(v)\right| \leq \sum_{r=0}^{q}\binom{q}{r}A_{\mu,r}|v|^{\mu+\frac{1}{2}-2r}\int_0^\infty \left|(vy)^{-(\mu+q-r)}J_{\mu+q-r}(vy)\right.$$
$$\left.\times\ y^{\mu+2q-2r+\frac{1}{2}}\psi(y)\right|dy.$$

From (3.4),

$$\left|\left(v^{-1}\frac{d}{dv}\right)^q (h_\mu\psi)(v)\right|$$
$$\leq \sum_{r=0}^{q}\binom{q}{r}A_{\mu,r}\ |v|^{\mu+\frac{1}{2}-2r}C\int_0^\infty e^{ky}y^{\mu+2q-2r+\frac{1}{2}}\ |\psi(y)|\,dy,\quad \text{if } |Im\,v|\leq k$$

$$\leq \sum_{r=0}^{q}\binom{q}{r}A_{\mu,r}\ C\ |v|^{\mu+\frac{1}{2}-2r}\int_0^\infty e^{ky}y^{2\mu+2q-2r+1}\ y^{\mu-\frac{1}{2}}\ |\psi(y)|\,dy$$
$$\leq \sum_{r=0}^{q}\binom{q}{r}C_\mu\ |v|^{\mu+\frac{1}{2}-2r}\sup_{y\in(0,\infty)}\left|e^{(k+1)y}y^{-\mu-\frac{1}{2}}\psi(y)\right|\int_0^\infty e^{-y}y^{2\mu+2q-2r+1}dy$$
$$\leq \sum_{r=0}^{q}\binom{q}{r}C_\mu\ |v|^{\mu+\frac{1}{2}-2r}\ \gamma^{\mu}_{k+1,0}(\psi)\,\Gamma(2\mu-2r+2q+1).$$

Putting $v = a\,(\xi + i(k+1))$, we have

$$\left|\left([a\,(\xi+i(k+1))]^{-1}\frac{d}{d[a\,(\xi+i(k+1))]}\right)^q (h_\mu\psi)\,(a\,(\xi+i(k+1)))\right|$$
$$\leq \sum_{r=0}^{q}\binom{q}{r}C_\mu a^{\mu-2r+\frac{1}{2}}\ |\xi+i(k+1)|^{\mu+\frac{1}{2}-2r}\ \gamma^{\mu}_{k+1,0}(\psi)\,\Gamma(2\mu-2r+2q+1)$$

so that

$$\left|\left(a^{-1}\frac{d}{da}\right)^q (h_\mu\psi)\,(a(\xi+i(k+1)))\right|$$
$$\leq \sum_{r=0}^{q}\binom{q}{r}C_\mu\,a^{\mu-2r+\frac{1}{2}}\ |\xi+i(k+1)|^{\mu+\frac{1}{2}-2r+2q}\ \gamma^{\mu}_{k+1,0}(\psi)\Gamma(2\mu-2r+2q+1).$$

Theorem 3.1 *The Bessel wavelet transform B_ψ is a continuous linear map from $\chi_\mu(I)$ to $\chi_\mu(I\times I)$ for $\mu\geq -\frac{1}{2}$.*

Proof Let $\phi \in \chi_\mu(I)$. Then by using (2.11), we have

$$
\begin{aligned}
&(-1)^q \left(b^{-1}\frac{d}{db}\right)^q b^{-\mu-\frac{1}{2}}(B_\psi\phi)(b,a)\\
&= (-1)^q \left(b^{-1}\frac{d}{db}\right)^q b^{-\mu-\frac{1}{2}} \int_0^\infty (bx)^{1/2} J_\mu(bx) x^{-\mu-\frac{1}{2}} \left(h_\mu\phi\right)(x) \left(h_\mu\psi\right)(ax)dx\\
&= (-1)^q \int_0^\infty \left(b^{-1}\frac{d}{db}\right)^q \left(b^{-\mu} J_\mu(bx)\right) x^{1/2} \left(x^{-\mu-\frac{1}{2}} \left(h_\mu\phi\right)(x)\right) \left(h_\mu\psi\right)(ax)dx\\
&= (-1)^{2q} \int_0^\infty \left\{b^{-\mu-q} x^q J_{\mu+q}(bx)\right\} x^{1/2} \left(x^{-\mu-\frac{1}{2}} \left(h_\mu\phi\right)(x)\right) \left(h_\mu\psi\right)(ax)dx\\
&= \int_0^\infty b^{-\mu-q} x^{q+\frac{1}{2}} J_{\mu+q}(bx) \left(x^{-\mu-\frac{1}{2}} \left(h_\mu\phi\right)(x)\right) \left(h_\mu\psi\right)(ax)dx.
\end{aligned}
$$

Taking [1], we get

$$
\begin{aligned}
(-1)^q \left(b^{-1}\frac{d}{db}\right)^q b^{-\mu-\frac{1}{2}}(B_\psi\phi)(b,a) &= \frac{1}{2}\int_{-\infty}^\infty b^{-\mu-q}(\xi+i\eta)^{q+\frac{1}{2}} H^{(1)}_{\mu+q}(b(\xi+i\eta))\\
&\quad \times \left((\xi+i\eta)^{-\mu-\frac{1}{2}} \left(h_\mu\phi\right)(\xi+i\eta)\right) \left(h_\mu\psi\right)(a(\xi+i\eta))d\xi.
\end{aligned}
$$

Therefore

$$
\begin{aligned}
&\left|(-1)^q \left(a^{-1}\frac{d}{da}\right)^l \left(b^{-1}\frac{d}{db}\right)^q b^{-\mu-\frac{1}{2}}\Phi(b,a)\right|\\
&\le \frac{1}{2}\int_{-\infty}^\infty \left|b^{-\mu-q}(\xi+i\eta)^{q+\frac{1}{2}} H^{(1)}_{\mu+q}(b(\xi+i\eta)) \left((\xi+i\eta)^{-\mu-\frac{1}{2}} \left(h_\mu\phi\right)(\xi+i\eta)\right)\right|\\
&\quad \times \left|\left(a^{-1}\frac{d}{da}\right)^l \left(h_\mu\psi\right)(a(\xi+i\eta))\right| d\xi\\
&= \int_{-\infty}^\infty b^{-\mu-q-\frac{1}{2}} \left|(b(\xi+i\eta))^{\frac{1}{2}} H^{(1)}_{\mu+q}(b(\xi+i\eta))\right|\\
&\quad \times \left|(\xi+i\eta)^q \left((\xi+i\eta)^{-\mu-\frac{1}{2}} \left(h_\mu\phi\right)(\xi+i\eta)\right)\right| \left|\left(a^{-1}\frac{d}{da}\right)^l \left(h_\mu\psi\right)(a(\xi+i\eta))\right| d\xi\\
&= b^{-\mu-q-\frac{1}{2}}\, C\, e^{-b\eta} \int_{-\infty}^\infty \left|(\xi+i\eta)^q \left((\xi+i\eta)^{-\mu-\frac{1}{2}} \left(h_\mu\phi\right)(\xi+i\eta)\right)\right|\\
&\quad \times \left|\left(a^{-1}\frac{d}{da}\right)^l \left(h_\mu\psi\right)(a(\xi+i\eta))\right| d\xi.
\end{aligned}
$$

Using Lemma 3.1, we get

$$\left|(-1)^q \left(a^{-1}\frac{d}{da}\right)^l \left(b^{-1}\frac{d}{db}\right)^q b^{-\mu-\frac{1}{2}}\Phi(b,a)\right|$$

$$\leq b^{-\mu-q-\frac{1}{2}} C\, e^{-b\eta} \int_{-\infty}^{\infty} \left|(\xi+i\eta)^q \left[(\xi+i\eta)^{-\mu-\frac{1}{2}} \left(h_\mu\phi\right)(\xi+i\eta)\right]\right|$$

$$\times \left(\sum_{r=0}^{l}\binom{l}{r} C_\mu\, a^{\mu-2r+\frac{1}{2}} |\xi+i\eta|^{\mu+\frac{1}{2}-2r+2l}\, \gamma^{\mu}_{k+1,0}(\psi)\, \Gamma(2\mu-2r+2l+1)\right) d\xi$$

$$\leq C\, b^{-\mu-q-\frac{1}{2}} a^{\mu-2r+\frac{1}{2}} e^{-b\eta} \sum_{r=0}^{l}\binom{l}{r} C_\mu\, \gamma^{\mu}_{k+1,0}(\psi)\, \Gamma(2\mu-2r+2l+1)$$

$$\times \int_{-\infty}^{\infty} \left|(\xi+i\eta)^{\mu-2r+2l+q+\frac{1}{2}} \left[(\xi+i\eta)^{-\mu-\frac{1}{2}} \left(h_\mu\phi\right)(\xi+i\eta)\right]\right| d\xi.$$

Putting $\eta = k+1$, we have

$$\left|e^{kb} \left(a^{-1}\frac{d}{da}\right)^l \left(b^{-1}\frac{d}{db}\right)^q b^{-\mu-\frac{1}{2}}\Phi(b,a)\right|$$

$$\leq C.C_\mu\, b^{-\mu-q-\frac{1}{2}} a^{\mu-2r+\frac{1}{2}} e^{-b} \sum_{r=0}^{l}\binom{l}{r} \gamma^{\mu}_{k+1,0}(\psi)\, \Gamma(2\mu-2r+2l+1)$$

$$\times \int_{-\infty}^{\infty} |\xi+i(k+1)|^{\mu-2r+2l+q+\frac{1}{2}} \left|(\xi+i(k+1))^{-\mu-\frac{1}{2}} \left(h_\mu\phi\right)(\xi+i(k+1))\right| d\xi.$$

Now let $z = \xi + i(k+1)$, we have

$$\left|e^{kb} \left(a^{-1}\frac{d}{da}\right)^l \left(b^{-1}\frac{d}{db}\right)^q b^{-\mu-\frac{1}{2}}\Phi(b,a)\right|$$

$$\leq C^{'}_{\mu} b^{-\mu-q-\frac{1}{2}} a^{\mu-2r+\frac{1}{2}} e^{-b} \sum_{r=0}^{l}\binom{l}{r} \gamma^{\mu}_{k+1,0}(\psi)\, \Gamma(2\mu-2r+2l+1)$$

$$\times \int_{-\infty}^{\infty} |z|^{\mu-2r+2l+q+\frac{1}{2}} \left|z^{-\mu-\frac{1}{2}} \left(h_\mu\phi\right)(z)\right| dz$$

$$\leq C^{'}_{\mu} b^{-\mu-q-\frac{1}{2}} a^{\mu-2r+\frac{1}{2}} e^{-b} \sum_{r=0}^{l}\binom{l}{r} \gamma^{\mu}_{k+1,0}(\psi)\, \Gamma(2\mu-2r+2l+1)$$

$$\times \int_{-\infty}^{\infty} \left(1+|z|^2\right)^{-m} |z|^{\mu-2r+2l+q+\frac{1}{2}} \left(1+|z|^2\right)^{m} \left|z^{-\mu-\frac{1}{2}} \left(h_\mu\phi\right)(z)\right| dz$$

$$\leq C^{'}_{\mu} b^{-\mu-q-\frac{1}{2}} a^{\mu-2r+\frac{1}{2}} e^{-b} \sum_{r=0}^{l}\binom{l}{r} \gamma^{\mu}_{k+1,0}(\psi)\, \Gamma(2\mu-2r+2l+1)$$

$$\times \sup_{|Imz|\leq k+1} \left(1+|z|^2\right)^{m} \left|z^{-\mu-\frac{1}{2}} \left(h_\mu\phi\right)(z)\right| \int_{-\infty}^{\infty} \left(1+|z|^2\right)^{-m} |z|^{\mu-2r+2l+q+\frac{1}{2}} dz.$$

The last integral is convergent for large value of m. Then

$$\left| e^{kb}\left(a^{-1}\frac{d}{da}\right)^{l}\left(b^{-1}\frac{d}{db}\right)^{q} b^{-\mu-\frac{1}{2}}\Phi(b,a)\right|$$
$$\leq C'_{\mu} b^{-\mu-q-\frac{1}{2}} a^{\mu-2r+\frac{1}{2}} e^{-b}\sum_{r=0}^{l}\binom{l}{r}\gamma^{\mu}_{k+1,0}(\psi)\,\Gamma(2\mu-2r+2l+1)$$
$$\times \sup_{|Imz|\leq k+1}\left(1+|z|^2\right)^m \left|z^{-\mu-\frac{1}{2}}\left(h_\mu\phi\right)(z)\right|. \tag{3.11}$$

Using [1, Theorem 2.1], we get

$$\left| e^{kb}\left(a^{-1}\frac{d}{da}\right)^{l}\left(b^{-1}\frac{d}{db}\right)^{q} b^{-\mu-\frac{1}{2}}\Phi(b,a)\right|$$
$$\leq C'_{\mu} b^{-\mu-q-\frac{1}{2}} a^{\mu-2r+\frac{1}{2}} e^{-b}\sum_{r=0}^{l}\binom{l}{r}\gamma^{\mu}_{k+1,0}(\psi)\,\Gamma(2\mu-2r+2l+1)$$
$$\times\left\{\eta^{\mu}_{k+2,0}(\phi)+\eta^{\mu}_{k+2,m}(\phi)\right\}.$$

Theorem 3.2 *The Bessel wavelet transform B_ψ is continuous linear mapping from $Q_\mu(I)$ to $Q_\mu(I\times I)$.*

Proof Let $\phi\in Q_\mu$. Suppose $\left(B_\psi\phi\right)(z,a)=\Phi(z,a)$ where $z=b+ib'$, $b,b'\in I$ and $a\in I$.

$$a^{-\mu-\frac{1}{2}}z^{-\mu-\frac{1}{2}}\Phi(z,a)$$
$$=a^{-\mu-\frac{1}{2}}z^{-\mu-\frac{1}{2}}\int_0^\infty (zx)^{\frac{1}{2}}J_\mu(zx)\left(h_\mu\phi\right)(x)x^{-\mu-\frac{1}{2}}\left(h_\mu\psi\right)(ax)dx$$
$$=a^{-\mu-\frac{1}{2}}z^{-\mu-\frac{1}{2}}\int_0^\infty (zx)^{-\mu}J_\mu(zx)(zx)^{\mu+\frac{1}{2}}\left(h_\mu\phi\right)(x)x^{-\mu-\frac{1}{2}}\left(h_\mu\psi\right)(ax)dx$$
$$=\int_0^\infty (zx)^{-\mu}J_\mu(zx)x^{\mu+\frac{1}{2}}\left(h_\mu\phi\right)(x)(ax)^{-\mu-\frac{1}{2}}\left(h_\mu\psi\right)(ax)dx.$$

Taking the absolute value of the above equation, we get

$$\begin{aligned}
&\left|a^{-\mu-\frac{1}{2}}z^{-\mu-\frac{1}{2}}\Phi(z,a)\right| \\
&\leq \int_0^\infty \left|(zx)^{-\mu}J_\mu(zx)\right| \left|x^{\mu+\frac{1}{2}}\left(h_\mu\phi\right)(x)\right| \left|(ax)^{-\mu-\frac{1}{2}}\left(h_\mu\psi\right)(ax)\right| dx \\
&\leq C\int_0^\infty e^{x|Imz|} \left|x^{\mu+\frac{1}{2}}\left(h_\mu\phi\right)(x)\right| \left|(ax)^{-\mu-\frac{1}{2}}\left(h_\mu\psi\right)(ax)\right| dx \\
&\leq C\int_0^\infty e^{xk} \left|x^{\mu+\frac{1}{2}}\left(h_\mu\phi\right)(x)\right| \left|(ax)^{-\mu-\frac{1}{2}}\left(h_\mu\psi\right)(ax)\right| dx \\
&\leq C\int_0^\infty e^{-akx}x^{2\mu+1} \left|e^{xk}x^{-\mu-\frac{1}{2}}\left(h_\mu\phi\right)(x)\right| \left|e^{akx}(ax)^{-\mu-\frac{1}{2}}\left(h_\mu\psi\right)(ax)\right| dx \\
&\leq C\sup_{x\in I}\left|e^{xk}x^{-\mu-\frac{1}{2}}\left(h_\mu\phi\right)(x)\right| \sup_{x\in I}\left|e^{akx}(ax)^{-\mu-\frac{1}{2}}\left(h_\mu\psi\right)(ax)\right| \int_0^\infty e^{-axk}x^{2\mu+1}dx
\end{aligned}$$

so that

$$\begin{aligned}
&\left|a^{-\mu-\frac{1}{2}}z^{-\mu-\frac{1}{2}}\Phi(z,a)\right| \\
&\leq C\sup_{x\in I}\left|e^{xk}x^{-\mu-\frac{1}{2}}\left(h_\mu\phi\right)(x)\right| \sup_{x\in I}\left|e^{akx}(ax)^{-\mu-\frac{1}{2}}\left(h_\mu\psi\right)(ax)\right| \frac{\Gamma(2\mu+1)}{(ak)^{2\mu+1}}.
\end{aligned}$$

In the view of [1, Theorem 2.1, pp. 38–39], we have

$$\left|a^{-\mu-\frac{1}{2}}z^{-\mu-\frac{1}{2}}\Phi(z,a)\right| \leq C\,\omega^\mu_{k+1,l}(\phi)\,\omega^\mu_{k+1,l}(\psi)\frac{\Gamma(2\mu+1)}{(ak)^{2\mu+1}} \quad \text{for } x>1. \tag{3.12}$$

For $x \in (0,1)$, using the arguments of [1, Theorem 2.1, pp. 38–39], we have

$$\left|a^{-\mu-\frac{1}{2}}z^{-\mu-\frac{1}{2}}\Phi(z,a)\right| \leq C\omega^\mu_{1,n}(\phi)\,\omega^\mu_{1,n}(\psi)\frac{\Gamma(2\mu+1)}{(ak)^{2\mu+1}}, \tag{3.13}$$

where $n \in \mathbb{N}$ and $n > \mu+1$. Taking (3.12) and (3.13), B_ψ is continuous from $Q_\mu(I)$ to $Q_\mu(I \times I)$. □

Lemma 3.2 *Let ψ be a Bessel wavelet, then it can be written in the terms of Hankel transform as*

$$\tau_b\psi_a(x) = b^{\mu+\frac{1}{2}}h_\mu\left[(bu)^{-\mu}J_\mu(bu)(h_\mu\psi)(au)\right](x), \tag{3.14}$$

where a, b are dilation and translation parameter respectively.

Proof From (3.7), we have

$$\begin{aligned}\tau_b\psi_a(x) &= a^{\mu-\frac{1}{2}}\int_0^\infty \psi(z)\, D_\mu\left(\frac{x}{a},\frac{b}{a},z\right)dz\\ &= a^{\mu-\frac{1}{2}}\int_0^\infty \psi(z)\Big(\int_0^\infty t^{-\mu-\frac{1}{2}}\left(\frac{xt}{a}\right)^{\frac{1}{2}} J_\mu\left(\frac{xt}{a}\right)\left(\frac{bt}{a}\right)^{\frac{1}{2}} J_\mu\left(\frac{bt}{a}\right)\\ &\quad\times (zt)^{\frac{1}{2}} J_\mu(zt)dt\Big)dz.\end{aligned}$$

Putting $\frac{t}{a}=u$, we have

$$\begin{aligned}\tau_b\psi_a(x) &= a^{\mu-\frac{1}{2}}\int_0^\infty \psi(z)\Big(\int_0^\infty (au)^{-\mu-\frac{1}{2}}(xu)^{\frac{1}{2}}J_\mu(x\mu)(bu)^{\frac{1}{2}}J_\mu(bu)\\ &\quad\times (zau)^{\frac{1}{2}}J_\mu(azu)adu\Big)dz\\ &= \int_0^\infty\Big(\int_0^\infty (zau)^{\frac{1}{2}}J_\mu(azu)\psi(z)dz\Big)u^{-\mu-\frac{1}{2}}(xu)^{\frac{1}{2}}J_\mu(xu)(bu)^{\frac{1}{2}}J_\mu(bu)du\\ &= \int_0^\infty u^{-\mu-\frac{1}{2}}(xu)^{\frac{1}{2}}J_\mu(xu)(bu)^{\frac{1}{2}}J_\mu(bu)(h_\mu\psi)(au)du\\ &= b^{\mu+\frac{1}{2}}h_\mu\left[(bu)^{-\mu}J_\mu(bu)(h_\mu\psi)(au)\right](x).\end{aligned}$$

Theorem 3.3 *If $f\in\chi_\mu'$ and $\psi\in\chi_\mu$ then $b^{-\mu-\frac{1}{2}}\left(B_\psi f\right)(b,a)\in\theta_{\chi_\mu}$, where χ_μ' and θ_{χ_μ} denote the dual and multiplier of χ_μ respectively.*

Proof Suppose $f\in\chi_\mu'$ and $\varphi\in\chi_\mu$.

$$\begin{aligned}\left(B_\psi f\right)(b,a) &= \left(f\#\overline{\psi_a}\right)(b)\\ &= \langle f,\tau_b\psi_a\rangle\\ &= \left\langle\sum_{k=0}^r S_\mu^k(e^{rx}x^{-\mu-\frac{1}{2}}f_k),\tau_b\psi_a\right\rangle\\ &= \left\langle\sum_{k=0}^r e^{rx}x^{-\mu-\frac{1}{2}}f_k,\tau_b(S_\mu^k\psi_a)\right\rangle\\ &= \sum_{k=0}^r\int_0^\infty e^{rx}x^{-\mu-\frac{1}{2}}f_k(x)\tau_b(S_\mu^k\psi_a)(x)dx\\ &= \sum_{k=0}^r\int_0^\infty e^{rx}x^{-\mu-\frac{1}{2}}f_k(x)b^{\mu+\frac{1}{2}}h_\mu\left[(bt)^{-\mu}J_\mu(bt)h_\mu(S_\mu^k\psi)(at)\right](x)dx\\ &= \sum_{k=0}^r\int_0^\infty e^{rx}x^{-\mu-\frac{1}{2}}f_k(x)b^{\mu+\frac{1}{2}}\,h_\mu\left[(bt)^{-\mu}J_\mu(bt)h_\mu\psi(at)(at)^{2k}(-1)^k\right](x)dx.\end{aligned}$$

Therefore,

$$b^{-\mu-\frac{1}{2}}\left(B_\psi f\right)(b,a) = \sum_{k=0}^{r}(-1)^k a^{2k}\int_0^\infty e^{rx}x^{-\mu-\frac{1}{2}}f_k(x) \times h_\mu\left[(bt)^{-\mu}J_\mu(bt)h_\mu\psi(at)t^{2k}\right](x)dx$$

$$\left(b^{-1}\frac{d}{db}\right)^n b^{-\mu-\frac{1}{2}}\left(B_\psi f\right)(b,a) = \sum_{k=0}^{r}(-1)^k a^{2k}\int_0^\infty e^{rx}x^{-\mu-\frac{1}{2}}f_k(x) \times h_\mu\left[(bt)^{-\mu-n}J_{\mu+n}(bt)h_\mu\psi(at)t^{2(k+n)}\right](x)dx.$$

Hence,

$$\begin{aligned}&\left|\left(b^{-1}\frac{d}{db}\right)^n b^{-\mu-\frac{1}{2}}\left(B_\psi f\right)(b,a)\right|\\&=\sum_{k=0}^{r}a^{2k}\int_0^\infty\left|e^{rx}x^{-\mu-\frac{1}{2}}f_k(x)h_\mu\left((bt)^{-\mu-n}J_{\mu+n}(bt)h_\mu\psi(at)t^{2(k+n)}\right)(x)\right|dx\\&\le\sup_{x\in I}\left|e^{(r+1)x}x^{-\mu-\frac{1}{2}}h_\mu\left((bt)^{-\mu-n}J_{\mu+n}(bt)t^{2(k+n)}h_\mu\psi(at)\right)(x)\right|\\&\quad\times\sum_{k=0}^{r}a^{2k}\int_0^\infty\left|e^{-x}f_k(x)\right|dx\\&\le\sup_{x\in I}\left|e^{(r+1)x}x^{-\mu-\frac{1}{2}}h_\mu\left((bt)^{-\mu-n}J_{\mu+n}(bt)t^{2(k+n)}h_\mu\psi(at)\right)(x)\right|\\&\quad\times r\,a^{2r}\int_0^\infty\left|e^{-x}f_k(x)\right|dx.\end{aligned}$$

The above implies that

$$\begin{aligned}&\left|\left(b^{-1}\frac{d}{db}\right)^n b^{-\mu-\frac{1}{2}}\left(B_\psi f\right)(b,a)\right|\\&\le C^{'}a^{2r}\sup_{x\in I}\left|e^{(r+1)x}x^{-\mu-\frac{1}{2}}h_\mu\left((bt)^{-\mu-n}J_{\mu+n}(bt)t^{2(k+n)}h_\mu\psi(at)\right)(x)\right|.\end{aligned}$$

Since $\psi\in\chi_\mu\Rightarrow(h_\mu\psi)(at)\in Q_\mu$ and $(bt)^{-\mu-n}J_{\mu+n}(bt)\in\theta_{Q_\mu}$ (Multiplier of Q_μ). Therefore, $t^{2(n+k)}(bt)^{-\mu-n}J_{\mu+n}(bt)(h_\mu\psi)(at)\in Q_\mu$.

So that,

$$\begin{aligned}\left|(b^{-1}\frac{d}{db})^n(b^{-\mu-1/2}\left(f\#\overline{\psi_a}\right)(b))\right| &\le C^{'}a^{2r}\omega^\mu_{l,m}\left(t^{2(n+k)}(bt)^{-\mu-n}J_{\mu+n}(bt)(h_\mu(at)\right)\\&\le C^{'}a^{2r}\omega^\mu_{l,m+k+n}\left(h_\mu(at)\right)e^{lb}\\&\le C^{'}a^{2r}e^{lb}.\end{aligned}$$

Hence,

$$\left|(b^{-1}\frac{d}{db})^n(1+a^{2r})^{-1}b^{-\mu-1/2}(B_\psi f)(b,a)\right| \le C^{'} e^{lb}.$$

This shows that $(1+a^{2r})^{-1}b^{-\mu-1/2}(B_\psi f)(b,a) \in \theta_{\chi_\mu}$. □

3.3 Applications

In this section, motivated from [3, p. 214], we introduce the Fredholm integral equation associated with the Hankel convolution on χ_μ space.
The Fredholm integral equation is defined by

$$\int_0^\infty f(t)g(x,t)dt + \lambda f(x) = u(x), \tag{3.15}$$

where g(x) and u(x) are given functions and λ is a known parameter.
From (1.79), we can write (3.15) as

$$(f\#g)(x) + \lambda f(x) = u(x). \tag{3.16}$$

Theorem 3.4 *Let* $f \in L^1(0,\infty)$ *and* $g \in L^1(0,\infty)$ *then solution of* (3.16) *is*

$$f(x) = \int_0^\infty (x\xi)^{1/2} J_\mu(x\xi)\frac{(h_\mu u)(\xi)}{(\xi^{-\mu-\frac{1}{2}}(h_\mu g)(\xi)+\lambda)}d\xi. \tag{3.17}$$

Proof Hankel transform of (3.16) is

$$h_\mu[(f\#g)](\xi) + \lambda(h_\mu f)(\xi) = (h_\mu u)(\xi).$$

Using (1.85), we get

$$\begin{aligned}\xi^{-\mu-\frac{1}{2}}(h_\mu f)(\xi)(h_\mu g)(\xi) + \lambda(h_\mu f)(\xi) &= (h_\mu u)(\xi)\\ (h_\mu f)(\xi)\left[\xi^{-\mu-\frac{1}{2}}(h_\mu g)(\xi)+\lambda\right] &= (h_\mu u)(\xi)\\ (h_\mu f)(\xi) &= \frac{(h_\mu u)(\xi)}{(\xi^{-\mu-\frac{1}{2}}(h_\mu g)(\xi)+\lambda)}.\end{aligned} \tag{3.18}$$

From the inversion formula (1.76), we can find the solution of (3.16)

$$f(x) = \int_0^\infty (x\xi)^{1/2} J_\mu(x\xi)\frac{(h_\mu u)(\xi)}{(\xi^{-\mu-\frac{1}{2}}(h_\mu g)(\xi)+\lambda)}d\xi. \tag{3.19}$$

Theorem 3.5 *Let $f \in \chi_\mu$, $g \in \chi_\mu$. Then*

$$(f\#g)(x) + \lambda f(x) \in \chi_\mu. \tag{3.20}$$

Proof From [1, Proposition 3.2], the Hankel convolution is a continuous linear mapping from $\chi_\mu \times \chi_\mu$ into χ_μ.

This implies that $(f\#g) \in \chi_\mu$.

Since $f \in \chi_\mu$ therefore

$$(f\#g)(x) + \lambda f(x) \in \chi_\mu.$$

Now we justify the above theorem with the following example.

Example 1

We take $u(x) = x^{\mu+\frac{1}{2}} e^{-ax^2}$ with $Re\, a > 0$, $Re\mu \geq -1$ and $f = g$ in (3.15). Then from (3.18), we have

$$\begin{aligned}\left[(h_\mu f)(\xi)\right]^2 &= \xi^{\mu+\frac{1}{2}}\, h_\mu\left(x^{\mu+\frac{1}{2}} e^{-ax^2}\right)(\xi) \\ &= \frac{\xi^{2\mu+1}}{(2a)^{\mu+1}} e^{-\xi^2/4a}.\end{aligned}$$

From [4], we have

$$f(x) = 2^{\frac{\mu+1}{2}} x^{\mu+1} e^{-2ax^2}.$$

This $x^{\mu+1} e^{-2ax^2} \in \chi_\mu$ and the solution $f(x) = 2^{\frac{\mu+1}{2}} x^{\mu+1} e^{-2ax^2} \in \chi_\mu$.

Theorem 3.6 *Let $\psi \in \chi_\mu \subset L^1(0, \infty)$ be a Bessel wavelet. Then*

$$f(b) = \int_0^\infty J_\mu(b\xi)(b\xi)^{1/2} \frac{(h_\mu u)(\xi)}{(\xi^{-\mu-\frac{1}{2}}(h_\mu \psi_a)(\xi) + \lambda)} d\xi. \tag{3.21}$$

Proof Putting $g = \psi_a(b)$ in (3.16), we have

$$(f\#\psi_a)(b) + \lambda f(b) = u(b). \tag{3.22}$$

Taking the Hankel transform to the both sides of (3.22), we get

$$\xi^{-\mu-\frac{1}{2}}(h_\mu f)(\xi)(h_\mu\psi_a)(\xi)+\lambda(h_\mu f)(\xi)=(h_\mu u)(\xi)$$

$$(h_\mu f)(\xi)\left[\xi^{-\mu-\frac{1}{2}}(h_\mu\psi_a)(\xi)+\lambda\right]=(h_\mu u)(\xi)$$

$$(h_\mu f)(\xi)=\frac{(h_\mu u)(\xi)}{(\xi^{-\mu-\frac{1}{2}}(h_\mu\psi_a)(\xi)+\lambda)}. \tag{3.23}$$

With the help of inversion formula, we have

$$f(b)=\int_0^\infty J_\mu(b\xi)(b\xi)^{1/2}\frac{(h_\mu u)(\xi)}{(\xi^{-\mu-\frac{1}{2}}(h_\mu\psi_a)(\xi)+\lambda)}d\xi. \tag{3.24}$$

Example 2
Solve the integral equation

$$\int_0^\infty f(t)\psi(\frac{t}{a},\frac{b}{a})dt=u(b),$$

where $\psi(x)=2^\nu\Gamma(\nu+1)x^{-\nu-\frac{1}{2}}J_{\mu+\nu+1}(x)$.

Solution. From (3.23) and [4, p. 26], we get

$$\begin{aligned}(h_\mu f)(\xi)&=(h_\mu u)(\xi)\frac{1}{\xi^{-\mu-\frac{1}{2}}h_\mu(2^\nu\Gamma(\nu+1)x^{-\nu-\frac{1}{2}}J_{\mu+\nu+1}(x))(a\xi)}\\&=(h_\mu u)(\xi)\frac{1}{[1-(a\xi)^2]^\nu},\quad Re\,\nu>-1,\ Re\,\mu>-1.\end{aligned} \tag{3.25}$$

Taking $\nu=(\mu+\frac{1}{2})$

$$(h_\mu f)(\xi)=(h_\mu u)(\xi)[1-(a\xi)^2]^{-\mu-\frac{1}{2}}. \tag{3.26}$$

Since [4, p. 32] we have

$$h_\mu\left(\pi^{-1/2}2^{-\mu}\Gamma(1/2-\mu)x^{\mu-\frac{1}{2}}sinx\right)(a\xi)=\xi^{\mu+\frac{1}{2}}[1-(a\xi)^2]^{-\mu-\frac{1}{2}}, \tag{3.27}$$

where $-1<Re\mu<\frac{1}{2}$.

From (3.26), we get

$$
\begin{aligned}
(h_\mu f)(\xi) &= \xi^{-\mu-\frac{1}{2}}(h_\mu u)(\xi)\; h_\mu\left(\pi^{-1/2}2^{-\mu}\Gamma(1/2-\mu)x^{\mu-\frac{1}{2}}sinx\right)(a\xi)\\
&= h_\mu\left(u\,\#\,\pi^{-1/2}2^{-\mu}\Gamma(1/2-\mu)\left(\frac{x}{a}\right)^{\mu-\frac{1}{2}} sin\frac{x}{a}\right)(\xi)\\
f(x) &= u\,\#\,\pi^{-1/2}2^{-\mu}\Gamma(1/2-\mu)\left(\frac{x}{a}\right)^{\mu-\frac{1}{2}} sin\frac{x}{a}.
\end{aligned}
$$

References

1. Betancor, J.J., Rodríguez-Mesa, L.: Hankel convolution on distribution spaces with exponential growth. Studia Math. **121**(1), 35–52 (1996)
2. Upadhyay, S.K., Yadav, R.N., Debnath, L.: On continuous Bessel wavelet transformation associated with the Hankel-Hausdorff operator. Integral transforms Spec. Funct. **23**(5), 315–323 (2012)
3. Debnath, L.: Wavelet Transforms and their Applications. Birkhäuser, Boston, MA (2002)
4. Erdélyi, A., Magnus, W., Oberhettinger, F., Tricomi F.G., (eds.).: Tables of integral transforms, vol., 2, McGraw-Hill, New York 19542 (1954)

Chapter 4
The Bessel Wavelet Convolution Product

4.1 Introduction

Convolution is an important integral operator and it is an efficient technique for the problems of signal processing, image processing, and integral equations. Different types of convolutions can be made using different integral transforms. Using Fourier transform techniques, many properties of convolutions are established and many applications have been done in different areas. Most of the research works and applications in convolutions are available in various literature exploring the theory of Fourier transform.

The convolution product is an important property of convolution and is heavily used to study the approximation properties of the Fourier transform and other integral transforms. The continuous wavelet transform with respect to certain wavelets is a convolution operator and it is useful in many applications of different areas of mathematics. Pathak [1] developed a convolution product and studied many properties by exploiting the theory of the Fourier transform. Cholewinski [2], Haimo [3], Hirschman Jr. [4], and others investigated definitions and properties of the Hankel transform which are quite useful for developing definitions and properties of the Hankel convolution. Later on, exploiting the aforesaid theory of Hankel convolution Pathak [1], Pathak and Dixit [5], and Triméche [6] found the theory of the Bessel wavelet transform and found many interesting results.

Our main aim in this chapter is to study the Bessel wavelet convolution and its properties by exploiting the theory of the Hankel transform and the Hankel convolution.

S. K. Upadhyay and J. S. Maurya, *The Bessel Wavelet Transform*,
Industrial and Applied Mathematics,
https://doi.org/10.1007/978-981-96-9938-4_4

4.2 Hankel Transform and Hankel Convolution

We say that $f \in L^p_\sigma(I)$, $1 \le p \le \infty$ and $I = (0, \infty)$, if

$$\|f\|_{p,\sigma} = \left(\int_0^\infty |f(x)|^p d\sigma(x) \right)^{\frac{1}{p}} < \infty, \tag{4.1}$$

$$\|f\|_{\infty,\sigma} = ess \sup_{0<x<\infty} |f(x)| < \infty. \tag{4.2}$$

Definition 4.1 Cholewinski [2], Haimo [3], Hirschman Jr. [4], and others studied the Hankel convolution for the following form of the Hankel transformation of a function $f \in L^1_\sigma(I)$. Namely,

$$\left(h_\mu f\right)(x) = \tilde{f}(x) = \int_0^\infty j_\mu(xt) f(t) d\sigma(t) \,, \tag{4.3}$$

where

$$j_\mu(x) = 2^{\mu-\frac{1}{2}} \Gamma\left(\mu + \frac{1}{2}\right) x^{\frac{1}{2}-\mu} J_{\mu-\frac{1}{2}}(x).$$

Here, $J_{\mu-\frac{1}{2}}(x)$ is the Bessel function of order $\mu - \frac{1}{2}$, and

$$d\sigma(t) = \frac{t^{2\mu}}{2^{\mu-\frac{1}{2}} \Gamma\left(\mu + \frac{1}{2}\right)} dt \,,$$

where $\mu > 0$.

If $f \in L^1_\sigma(I)$ and $h_\mu f \in L^1_\sigma(I)$, then the inverse Hankel transform is given by

$$f(x) = \left(h_\mu^{-1}[\tilde{f}]\right)(x) = \int_0^\infty j_\mu(xt) \left(h_\mu f\right)(t) d\sigma(t). \tag{4.4}$$

Definition 4.2 If $f \in L^1_\sigma(I)$, $g \in L^1_\sigma(I)$ then the Hankel convolution is defined by

$$(f\#g)(x) := \int_0^\infty \left(\tau_x f\right)(y) g(y) d\sigma(y), \tag{4.5}$$

where the Hankel translation τ_x is given by

$$\left(\tau_x f\right)(y) := \tilde{f}(x, y) = \int_0^\infty D(x, y, z) f(z) d\sigma(z), \tag{4.6}$$

and the basic function

$$D(x, y, z) := \int_0^\infty j_\mu(xt) j_\mu(yt) j_\mu(zt) d\sigma(t), \quad 0 < x, y, z < \infty, \ 0 \leq t < \infty$$
$$= \frac{2^{3\mu-5/2}\,[\Gamma\,(\mu + 1/2)]^2}{\Gamma\,(\mu)\,\pi^{1/2}} (xyz)^{-2\mu+1}[\Delta(x, y, z)]^{2\mu-2}, \tag{4.7}$$

for $\mu > 0$, where $\Delta(x, y, z)$ is the area of a triangle with sides x, y, z if such a triangle exists and zero otherwise.
Here we note that $D(x, y, z) \geq 0$ is symmetric in x, y, z. Applying (4.4) to (4.6), we get the formula

$$\int_0^\infty j_\mu(zt) D(x, y, z) d\sigma(z) = j_\mu(xt) j_\mu(yt). \tag{4.8}$$

Setting $t = 0$, we get

$$\int_0^\infty D(x, y, z) d\sigma(z) = 1. \tag{4.9}$$

Therefore in view of (4.6),

$$\|\tilde{f}(x, y)\|_{1,\sigma} \leqslant \|f\|_{1,\sigma}. \tag{4.10}$$

Now, using (4.6) we can write (4.5) in the following form:

$$(f\#g)(x) = \int_0^\infty \int_0^\infty D(x, y, z) f(z) g(y) d\sigma(z) d\sigma(y). \tag{4.11}$$

Some important properties of the Hankel transform and the Hankel convolution relevant to this chapter are

1. If $f, g \in L^1_\sigma(I)$, then from [3]

$$\|f\#g\|_{1,\sigma} \leqslant \|f\|_{1,\sigma} \|g\|_{1,\sigma}. \tag{4.12}$$

2. With the same assumptions,

$$h_\mu(f\#g)(x) = \left(h_\mu f\right)(x) \left(h_\mu g\right)(x). \tag{4.13}$$

3. Let $f \in L^1_\sigma(I)$ and $g \in L^p_\sigma(I)$, $p \geqslant 1$. Then $(f\#g)$ exists, is continuous and from [7], we get the inequality

$$\|f\#g\|_{p,\sigma} \leqslant \|f\|_{1,\sigma} \|g\|_{p,\sigma}. \tag{4.14}$$

4. Let $f \in L^p_\sigma(I)$, $g \in L^q_\sigma(I)$, $1/p + 1/q = 1$. Then $f\#g$ exists, is continuous and from [7], we have
$$\|f\#g\|_{\infty,\sigma} \leqslant \|f\|_{p,\sigma}\|g\|_{q,\sigma}. \tag{4.15}$$

5. Let $f \in L^p_\sigma(I)$ and $g \in L^q_\sigma(I)$, $1/r = 1/p + 1/q - 1$. Then $(f\#g)$ exists, is continuous and from [7], we get the inequality:
$$\|f\#g\|_{r,\sigma} \leqslant \|f\|_{p,\sigma}\|g\|_{q,\sigma}. \tag{4.16}$$

6. Let $f \in L^p_\sigma(I)$, $g \in L^q_\sigma(I)$ and $h \in L^r_\sigma(I)$. Then the weighted norm inequality
$$\left|\int_0^\infty f(x)(g\#h)(x)d\sigma(x)\right| \leqslant \|f\|_{p,\sigma}\|g\|_{q,\sigma}\|h\|_{r,\sigma}\,, \tag{4.17}$$

holds for $\frac{1}{p} + \frac{1}{q} + \frac{1}{r} = 2$.

As indicated above, the proof of properties 1 to 5 is well known. Hence, we next give the proof of property 6.

Proof Using Holder's inequality, we get
$$\left|\int_0^\infty f(x)(g\#h)(x)d\sigma(x)\right| \leqslant \|f\|_{p,\sigma}\|g\#h\|_{s,\sigma}, \quad \frac{1}{p} + \frac{1}{s} = 1. \tag{4.18}$$

Therefore, using (4.15) we have
$$\left|\int_0^\infty f(x)(g\#h)(x)d\sigma(x)\right| \leq \|f\|_{p,\sigma}\|g\|_{q,\sigma}\|h\|_{s,\sigma}, \quad \frac{1}{s} = \frac{1}{q} + \frac{1}{r} - 1. \tag{4.19}$$

7. From [8], h_μ is isometric on $L^2_\sigma(I)$, that is $\left(h_\mu^{-1}h_\mu f\right) = f$, then Parseval's formula of the Hankel transformation for $f, g \in L^2_\sigma(I)$ is given by
$$\int_0^\infty f(x)g(x)d\sigma(x) = \int_0^\infty \left(h_\mu f\right)(y)\left(h_\mu g\right)(y)d\sigma(y). \tag{4.20}$$

   Furthermore, this relation also holds for $f, g \in L^1_\sigma(I)$, see [9].

Now, we also state some results from [4, Theorem 2c, p. 312] and [4, corollary 2c, p. 313], which are useful for our approximation results:

Theorem 4.1 *Suppose that*

1. $k_n(x) \geq 0, \quad 0 < x < \infty,$
2. $\int_0^\infty k_n(x)d\sigma(x) = 1, \quad n = 0, 1, 2, 3, \ldots$

3. $\lim_{n\to\infty}\int_{\delta}^{\infty} k_n(x)d\sigma(x) = 0$ *for each* $\delta > 0$,
4. $\varphi(x) \in L_{\sigma}^{\infty}(I)$,
5. φ *is continuous at* x_0, $x_0 \in [x-\delta, x+\delta]$ *and* $\delta > 0$.

Then

$$\lim_{n\to\infty} (\varphi\#k_n)(x_0) = \varphi(x_0). \tag{4.21}$$

Corollary 4.1 *With the same assumptions on* $k_n(x)$, *if* $f(x) \in L_{\sigma}^{1}(I)$, *then*

$$\lim_{n\to\infty} \| f\#k_n - f\|_1 = 0. \tag{4.22}$$

4.3 Continuous Bessel Wavelet Transform

Definition 4.3 For $\psi \in L_{\sigma}^{1}(I)$, using translation τ given in (4.6) and dilation $D_a f(x, y) = f(ax, ay)$, the Bessel wavelet [5] is defined by

$$\psi_{a,b}(t) = \psi\left(\frac{t}{a}, \frac{b}{a}\right) = D_{1/a}\tau_b\psi(t) = a^{-2\mu-1}\int_0^{\infty} \psi(z)D\left(\frac{t}{a}, \frac{b}{a}, z\right)d\sigma(z). \tag{4.23}$$

Definition 4.4 The continuous Bessel wavelet transform [5] of a function $f \in L_{\sigma}^{1}(I)$ with respect to wavelet $\psi \in L_{\sigma}^{1}(I)$ is defined by

$$\left(B_{\psi} f\right)(b, a) = a^{-2\mu-1}\int_0^{\infty} \psi\left(\frac{t}{a}, \frac{b}{a}\right) f(t)d\sigma(t), \quad a > 0. \tag{4.24}$$

By simple modification of (4.24), we can get

$$\left(B_{\psi} f\right)(b, a) = (f\#\psi)\left(\frac{b}{a}\right), \quad a > 0. \tag{4.25}$$

From (4.5) and (4.6), the continuous Bessel wavelet transform of a function $f \in L_{\sigma}^{1}(I)$ can be written in the form:

$$\left(B_{\psi} f\right)(b, a) = \int_0^{\infty} j_{\mu}(bw)\left(h_{\mu} f\right)(w)\overline{\left(h_{\mu}\psi\right)(aw)}d\sigma(w). \tag{4.26}$$

Now, we state the Parseval formula of the Bessel wavelet transform from [5, p. 245]

$$\int_0^{\infty}\int_0^{\infty} (B_{\psi} f)(b, a)\overline{(B_{\psi} g)(b, a)}\,\frac{d\sigma(a)d\sigma(b)}{a^{2\mu+1}} = C_{\psi}\langle f, g\rangle, \tag{4.27}$$

for $f \in L_{\sigma}^{2}(I)$ and $g \in L_{\sigma}^{2}(I)$.

4.4 The Bessel Wavelet Convolution Product

In this section, using properties (4.10), (4.20), and (4.23), we formally define the convolution product for the Bessel wavelet transformation by the relation

$$B_\psi(f \otimes g)(b,a) = \left(B_\psi f\right)(b,a)\left(B_\psi g\right)(b,a)\,, \tag{4.28}$$

and investigate its boundedness and approximation properties. This in turn implies that the product of two Bessel wavelet transforms could be wavelet transforms under certain conditions.

Theorem 4.2 *Let $f, g, \psi \in L^1_\sigma(I)$ and $h_\mu(\psi)(w) \neq 0$. Then the Bessel wavelet convolution can be written in the form*

$$(f \otimes g)(z) = \int_0^\infty \left(\tau_{z,a} f\right)(y) g(y) d\sigma(y)\,, \tag{4.29}$$

where

$$\left(\tau_{z,a} f\right)(y) = \int_0^\infty f(x) D_a(x,y,z) d\sigma(x)\,,$$

$$D_a(x,y,z) = \int_0^\infty \int_0^\infty \left(h_\mu\psi\right)(at)\left(h_\mu\psi\right)(a\xi) j_\mu(xt) j_\mu(y\xi) L_a(t,\xi,z) d\sigma(t) d\sigma(\xi), \tag{4.30}$$

and

$$L_a(t,\xi,z) = \int_0^\infty j_\mu(y\xi) j_\mu(yt) Q_a(y,z) d\sigma(y), \tag{4.31}$$

$$Q_a(y,z) = \int_0^\infty \frac{j_\mu(wz) j_\mu(wy)}{\left(h_\mu\psi\right)(aw)} d\sigma(w). \tag{4.32}$$

Proof From (4.26), we have

$$h_\mu\left[\left(B_\psi f\right)(b,a)\right](w) = \left(h_\mu\psi\right)(aw)\left(h_\mu f\right)(w). \tag{4.33}$$

Using (4.28) and (4.33), we get

$$\begin{aligned} &h_\mu\left[\left(B_\psi(f \otimes g)\right)(b,a)\right](w) \\ &= h_\mu\left[\left(B_\psi f\right)(b,a)\left(B_\psi g\right)(b,a)\right](w) \\ &= h_\mu\left[h_\mu^{-1}\left(\left(h_\mu\psi\right)(a\cdot)\left(h_\mu f\right)(\cdot)\right) h_\mu^{-1}\left(\left(h_\mu\psi\right)(a\cdot)\left(h_\mu g\right)(\cdot)\right)\right](w). \end{aligned}$$

By the property (4.13) of the Hankel convolution, we have

$$h_\mu\left[\left(B_\psi(f \otimes g)\right)(b,a)\right](w) = \left[\left(h_\mu\psi\right)(a\cdot)\left(h_\mu f\right)(\cdot)\#\left(h_\mu\psi\right)(a\cdot)\left(h_\mu g\right)(\cdot)\right](w).$$

Therefore by (4.33), we get

$$\left(h_\mu\psi\right)(aw)h_\mu[(f\otimes g)](w)=\left[\left(h_\mu\psi\right)(a\cdot)\left(h_\mu f\right)(\cdot)\#\left(h_\mu\psi\right)(a\cdot)\left(h_\mu g\right)(\cdot)\right](w). \tag{4.34}$$

This gives a relation between the Bessel wavelet transform-convolution and the Hankel transform-convolution. Let us set

$$\begin{aligned}F_a&=\left(h_\mu\psi\right)(a\cdot)\left(h_\mu f\right)(\cdot)\,,\\ G_a&=\left(h_\mu\psi\right)(a\cdot)\left(h_\mu g\right)(\cdot)\,.\end{aligned}$$

Then, by (4.5) and (4.6) we get

$$\begin{aligned}&\left(h_\mu\psi\right)(aw)h_\mu[(f\otimes g)](w)\\ &=\int_0^\infty\left(\tau_w G_a\right)(\eta)F_a(\eta)d\sigma(\eta)\\ &=\int_0^\infty F_a(\eta)\left(\int_0^\infty D(w,\eta,\xi)G_a(\xi)d\sigma(\xi)\right)d\sigma(\eta)\\ &=\int_0^\infty\int_0^\infty F_a(\eta)G_a(\xi)D(w,\eta,\xi)d\sigma(\xi)d\sigma(\eta)\\ &=\int_0^\infty\int_0^\infty F_a(\eta)G_a(\xi)\left(\int_0^\infty j_\mu(wy)j_\mu(\eta y)j_\mu(\xi y)d\sigma(y)\right)d\sigma(\xi)d\sigma(\eta)\\ &=\int_0^\infty\left(\int_0^\infty F_a(\eta)j_\mu(\eta y)d\sigma(\eta)\right)\left(\int_0^\infty G_a(\xi)j_\mu(\xi y)d\sigma(\xi)\right)j_\mu(wy)d\sigma(y)\\ &=\int_0^\infty\left(h_\mu F_a\right)(y)\left(h_\mu G_a\right)(y)j_\mu(wy)d\sigma(y).\end{aligned}$$

Therefore by the inversion formula of the Hankel transformation (4.4), we have

$$\begin{aligned}&(f\otimes g)(z)\\ &=\int_0^\infty\frac{j_\mu(wz)}{\left(h_\mu\psi\right)(aw)}\left(\int_0^\infty\left(h_\mu F_a\right)(y)\left(h_\mu G_a\right)(y)j_\mu(wy)d\sigma(y)\right)d\sigma(w)\\ &=\int_0^\infty\left(h_\mu F_a\right)(y)\left(h_\mu G_a\right)(y)\left(\int_0^\infty\frac{j_\mu(wz)j_\mu(wy)}{\left(h_\mu\psi\right)(aw)}d\sigma(w)\right)d\sigma(y)\\ &=\int_0^\infty\left(h_\mu F_a\right)(y)\left(h_\mu G_a\right)(y)Q_a(y,z)d\sigma(y),\end{aligned}$$

where $Q_a(y,z)$ is given by (4.32).

Then by the definition of the Hankel transformation (4.3)

$$
\begin{aligned}
&(f \otimes g)(z) \\
&= \int_0^\infty \int_0^\infty j_\mu(yt)\left(h_\mu \psi\right)(at)\left(h_\mu f\right)(t) d\sigma(t) \\
&\quad \left(\int_0^\infty j_\mu(y\xi)\left(h_\mu \psi\right)(a\xi)\left(h_\mu g\right)(\xi) d\sigma(\xi)\right) Q_a(y, z) d\sigma(y) \\
&= \int_0^\infty \int_0^\infty \left(h_\mu \psi\right)(at)\left(h_\mu \psi\right)(a\xi)\left(h_\mu f\right)(t)\left(h_\mu g\right)(\xi) \\
&= \int_0^\infty \int_0^\infty \left(h_\mu \psi\right)(at)\left(h_\mu \psi\right)(a\xi)\left(h_\mu f\right)(t)\left(h_\mu g\right)(\xi) L_a(t, \xi, z) d\sigma(t) d\sigma(\xi).
\end{aligned}
$$

Therefore,

$$
\begin{aligned}
&(f \otimes g)(z) \\
&= \int_0^\infty \int_0^\infty \left(h_\mu \psi\right)(at)\left(h_\mu \psi\right)(a\xi)\left(\int_0^\infty j_\mu(xt) f(x) d\sigma(x)\right) \\
&\quad \times \left(\int_0^\infty j_\mu(y\xi) g(y) d\sigma(y)\right) L_a(t, \xi, z) d\sigma(t) d\sigma(\xi) \\
&= \int_0^\infty \int_0^\infty f(x) g(y)\left(\int_0^\infty \int_0^\infty j_\mu(xt) j_\mu(y\xi)\left(h_\mu \psi\right)(at)\left(h_\mu \psi\right)(a\xi)\right. \\
&\quad \left. L_a(t, \xi, z) d\sigma(t) d\sigma(\xi)\right) d\sigma(x) d\sigma(y) \\
&= \int_0^\infty f(x) g(y) D_a(x, y, z) d\sigma(x) d\sigma(y),
\end{aligned}
$$

where

$$
D_a(x, y, z) = \int_0^\infty \int_0^\infty j_\mu(xt) j_\mu(y\xi)\left(h_\mu \psi\right)(at)\left(h_\mu \psi\right)(a\xi) L_a(t, \xi, z) d\sigma(t) d\sigma(\xi).
$$

If we define the generalized translation by

$$
F_a(z, y) = \left(\tau_{z,a} f\right)(y) = \int_0^\infty D_a(x, y, z) f(x) d\sigma(x),
$$

then

$$
(f \otimes g)(z) = \int_0^\infty \left(\tau_{z,a} f\right)(y) g(y) d\sigma(y).
$$

Theorem 4.3 *Assume that* $\inf_{w} \left|\left(h_\mu\psi\right)(aw)\right| = B_\psi(a) > 0$. *Then*

$$\|D_a(x, y, z)\| \leqslant \frac{1}{B_\psi(a)} a^{-2\mu-1}\|\psi\|^2_{1,\sigma}. \tag{4.35}$$

Proof From (4.30), we have

$$\begin{aligned}
&D_a(x, y, z)\\
&= \int_0^\infty \int_0^\infty j_\mu(xt)j_\mu(y\xi)\left(h_\mu\psi\right)(at)\left(h_\mu\psi\right)(a\xi)L_a(t,\xi,z)d\sigma(t)d\sigma(\xi)\\
&= \int_0^\infty \int_0^\infty j_\mu(xt)j_\mu(y\xi)\left(h_\mu\psi\right)(at)\left(h_\mu\psi\right)(a\xi)\\
&\times\left(\int_0^\infty j_\mu(n\xi)j_\mu(\eta t)Q_a(\eta,z)d\sigma(\eta)\right)d\sigma(t)d\sigma(\xi)\\
&= \int_0^\infty \int_0^\infty j_\mu(xt)j_\mu(y\xi)\left(h_\mu\psi\right)(at)\left(h_\mu\psi\right)(a\xi)\\
&\times\left(\int_0^\infty j_\mu(\eta\xi)j_\mu(\eta t)\left(\int_0^\infty \frac{j_\mu(wz)j_\mu(\eta w)}{\left(h_\mu\psi\right)(aw)}d\sigma(w)\right)d\sigma(\eta)\right)d\sigma(t)d\sigma(\xi)\\
&= \int_0^\infty\left(\int_0^\infty j_\mu(xt)j_\mu(\eta t)\left(h_\mu\psi\right)(at)d\sigma(t)\right)\\
&\times\left(\int_0^\infty j_\mu(y\xi)j_\mu(\eta\xi)(h_\mu\psi)(a\xi)d\sigma(\xi)\right)Q_a(z,\eta)d\sigma(\eta)\\
&= \int_0^\infty h_\mu\left[j_\mu^\infty j_\mu(xt)\left(h_\mu\psi\right)(at)\right](\eta)h_\mu\left[j_\mu(y\xi)\left(h_\mu\psi\right)(a\xi)\right](\eta)Q_a(z,\eta)d\sigma(\eta)\\
&= \int_0^\infty \int_0^\infty h_\mu\left[j_\mu(xt)\left(h_\mu\psi\right)(at)\# j_\mu(y\xi)\left(h_\mu\psi\right)(a\xi)\right](\eta)\\
&\times j_\mu(w\eta)j_\mu(wz)\left[\left(h_\mu\psi\right)(aw)\right]^{-1}d\sigma(w)d\sigma(\eta)\\
&= \int_0^\infty\left[j_\mu(x\cdot)\left(h_\mu\psi\right)(a\cdot)\# j_\mu(y\cdot)\left(h_\mu\psi\right)(a\cdot)\right](w)j_\mu(wz)\left[\left(h_\mu\psi\right)(aw)\right]^{-1}d\sigma(w).
\end{aligned}$$

Now, set $F_a(t) = j_\mu(xt)h_\mu\psi(at)$ and assume that $\inf_{w}\left|\left(h_\mu\psi\right)(aw)\right| = B_\psi(a) > 0$. Since $\left|j_\mu(z)\right| \leqslant 1$, [3, p. 336], we have

$$|D_a(x, y, z)| \leqslant \frac{1}{B_\psi(a)}\int_0^\infty |(F_a\# F_a)(w)|\,d\sigma(w).$$

Using (4.12), we have

$$\begin{aligned}
|D_a(x, y, z)| &\leqslant \frac{1}{B_\psi(a)} \|F\|_{1,\sigma} \|F\|_{1,\sigma} \\
&\leqslant \frac{1}{B_\psi(a)} \left[\int_0^\infty \left| j_\mu(xv) \left(h_\mu \psi\right)(av) \right| d\sigma(v) \right]^2 \\
&\leqslant \frac{1}{B_\psi(a)} \left[\int_0^\infty |\psi(av)| d\sigma(v) \right]^2 \\
&\leqslant \frac{1}{B_\psi(a)} \left[\|\psi_a\|_{1,\sigma} \right]^2 \\
&\leqslant \frac{a^{-2\mu-1}}{B_\psi(a)} \left[\|\psi\|_{1,\sigma} \right]^2 .
\end{aligned}$$

In order to obtain Plancheral formula for the Bessel wavelet transform, we define the space

$$W^2(I \times I) = \left\{ g(b, a) : \|g\|_{W^2} = \left(\int_0^\infty \int_0^\infty |g(b, a)|^2 \frac{d\sigma(b) d\sigma(a)}{a^{2\mu+1}} \right)^{\frac{1}{2}} < \infty \right\}.$$

.

Theorem 4.4 *Let $f \in L^2_\sigma(I)$, $\psi \in L^2_\sigma(I)$. Then*

$$\left\| \left(B_\psi f\right)(b, a) \right\|_{W^2} = \sqrt{C_\psi} \|f\|_{2,\sigma} .$$

Proof Putting $f = g$ in (4.27), we prove the above theorem. □

Theorem 4.5 *Let $f, g \in L^2_\sigma(I)$ and let $\psi \in L^2_\sigma(I)$ be a Bessel wavelet which satisfies $C_\psi := \int_0^\infty \left| \left(h_\mu \psi\right)(aw) \right|^2 \frac{d\sigma(a)}{a^{2\mu+1}} > 0$. Then*

$$\|f \otimes g\|_{2,\sigma} \leqslant \|f\|_{2,\sigma} \|g\|_{2,\sigma} \|\psi\|_{2,\sigma} .$$

Proof Using Theorem 4.4 and (4.28)

$$\begin{aligned}
&\sqrt{C_\psi} \|f \otimes g\|_{2,\sigma} \\
&= \left\| B_\psi (f \otimes g) \right\|_{W^2} \\
&= \left\| B_\psi f(b, a) B_\psi g(b, a) \right\|_{W^2} \\
&= \left(\int_0^\infty \int_0^\infty \left| B_\psi f(b, a) B_\psi g(b, a) \right|^2 \frac{d\sigma(a) d\sigma(b)}{a^{2\mu+1}} \right)^{\frac{1}{2}} .
\end{aligned} \tag{4.36}$$

From (4.26) and (4.15), we have

$$\left| B_\psi g(b, a) \right| \leqslant |(g(a\cdot)\#\psi(\cdot))(b/a)| \leqslant \|g\|_{2,\sigma} \|\psi\|_{2,\sigma} . \tag{4.37}$$

Applying (4.36) and (4.37), we get

$$\sqrt{C_\psi}\|f \otimes g\|_{2,\sigma} \leqslant \|g\|_{2,\sigma}\|\psi\|_{2,\sigma}\left(\int_0^\infty\int_0^\infty \left|B_\psi f(b,a)\right|^2 \frac{d\sigma(a)d\sigma(b)}{a^{2\mu+1}}\right)^{\frac{1}{2}}.$$

From Theorem 4.4, we obtain

$$\sqrt{C_\psi}\|f \otimes g\|_{2,\sigma} \leqslant \|g\|_{2,\sigma}\|\psi\|_{2,\sigma}\sqrt{C_\psi}\|f\|_{2,\sigma}.$$

Hence,

$$\|f \otimes g\|_{2,\sigma} \leqslant \|g\|_{2,\sigma}\|\psi\|_{2,\sigma}\|f\|_{2,\sigma}.$$

4.5 Weighted Sobolev Space

In this section, we study certain properties of the Bessel wavelet convolution on a weighted Sobolev space defined below.

Definition 4.5 The Zemanian space $H_\mu(I)$, $I = (0,\infty)$, is the set of all infinitely differentiable functions φ on $(0,\infty)$ such that

$$\gamma^\mu_{m,k}(\varphi) = \sup_{x\in(0,\infty)}\left|x^m\left(x^{-1}\frac{d}{dx}\right)^k x^{-\mu-\frac{1}{2}}\varphi(x)\right| < \infty,$$

for all $m, k \in \mathbb{N}_0$. Then $f \in H'_\mu(I)$ is defined by the following way:

$$\langle f,\varphi\rangle = \int_0^\infty f(x)\varphi(x)dx,\ \varphi \in H_\mu(I).$$

Definition 4.6 Let $k(w)$ be an arbitrary weight function. Then a function $\Phi \in \left[H_\mu(I)\right]'$ is said to belong to the weighted Sobolev space $G^p_{\mu,k}(I)$ for $\mu \in \mathbb{R}$, $1 \leqslant p < \infty$, if it satisfies

$$\|\Phi\|_{p,\mu,\sigma,k} = \left(\int_0^\infty \left|k(w)\left(h_\mu\Phi\right)(w)\right|^p d\sigma(w)\right)^{1/p}, \tag{4.38}$$

where $a > 0$ and $\Phi \in L^p_\sigma(I)$.

In what follows we shall assume that $k(w) = \left|\left(h_\mu\psi\right)(aw)\right|$ for fixed $a > 0$.

Theorem 4.6 *Let $f \in G^1_{\mu,k}(I)$ and $g \in G^p_{\mu,k}(I)$, $p \geq 1$. Then*

$$\|f \otimes g\|_{p,\mu,\sigma,k} \leqslant \|f\|_{1,\mu,\sigma,k}\|g\|_{p,\mu,\sigma,k}.$$

Proof In view of (4.38), we have

$$\|f \otimes g\|_{p,\mu,\sigma,k} = \left(\int_0^\infty \left|k(w)h_\mu(f \otimes g)(w)\right|^p d\sigma(w)\right)^{1/p}.$$

By (4.14) and (4.34), we have

$$\begin{aligned}\|f \otimes g\|_{p,\mu,\sigma,k} &\le \|F_a(w)\|_{1,\mu,\sigma,k}\, \|G_a(w)\|_{p,\mu,\sigma,k} \\ &\le \left\|\left(h_\mu\psi\right)(aw)\left(h_\mu f\right)(w)\right\|_{1,\mu,\sigma,k} \\ &\quad \times \left\|\left(h_\mu\psi\right)(aw)\left(h_\mu g\right)(w)\right\|_{p,\mu,\sigma,k}.\end{aligned}$$

From Definition 4.6, we get

$$\|f \otimes g\|_{p,\mu,\sigma,k} \leqslant \|f\|_{1,\mu,\sigma,k}\|g\|_{p,\mu,\sigma,k}.$$

Theorem 4.7 *Let $f \in G^p_{\mu,k}(I)$ and $g \in G^q_{\mu,k}(I)$, with $1 \leqslant p, q < \infty$ and $1/r = 1/p + 1/q - 1$. Then*

$$\|f \otimes g\|_{r,\mu,\sigma,k} \leqslant \|f\|_{p,\mu,\sigma,k}\|g\|_{q,\mu,\sigma,k}. \tag{4.39}$$

Proof Using (4.16) and (4.38), we get (4.39). □

Approximation properties of the Bessel wavelet convolution are given next.

Theorem 4.8 *Let $\psi_{n,a}(w) = \psi_n(aw)$, $n = 0, 1, 2, \ldots$ be the sequence of basic wavelet functions such that*

1. $\psi_{n,a}(w) \geqslant 0, \quad 0 < w < \infty,$
2. $\int_0^\infty \psi_{n,a}(w)d\sigma(w) = 1,$
3. $\lim_{n\to\infty} \int_\varepsilon^\infty \psi_{n,a}(w)d\sigma(w) = 0,$ *for each* $\varepsilon > 0,$
4. $\left(h_\mu\psi_{n,a}\right)(w) \in L^1_\sigma(I),$
5. $h_\mu^{-1}\left[\left(h_\mu\psi_{n,a}\right)(w)\right] = \psi_{n,a}(w).$

Then

$$\lim_{n\to\infty} \left\|f(b) - \left(B_{\psi_n} f\right)(b, a)\right\|_{1,\sigma} = 0.$$

Proof See [4, pp. 315–316]. □

Theorem 4.9 *Let $k_n(w) = \left(h_\mu\psi\right)(aw)\left(h_\mu g_n\right)(w)$ for fixed $a > 0, n \in \mathbb{N}$, and $\varphi(w) = \left(h_\mu\psi\right)(aw)\left(h_\mu f\right)(w)$ satisfy:*

1. $k_n(w) \geqslant 0, \quad 0 < w < \infty,$
2. $\int_0^\infty k_n(w)d\sigma(w) = 1, \quad w = 0, 1, 2, 3, \ldots,$

3. $\lim_{n\to\infty}\int_\delta^\infty k_n(w)d\sigma(w)=0$, *for each* $\delta>0$,
4. $\varphi(w)\in L_\sigma^\infty(I)$,
5. φ *is continuous at* w_0, *and* $\left(h_\mu\psi\right)(aw_0)\neq 0$ *for* $w_0\in[w-\delta,w+\delta]$, $\delta>0$.

Then

$$\lim_{n\to\infty} h_\mu\left(f\otimes g_n\right)(w_0)=\left(h_\mu f\right)(w_0). \tag{4.40}$$

Proof In view of relation (4.34), we have

$$\left(h_\mu\psi\right)(aw)h_\mu\left(f\otimes g_n\right)(w)=\left(\varphi\#k_n\right)(w).$$

Now, using Theorem 4.1, we have

$$\begin{aligned}\lim_{n\to\infty}\left(h_\mu\psi\right)(aw_0)\,h_\mu\left(f\otimes g_n\right)(w_0)&=\lim_{n\to\infty}\left(\varphi\#k_n\right)(w_0)\\&=\varphi\left(w_0\right)\\&=\left(h_\mu\psi\right)(aw_0)\left(h_\mu f\right)(w_0).\end{aligned}$$

This implies that

$$\lim_{n\to\infty} h_\mu\left(f\otimes g_n\right)(w_0)=\left(h_\mu f\right)(w_0).$$

Theorem 4.10 *Let* $f,\psi\in L_\sigma^1(I)$, *and* $k_n(w)$ *be the same as Theorem 4.9, which satisfies all the four properties of Theorem 4.8. Then*

$$\lim_{n\to\infty}\left\|\left(h_\mu\psi\right)(aw_0)\left(h_\mu f\right)(w_0)-\left(h_\mu\psi\right)(aw_0)\,h_\mu\left(f\otimes g_n\right)(w_0)\right\|_{1,\sigma}=0.$$

Proof Using (4.34), we have

$$\begin{aligned}&\lim_{n\to\infty}\left\|\left(h_\mu\psi\right)(aw_0)\left(h_\mu f\right)(w_0)-\left(h_\mu\psi\right)(aw_0)\,h_\mu\left(f\otimes g_n\right)(w_0)\right\|_{1,\sigma}\\&=\lim_{n\to\infty}\|\left(h_\mu\psi\right)(aw_0)\left(h_\mu f\right)(w_0)\\&\quad-\left[\left(h_\mu\psi\right)(a\cdot)\left(h_\mu f\right)(\cdot)\#\left(h_\mu\psi\right)(a\cdot)\left(h_\mu g_n\right)(a\cdot)\right](w_0)\|_{1,\sigma}\\&=\lim_{n\to\infty}\|\varphi\left(w_0\right)-\left(\varphi\#k_n\right)(w_0)\|_{1,\sigma}\,.\end{aligned}$$

Since $f,\psi_a\in L_\sigma^1(I)$, $\varphi(w)=\left(h_\mu f\right)\left(h_\mu\psi_a\right)=h_\mu\left(f\#\psi_a\right)\in L_\sigma^1(I)$. Therefore using the tools of [4, Corollary 2c, pp. 313–314], we have

$$\lim_{n\to\infty}\left\|\left(h_\mu\psi\right)(aw_0)\left(h_\mu f\right)(w_0)-\left(h_\mu\psi\right)(aw_0)\,h_\mu\left(f\otimes g_n\right)(w_0)\right\|_{1,\sigma}=0.$$

References

1. Pathak, R.S.: The wavelet transform. Atlantic Press/World Scientific, Paris, France (2009)
2. Cholewinski, F.M.: A Hankel convolution complex inversion theory. Mem. Amer. Math, Soc (1965)
3. Haimo, D.T.: Integral equations associated with Hankel convolutions. Trans. Amer. Math. Soc. **116**, 330–375 (1965)
4. Hirschman, I.: Variation diminishing Hankel transforms. J. Analyse Math. **8**(1), 307–336 (1960–61)
5. Pathak, R.S., Dixit, M.M.: Continuous and discrete Bessel wavelet transforms. J. Comput. Appl. Math. **160**(1–2), 241–250 (2003)
6. Triméche, K.: Generalized wavelets and hypergroups. Routledge (2019)
7. Pathak, R.S., Pandey, P.K.: Sobolev type spaces associated with Bessel operators. J. Math. Anal. Appl. **215**(1), 95–111 (1997)
8. Kanjin, Y.: A translation theorem for the Hankel transformation on the Hardy space. Tohoku Math. J. **57**, 231–246 (2005)
9. Zemanian, A.H.: Generalized integral transformations. Pure and applied mathematics XVIII. Interscience Publishers, New York (1968)

Chapter 5
Relation Between the Bessel Wavelet Convolution Product and the Hankel Convolution Product

5.1 Introduction

The concept of wavelet convolution product and their properties are extensively discussed by Pathak [1] and [2], utilizing the theory of Fourier transform. Using the Bessel wavelet transform Pathak, Upadhyay, and Pandey [3] formally introduced the Bessel wavelet convolution product, deriving key approximations and significant results. Additionally, Pinsky [4] introduced the concept of Heuristic treatment of wavelet transform by exploiting the Fourier transform technique, leading to several important characterizations. These developments inspire our investigation into the relationship between the Bessel wavelet convolution product and the Hankel convolution product, the heuristic treatment to the Bessel wavelet transform using the Hankel transform.

The present chapter is divided into three sections. Present Sect. 5.1 gives definitions and other important results. The Sect. 5.2 contains the relation between the Bessel wavelet convolution product and Hankel convolution product and related approximation properties of the Bessel wavelet convolution product. Section 5.3 presents the heuristic treatment of the Bessel wavelet transform and examines its various properties.

Definition 5.1 The Bessel wavelet for $\psi \in L^p_\sigma(0,\infty)$, $1 \le p < \infty$, $b \ge 0$ and $a > 0$ is defined by

$$\psi_{b,a}(x) := D_a \tau_b \psi(x) = a^{-2\mu-1} \int_0^\infty D(b/a, x/a, z)\psi(z)d\sigma(z), \tag{5.1}$$

where D_a and τ_b denote the dilation and the translation of $\psi \in L^p_\sigma(0,\infty)$ at a, b respectively and $D(b/a, x/a, z)$ is the basic function which is given in (4.7).

S. K. Upadhyay and J. S. Maurya, *The Bessel Wavelet Transform*,
Industrial and Applied Mathematics,
https://doi.org/10.1007/978-981-96-9938-4_5

Definition 5.2 The continuous Bessel wavelet transform of $f \in L^1_\sigma(I) \cap L^2_\sigma(I)$ with respect to a wavelet $\psi \in L^2_\sigma(I)$ is defined as

$$(B_\psi f)(b,a) := a^{-2\mu-1} \int_0^\infty \int_0^\infty f(t)\bar{\psi}(z) D(b/a, t/a, z) d\sigma(z) d\sigma(t). \quad (5.2)$$

From (5.1), the continuous Bessel wavelet transform of a function $f \in L^1_\sigma(I) \cap L^2_\sigma(I)$ with respect to wavelet $\psi \in L^2_\sigma(I)$ in terms of Hankel transform is defined as

$$(B_\psi f)(b,a) = \int_0^\infty j_\mu(b\omega)(h_\mu f)(\omega)\overline{(h_\mu \psi)(a\omega)} d\sigma(\omega). \quad (5.3)$$

5.2 The Bessel Wavelet Convolution Product

In this section, using the Bessel wavelet convolution product

$$B_\psi \left(f \otimes g\right)(b,a) = (B_\psi f)(b,a)(B_\psi g)(b,a), \quad (5.4)$$

we find the relation between the Bessel wavelet convolution product and the Hankel convolution product and obtain boundedness results of the Bessel wavelet convolution product.

Theorem 5.1 *Let $f, g \in L^1_\sigma(I) \cap L^2_\sigma(I)$. Then the Bessel wavelet convolution product can be written in the following form:*

$$\begin{aligned} E_\psi[h_\mu (f \otimes g)](\omega) = & \int_0^\infty \int_0^\infty (h_\mu f)(\eta)\, (h_\mu g)(\xi)\, D(\omega, \xi, \eta) \\ & \times \left(\int_0^\infty \overline{(h_\mu \psi)(a\eta)}\ \overline{(h_\mu \psi)(a\xi)} \frac{d\sigma(a)}{a^{2\mu+1}} \right) d\sigma(\eta) d\sigma(\xi) \end{aligned} \quad (5.5)$$

where

$$E_\psi := \int_0^\infty \frac{\overline{(h_\mu \psi)(a\omega)}}{a^{2\mu+1}} d\sigma(a). \quad (5.6)$$

Proof From (5.3), we have

$$h_\mu \left[(B_\psi f)(b,a)\right](\omega) = \overline{(h_\mu \psi)(a\omega)}\ (h_\mu f)(\omega).$$

Hence

$$h_\mu \left[B_\psi (f \otimes g)(b,a)\right](\omega) = \overline{(h_\mu \psi)(a\omega)}\ [h_\mu (f \otimes g)](\omega),$$

so that, using (5.4) and [3, pp. 271] we have

$$\begin{aligned}
&\overline{(h_\mu\psi)(a\omega)}\ [h_\mu(f\otimes g)](\omega)\\
&= h_\mu\left[(B_\psi f)(b,a)(B_\psi g)(b,a)\right](\omega)\\
&= h_\mu\left[h_\mu^{-1}\left\{\overline{(h_\mu\psi)(a.)}(h_\mu f)(.)\right\}\ h_\mu^{-1}\left\{\overline{(h_\mu\psi)(a.)}(h_\mu g)(.)\right\}\right](\omega)\\
&= h_\mu\left[h_\mu^{-1}\left\{\overline{(h_\mu\psi)(a.)}(h_\mu f)(.)\#\overline{(h_\mu\psi)(a.)}(h_\mu g)(.)\right\}\right](\omega)\\
&= \left(\overline{(h_\mu\psi)(a.)}(h_\mu f)(.)\#\overline{(h_\mu\psi)(a.)}(h_\mu g)(.)\right)(\omega).
\end{aligned}$$

If we set $F_a=\overline{(h_\mu\psi)(a.)}\,(h_\mu f)(.)$ and $G_a=\overline{(h_\mu\psi)(a.)}(h_\mu g)(.)$, then we have

$$\begin{aligned}
&\overline{(h_\mu\psi)(a\omega)}\ [h_\mu(f\otimes g)](\omega)\\
&=(F_a\#G_a)(\omega)\\
&=\int_0^\infty\int_0^\infty F_a(\eta)G_a(\xi)D(\omega,\xi,\eta)\,d\sigma(\eta)\,d\sigma(\xi)\\
&=\int_0^\infty\int_0^\infty \overline{(h_\mu\psi)(a\eta)}(h_\mu f)(\eta)\overline{(h_\mu\psi)(a\xi)}(h_\mu g)(\xi)D(\omega,\xi,\eta)\,d\sigma(\eta)\,d\sigma(\xi).
\end{aligned}$$

Therefore,

$$\begin{aligned}
\int_0^\infty \frac{\overline{(h_\mu\psi)(a\omega)}}{a^{2\mu+1}}\ [h_\mu(f\otimes g)](\omega)d\sigma(a) = \int_0^\infty\Bigg(\int_0^\infty\int_0^\infty &\overline{(h_\mu\psi)(a\eta)}\,(h_\mu f)(\eta)\,\overline{(h_\mu\psi)(a\xi)}\\
&\times(h_\mu g)(\xi)D(\omega,\xi,\eta)\,d\sigma(\eta)\,d\sigma(\xi)\Bigg)\frac{d\sigma(a)}{a^{2\mu+1}}.
\end{aligned}$$

Thus, the above expression can be written as

$$\begin{aligned}
&E_\psi\ [h_\mu(f\otimes g)](\omega)\\
&=\int_0^\infty\int_0^\infty (h_\mu f)(\eta)(h_\mu g)(\xi)D(\omega,\xi,\eta)\left(\int_0^\infty \overline{(h_\mu\psi)(a\eta)}\ \overline{(h_\mu\psi)(a\xi)}\ \frac{d\sigma(a)}{a^{2\mu+1}}\right)d\sigma(\eta)\,d\sigma(\xi).
\end{aligned}$$

□

Theorem 5.2 *Let $\psi\in L^2_\sigma(I)$ be the basic wavelet and it satisfies the admissibility condition*

$$C_\psi := \int_0^\infty \frac{|(h_\mu\psi)(a\omega)|^2}{a^{2\mu+1}}d\sigma(a). \tag{5.7}$$

Then

$$\int_0^\infty \frac{|(h_\mu\psi)(a\omega)(h_\mu\psi)(a\eta)|}{a^{2\mu+1}}d\sigma(a) < C_\psi. \tag{5.8}$$

Proof We have

$$\int_0^\infty \frac{|(h_\mu\psi)(a\omega)(h_\mu\psi)(a\eta)|}{a^{2\mu+1}} d\sigma(a) = \int_0^\infty \frac{|(h_\mu\psi)(a\omega)(h_\mu\psi)(a\eta)|}{a^{\frac{2\mu+1}{2}} a^{\frac{2\mu+1}{2}}} d\sigma(a)$$
$$\leq \left(\int_0^\infty \frac{|(h_\mu\psi)(a\omega)|^2}{a^{2\mu+1}} d\sigma(a)\right)^{\frac{1}{2}} \left(\int_0^\infty \frac{|(h_\mu\psi)(a\eta)|^2}{a^{2\mu+1}} d\sigma(a)\right)^{\frac{1}{2}}.$$

From equation (5.7), we get

$$\int_0^\infty \frac{|(h_\mu\psi)(a\omega)(h_\mu\psi)(a\eta)|}{a^{2\mu+1}} d\sigma(a) \leq C_\psi^{\frac{1}{2}} \times C_\psi^{\frac{1}{2}}$$
$$= C_\psi.$$

This implies that

$$\int_0^\infty \frac{|(h_\mu\psi)(a\omega)(h_\mu\psi)(a\eta)|}{a^{2\mu+1}} d\sigma(a) < C_\psi.$$

Theorem 5.3 *Let $f, g \in L^1_\sigma(I) \cap L^2_\sigma(I)$. Then we get the following estimate*

$$\left|h_\mu (f \otimes g)(\omega)\right| \leq C'_\psi \left(\left|h_\mu f\right| \# \left|h_\mu g\right|\right)(\omega), \tag{5.9}$$

where $C'_\psi = \frac{C_\psi}{E_\psi}$ and value of C_ψ is defined in (5.7) and E_ψ defined in (5.6).

Proof From (5.5), we have

$$E_\psi \left|h_\mu(f \otimes g)(\omega)\right| \leq \int_0^\infty \int_0^\infty \left|(h_\mu f)(\eta)\,(h_\mu g)(\xi)\, D(\omega, \xi, \eta)\right|$$
$$\times \left(\int_0^\infty \left|\overline{(h_\mu\psi)(a\eta)}\ \ \overline{(h_\mu\psi)(a\xi)}\right| \frac{d\sigma(a)}{a^{2\mu+1}}\right) d\sigma(\eta) d\sigma(\xi).$$

Using Theorem 5.2 and Holder inequality, we get

$$E_\psi \left|h_\mu(f \otimes g)(\omega)\right|$$
$$\leq \int_0^\infty \int_0^\infty \left|(h_\mu f)(\eta)\,(h_\mu g)(\xi)\, D(\omega, \xi, \eta)\right|$$
$$\times \left(\int_0^\infty \frac{|(h_\mu\xi)(a\eta)|^2}{a^{2\mu+1}} d\sigma(a)\right)^{1/2} \left(\int_0^\infty \frac{|(h_\mu\xi)(a\xi)|^2}{a^{2\mu+1}} d\sigma(a)\right)^{1/2} d\sigma(\eta)\, d\sigma(\xi)$$
$$\leq \int_0^\infty \int_0^\infty \left|(h_\mu f)(\eta)\,(h_\mu g)(\xi)\, D(\omega, \xi, \eta)\right| (C_\psi)^{1/2} (C_\psi)^{1/2}\, d\sigma(\eta)\, d\sigma(\xi).$$

Hence,

$$\begin{aligned}\left|h_\mu(f\otimes g)(\omega)\right| &\le \frac{C_\psi}{E_\psi}\left(|h_\mu f|\,\#\,|h_\mu g|\right)(\omega)\\ &\le C_\psi^{'}\left(|h_\mu f|\,\#\,|h_\mu g|\right)(\omega).\end{aligned}$$

□

Theorem 5.4 ***(i).*** *Assume that* $f\in L^p_\sigma(I), g\in L^{p'}_\sigma(I)$. $1\le p, p'<\infty$ *and* $\psi\in L^q_\sigma(I)\cap L^{q'}_\sigma(I)$ *such that* $\frac{1}{p}+\frac{1}{q}=1\,,\ \frac{1}{p'}+\frac{1}{q'}=1$.
Then

$$|B_\psi(f\otimes g)(b,a)| \le a^{-2\mu-1}\,||f||_{p,\sigma}\ ||g||_{p',\sigma}\ ||\psi||_{q,\sigma}\ ||\psi||_{q',\sigma}. \tag{5.10}$$

(ii). *Assume that* $f,g\in L^2_\sigma(I)$ *and* $\psi\in L^2_\sigma(I)$ *is a Bessel wavelet which satisfies*

$$C_\psi := \int_0^\infty \frac{|(h_\mu\psi)(a\omega)|^2}{a^{2\mu+1}}d\sigma(a), \tag{5.11}$$

then

$$\left|\int_0^\infty\int_0^\infty B_\psi\left(f\otimes g\right)(b,a)\frac{d\sigma(a)d\sigma(b)}{a^{2\mu+1}}\right| \le C_\psi||f||_{2,\sigma}||g||_{2,\sigma}. \tag{5.12}$$

Proof **(i).** Using (5.4), we have

$$\begin{aligned}|B_\psi\left(f\otimes g\right)(b,a)| &= |(B_\psi f)(b,a)(B_\psi g)(b,a)|\\ &= |a^{-2\mu-1}(f\#\overline{\psi_a})(b)|\ |a^{-2\mu-1}(g\#\overline{\psi_a})(b)|\\ &\le a^{-4\mu-2}\ ||f||_{p,\sigma}\ ||\bar{\psi_a}||_{q,\sigma}\ ||g||_{p',\sigma}\ ||\bar{\psi_a}||_{q',\sigma}\\ &= a^{-4\mu-2}\ \ ||f||_{p,\sigma}\ (a^{\frac{2\mu+1}{q}}\ \ ||\psi||_{q,\sigma})\ \ ||g||_{p',\sigma}\ \ (a^{\frac{2\mu+1}{q'}}\ \ ||\psi||_{q',\sigma})\\ &= a^{-4\mu-2}\ a^{(2\mu+1)(\frac{1}{q}+\frac{1}{q'})}\ \ ||f||_{p,\sigma}\ ||\psi||_{q,\sigma}\ ||g||_{p'}\ ||\psi||_{q'}\\ &= a^{-2\mu-1}\ ||f||_{p,\sigma}\ ||\psi||_{q,\sigma}\ ||g||_{p',\sigma}\ ||\psi||_{q',\sigma}.\end{aligned}$$

Proof. (ii). Using (5.4), we have

$$\begin{aligned}\left|\int_0^\infty\int_0^\infty B_\psi\,(f\otimes g)\,(b,a)\frac{d\sigma(a)d\sigma(b)}{a^{2\mu+1}}\right| &= \left|\int_0^\infty\int_0^\infty (B_\psi f)(b,a)(B_\psi g)(b,a)\frac{d\sigma(a)d\sigma(b)}{a^{2\mu+1}}\right|\\ &= |C_\psi < f, g > |\\ &= C_\psi\left|\int_0^\infty f(x)\overline{g}(x)d\sigma(x)\right|\\ &\le C_\psi\int_0^\infty |f(x)\overline{g}(x)|\,d\sigma(x)\\ &\le C_\psi||f||_{2,\sigma}\,||g||_{2,\sigma}.\end{aligned}$$

Theorem 5.5 *Let $(h_\mu f)\in L^p_\sigma(I)$ and $(h_\mu g)\in L^q_\sigma(I)$, then we have the following inequality*

$$\left\|h_\mu\,(f\otimes g)\right\|_{r,\sigma}\le C_\psi^{'}\,\left\|h_\mu f\right\|_{p,\sigma}\left\|h_\mu g\right\|_{q,\sigma}, \tag{5.13}$$

where $\frac{1}{p}+\frac{1}{q}-1=\frac{1}{r}$.

Proof We have

$$\left\|h_\mu\,(f\otimes g)\right\|^r_{r,\sigma}=\int_0^\infty\left|h_\mu\,(f\otimes g)\,(x)\right|^r d\sigma(x).$$

Using Theorem 5.3, we have

$$\begin{aligned}\left\|h_\mu\,(f\otimes g)\right\|^r_{r,\sigma} &\le \int_0^\infty\left[C_\psi^{'}\,\left(|h_\mu f|\#|h_\mu g|\right)(x)\right]^r d\sigma(x)\\ &\le (C_\psi^{'})^r\int_0^\infty\left|\left(|h_\mu f|\#|h_\mu g|\right)(x)\right|^r d\sigma(x)\\ &\le (C_\psi^{'})^r\,\left\|\,|h_\mu f|\#|h_\mu g|\,\right\|^r_{r,\sigma}.\end{aligned}$$

From (4.16), we have

$$\left\|h_\mu\,(f\otimes g)\right\|_{r,\sigma}\le C_\psi^{'}\left\|h_\mu f\right\|_{p,\sigma}\left\|h_\mu g\right\|_{q,\sigma}.$$

Theorem 5.6 *Let $k_n(w)=(h_\mu g_n)(w)$ for $n\in\mathbb{N}$ and $\phi(w)=(h_\mu f)(w)$ satisfy the following conditions :*

1. $k_n(w)\ge 0,\quad 0<w<\infty,$
2. $\int_0^\infty k_n(w)\,d\sigma(w)=1,\quad w=0,1,2,3,.....,$
3. $\lim\limits_{n\to\infty}\int_\delta^\infty k_n(w)\,d\sigma(w)=0,\quad for\ each\ \delta>0,$
4. $\phi(w)\in L^\infty_\sigma(I),$
5. *ϕ is continuous at w_0,*

then

$$\lim_{n\to\infty} \left|h_\mu(f \otimes g_n)(w_0)\right| \leq C'_\psi (h_\mu f)(w_0), \tag{5.14}$$

where $C'_\psi = \frac{C_\psi}{E_\psi}$ *and* C_ψ, E_ψ *are given in (5.7) and (5.6) respectively.*

Proof From (5.9), we have

$$\left|h_\mu(f \otimes g_n)(w_0)\right| \leq C'_\psi \left(\left|h_\mu f\right| \# \left|h_\mu g_n\right|\right)(w_0).$$

Therefore,

$$\lim_{n\to\infty} \left|h_\mu(f \otimes g_n)(w_0)\right| \leq \lim_{n\to\infty} C'_\psi (|\phi| \# |k_n|)(w_0).$$

Using [5, Theorem 2(c)], we have

$$\begin{aligned}\lim_{n\to\infty} \left|h_\mu(f \otimes g_n)(w_0)\right| &\leq C'_\psi \, |\phi(w_0)| \\ &= C'_\psi \left|(h_\mu f)(w_0)\right|.\end{aligned}$$

□

Theorem 5.7 *Let* $f \in L^1_\sigma(I)$, $\phi(w) = (h_\mu f)(w)$ *and* $k_n(w)$ *be same as Theorem 5.6, satisfies all the four properties of Theorem 5.6. Then*

$$\lim_{n\to\infty} \left\| \frac{1}{C'_\psi} h_\mu(f \otimes g_n) - (h_\mu f) \right\|_{1,\sigma} = 0. \tag{5.15}$$

Proof From (5.9), we have

$$\begin{aligned}\lim_{n\to\infty} \left\| \frac{1}{C'_\psi} h_\mu(f \otimes g_n) - (h_\mu f) \right\|_{1,\sigma} &\leq \lim_{n\to\infty} ||(\left|h_\mu f\right| \# \left|h_\mu g_n\right|) - (h_\mu f)||_{1,\sigma} \\ &\leq \lim_{n\to\infty} ||\,(|\phi| \# |k_n|) - |\phi|\,||_{1,\sigma}.\end{aligned}$$

□

Since $f \in L^1_\sigma(I)$, $h_\mu f(w) \in L^1_\sigma(I)$. Therefore using the tools of [5, corollary 2c, pp. 313–314], we have

$$\lim_{n\to\infty} \left\| \frac{1}{C'_\psi} h_\mu(f \otimes g_n) - (h_\mu f) \right\|_{1,\sigma} = 0.$$

5.3 Heuristic Treatment of the Bessel Wavelet Transform

In this section, we shall study the properties of Heuristic treatment of the Bessel wavelet transform (5.2).

Theorem 5.8 *Let $(B_\psi f)(b,a)$ be the Bessel wavelet transform and $(B_\psi^* f)(b,a)$ be the adjoint Bessel wavelet operator on a function $f \in L^2_\sigma(I)$ with respect to wavelet $\psi \in L^2_\sigma(I)$. Then*

$$f = \int_0^\infty B_\psi^* \, B_\psi \, f \, \frac{d\sigma(a)}{a^{2\mu+1}}, \tag{5.16}$$

where $f(t) = j_\mu(\xi t)$.

Proof Putting $f(t) = j_\mu(\xi t)$ in (5.2), we get

$$\begin{aligned}(B_\psi f)(b,a) &= a^{-2\mu-1} \int_0^\infty j_\mu(\xi t)\, \bar{\psi}(\frac{t}{a}, \frac{b}{a})\, d\sigma(t) \\ &= a^{-2\mu-1} \int_0^\infty \left(\int_0^\infty \bar{\psi}(z)\, D(\frac{t}{a}, \frac{b}{a}, z) d\sigma(z) \right) j_\mu(\xi t) d\sigma(t) \\ &= a^{-2\mu-1} \int_0^\infty \left(\int_0^\infty j_\mu(\xi t)\, D(\frac{t}{a}, \frac{b}{a}, z) d\sigma(t) \right) \bar{\psi}(z)\, d\sigma(z).\end{aligned}$$

Substituting $\frac{t}{a} = u$, we obtain

$$\begin{aligned}(B_\psi f)(b,a) &= a^{-2\mu-1} \int_0^\infty \left(\int_0^\infty j_\mu(ua\xi)\, D(u, \frac{b}{a}, z) a^{2\mu+1} d\sigma(u) \right) \bar{\psi}(z)\, d\sigma(z) \\ &= \int_0^\infty j_\mu(b\xi) j_\mu(za\xi) \bar{\psi}(z)\, d\sigma(z) \\ &= j_\mu(b\xi) \int_0^\infty j_\mu(za\xi) \bar{\psi}(z)\, d\sigma(z) \\ &= j_\mu(b\xi)\, \overline{(h_\mu \psi)}(a\xi).\end{aligned}$$

Now, we construct the adjoint operator

$$\begin{aligned}B_\psi^* \, B_\psi f(t) &= a^{-2\mu-1} \int_0^\infty (B_\psi f)(b,a) \psi(\frac{t}{a}, \frac{b}{a}) d\sigma(b) \\ &= a^{-2\mu-1} \overline{(h_\mu \psi)}(a\xi) \int_0^\infty j_\mu(b\xi) \left(\int_0^\infty \psi(z)\ D(\frac{t}{a}, \frac{b}{a}, z) d\sigma(z) \right) d\sigma(b) \\ &= a^{-2\mu-1} \overline{(h_\mu \psi)}(a\xi) \int_0^\infty \left(\int_0^\infty D(\frac{t}{a}, \frac{b}{a}, z)\ j_\mu(b\xi) d\sigma(b) \right) \psi(z)\, d\sigma(z).\end{aligned}$$

Putting $\frac{b}{a} = v$, we get

$$\begin{aligned} B_\psi^* B_\psi f(t) &= a^{-2\mu-1}\overline{(h_\mu\psi)}(a\xi)\int_0^\infty \left(\int_0^\infty D(\frac{t}{a}, v, z)\, j_\mu(va\xi)a^{2\mu+1}d\sigma(v)\right)\psi(z)\,d\sigma(z)\\ &= \overline{(h_\mu\psi)}(a\xi)\int_0^\infty j_\mu(t\xi)\, j_\mu(za\xi)\,\psi(z)d\sigma(z)\\ &= \overline{(h_\mu\psi)}(a\xi)\,(h_\mu\psi)(a\xi)\, j_\mu(t\xi)\\ &= \left|(h_\mu\psi)(a\xi)\right|^2 j_\mu(t\xi).\\ \int_0^\infty B_\psi^* B_\psi\, f(t)\,\frac{d\sigma(a)}{a^{2\mu+1}} &= j_\mu(t\xi)\int_0^\infty \frac{\left|(h_\mu\psi)(a\xi)\right|^2}{a^{2\mu+1}}d\sigma(a). \end{aligned}$$

Therefore,

$$\begin{aligned} f(t) = j_\mu(t\xi) &= \frac{\int_0^\infty B_\psi^*\, B_\psi\, f(t)\,\frac{d\sigma(a)}{a^{2\mu+1}}}{\int_0^\infty \frac{\left|(h_\mu\psi)(a\xi)\right|^2}{a^{2\mu+1}}d\sigma(a)}\\ &= \frac{\int_0^\infty B_\psi^*\, B_\psi\, f(t)\,\frac{d\sigma(a)}{a^{2\mu+1}}}{\int_0^\infty \frac{\left|(h_\mu\psi)(\nu)\right|^2}{\nu^{2\mu+1}}d\sigma(\nu)}. \end{aligned}$$

By imposing the normalization $\int_0^\infty \frac{\left|(h_\mu\psi)(\nu)\right|^2}{\nu^{2\mu+1}}d\sigma(\nu) = 1$, we obtain the Bessel wavelet representation

$$f(t) = \int_0^\infty B_\psi^*\, B_\psi\, f(t)\,\frac{d\sigma(a)}{a^{2\mu+1}},$$

valid for $f(t) = j_\mu(t\xi)$.

□

Theorem 5.9 *Suppose that ψ is a continuum Bessel wavelet with*

$$A_\psi := \int_0^\infty \omega^{-2\mu-1}\,|\psi(\omega)|^2\,d\sigma(\omega) = 1.$$

Then for any $f \in L^2_\sigma(I)$ we have the L^2_σ inversion formula

$$\begin{aligned} f(x) &= \int_{\mathbb{R}^2_+} (B_\psi f)(b, a)\psi_{b,a}(x)\frac{d\sigma(a)d\sigma(b)}{a^{2\mu+1}}\\ &= \lim_{\epsilon\to\infty, A, B\to\infty}\int_{\epsilon<a<A, b<B} (B_\psi f)(b, a)\psi_{b,a}(x)\frac{d\sigma(a)d\sigma(b)}{a^{2\mu+1}}, \end{aligned}$$

where $S(\epsilon, A, B)f = \int_{\epsilon<a<A,b<B}(B_\psi f)(b, a)\psi_{b,a}(x)\frac{d\sigma(a)d\sigma(b)}{a^{2\mu+1}}$.

Proof Let the integral belongs in $L^2_\sigma(\mathbb{R}^2_+, \frac{d\sigma(a)d\sigma(b)}{a^{2\mu+1}})$.
Now, we have

$$\|f - S(\epsilon, A, B)f\|_{2,\sigma} = \sup_{\|g\|_{2,\sigma}=1} |\langle f - S(\epsilon, A, B)f, g\rangle| .$$

Applying Fubini's Theorem, we have

$$\begin{aligned}\langle S(\epsilon, A, B)f, g\rangle &= \int_{\mathbb{R}_+} \bar{g}(x)\left(\int_{\epsilon<a<A,b<B} (B_\psi f)(b,a)\psi_{b,a}(x)\frac{d\sigma(a)d\sigma(b)}{a^{2\mu+1}}\right)d\sigma(x)\\ &= \int_{\epsilon<a<A,b<B} (B_\psi f)(b,a)\left(\int_{\mathbb{R}_+} \bar{g}(x)\psi_{b,a}(x)d\sigma(x)\right)\frac{d\sigma(a)d\sigma(b)}{a^{2\mu+1}}\\ &= \int_{\epsilon<a<A,b<B} (B_\psi f)(b,a)\,\overline{(B_\psi g)(b,a)}\,\frac{d\sigma(a)d\sigma(b)}{a^{2\mu+1}}.\end{aligned}$$

Thus, by Parseval's formula of the Hankel transform and Cauchy-Schwarz inequality, we have

$$\begin{aligned}&\langle f - S(\epsilon, A, B)f, g\rangle\\ &= \left|\int_{(\epsilon<a<A,b<B)^c} (B_\psi f)(b,a)\,\overline{B_\psi g}(b,a)\frac{d\sigma(a)d\sigma(b)}{a^{2\mu+1}}\right|\\ &\leq \left(\int_{(\epsilon<a<A,b<B)^c} |(B_\psi f)(b,a)|^2\,\frac{d\sigma(a)d\sigma(b)}{a^{2\mu+1}}\right)^{1/2}\left(\int_{\mathbb{R}^2_+} |(B_\psi g)(b,a)|^2\,\frac{d\sigma(a)d\sigma(b)}{a^{2\mu+1}}\right)^{1/2}\\ &= \left(\int_{(\epsilon<a<A,b<B)^c} |(B_\psi f)(b,a)|^2\,\frac{d\sigma(a)d\sigma(b)}{a^{2\mu+1}}\right)^{1/2} C_\psi \,\|g\|_{2,\sigma} .\end{aligned}$$

When $\epsilon \to 0$ and $A, B \to \infty$, the region of integration decreases to the empty set, hence the last integral tends to zero by the dominated convergence theorem.
This gives that

$$\|S(\epsilon, A, B)f - f\|_{2,\sigma} \to 0.$$

□

Theorem 5.10 *Suppose that ψ is a continuum Bessel wavelet with $\langle\psi, \psi\rangle_\omega = 1$ and*

$$C_{\psi,\mu,s} := \int_0^\infty \frac{|(h_\mu\psi)(\xi)|^2}{\xi^{1+2\mu+2s}}d\sigma(\xi) < \infty,$$

for some $s > 0$.

Then

$$\int_0^\infty \int_0^\infty \frac{\left|(B_\psi f)(b,a)\right|^2}{a^{2\mu+2s+1}} d\sigma(a) d\sigma(b) = C_{\psi,\mu,s} \left\| f \right\|_{2,s}^2 , \tag{5.17}$$

where $\| f \|_{2,s} = \int_0^\infty \xi^{2s} |(h_\mu f)(\xi)|^2 d\sigma(\xi)$ *defined the Sobolev norm [4, p. 290].*

Proof From (4.27), we have

$$\begin{aligned}
&\int_0^\infty [(B_\psi f)(b,a)\overline{(B_\psi g)}(b,a)] d\sigma(b) \\
&= \int_0^\infty h_\mu^{-1}\{(h_\mu f)(u)\,(\overline{h_\mu \psi})(au)\}(b)\, \overline{h_\mu^{-1}\{(h_\mu g)(u)(\overline{h_\mu \psi})(au)\}(b)} d\sigma(b).
\end{aligned}$$

Now, using Parseval formula of the Hankel transform the last expression becomes

$$\begin{aligned}
&\int_0^\infty \int_0^\infty \frac{(B_\psi f)(b,a)\overline{(B_\psi g)}(b,a)}{a^{2\mu+2s+1}} d\sigma(a) d\sigma(b) \\
&= \int_0^\infty \int_0^\infty \frac{(h_\mu f)(u)(\overline{h_\mu \psi})(au)\overline{(h_\mu g)(u)(\overline{h_\mu \psi})(au)}}{a^{2\mu+2s+1}} d\sigma(a) d\sigma(u) \\
&= \int_0^\infty \int_0^\infty (h_\mu f)(u)\overline{(h_\mu g)(u)}\, \frac{|(h_\mu \psi)(au)|^2}{a^{2\mu+2s+1}} d\sigma(a) d\sigma(u).
\end{aligned}$$

If we take $f = g$, then we obtain

$$\int_0^\infty \int_0^\infty \frac{|(B_\psi f)(b,a)|^2}{a^{2\mu+2s+1}} d\sigma(a) d\sigma(b) = \int_0^\infty \int_0^\infty |(h_\mu f)(u)|^2\, \frac{|(h_\mu \psi)(au)|^2}{a^{2\mu+2s+1}} d\sigma(a) d\sigma(u).$$

Putting $au = \xi$, we get

$$\begin{aligned}
\int_0^\infty \int_0^\infty \frac{|(B_\psi f)(b,a)|^2}{a^{2\mu+2s+1}} d\sigma(a) d\sigma(b) &= \int_0^\infty |(h_\mu f)(u)|^2 \left(\int_0^\infty \frac{|(h_\mu \psi)(\xi)|^2}{\xi^{2\mu+2s+1}} d\sigma(\xi) \right) u^{2s} d\sigma(u) \\
&= C_{\psi,\mu,s} \int_0^\infty |(h_\mu f)(u)|^2\, u^{2s} d\sigma(u) \\
&= C_{\psi,\mu,s}\, ||f||_{2,s}^2 .
\end{aligned}$$

□

References

1. Pathak, R.S.: The Wavelet Transform. Atlantic Press/World Scientific, Paris, France (2009)
2. Pathak, R.S.: The wavelet convolution product, Investigation in Mathematical. Sciences **4**(2), 101–113 (2014)
3. Pathak, R.S., Upadhyay, S.K., Pandey, R.S.: The Bessel wavelet convolution product. Rend. Semin. Mat. Univ. Politec. Torino **69**(3), 267–279 (2011)
4. Pinsky, M.: Introduction to Fourier Analysis and Wavelets. (American Mathematical Society, 2002)
5. Hirschman, I.: Variation diminishing Hankel transforms. J. Analyse Math. **8**(1), 307–336 (1960-61)

Chapter 6
Integrability of the Continuum Bessel Wavelet Kernel

6.1 Introduction

Pinsky [1, 2] studied the continuum wavelet, and the integrability conditions of the continuum wavelet kernel, and obtained many useful results using the Fourier transform technique. In the present chapter, integrability conditions of the kernel of the Bessel wavelet transform and its various properties are discussed exploiting the theory of Hankel transform and Hankel convolution. Properties of the partial inverse wavelet transform which is deeply connected with the integrability of the kernel of the Bessel wavelet are also established.

The entire chapter is organized in the following way:
Section 6.1 is introductory, giving various definitions, properties, and formulae. Section 6.2 discusses multiple estimates of the continuum Bessel wavelet transform. In Sect. 6.3, partial inverse Bessel wavelet transform is defined, and many properties of its kernel are found. In the last section, sufficient conditions for the Bessel wavelet kernel's integrability are investigated using the Hankel transform.

6.2 Properties of the Continuous Bessel Wavelet Transform

In this section, we discuss some properties of the continuous Bessel wavelet transform which are helpful to give the sufficient conditions for the integrability of the Bessel wavelet kernel.

Definition 6.1 A function $\psi \in L^2_\sigma(I)$ is a normalized continuum Bessel wavelet if $\|\psi\|_{2,\sigma} = 1$ and its Hankel transform satisfies the admissibility condition

$$C_\psi := \int_0^\infty \frac{|(h_\mu \psi)(\omega)|^2}{\omega^{2\mu+1}} d\sigma(\omega) < \infty. \tag{6.1}$$

S. K. Upadhyay and J. S. Maurya, *The Bessel Wavelet Transform*,
Industrial and Applied Mathematics,
https://doi.org/10.1007/978-981-96-9938-4_6

The admissibility condition (6.1) satisfies only if $(h_\mu\psi)(0) = 0$ which implies that $\int_0^\infty \psi(t)d\sigma(t) = 0$ by (4.3).

By rescaling the spatial coordinate, we may assume that both $\|\psi\|_{2,\sigma} = 1$ and C_ψ=1. Then, for any $\psi \in L^2_\sigma(I)$ with $C_\psi < \infty$, we can define

$$\left(h_\mu\psi_{new}\right)(\xi) = \frac{1}{C_\psi^{\mu+1/2}}\, h_\mu\psi\left(\frac{\xi||\psi||_{2,\sigma}^{2/2\mu+1}}{C_\psi}\right). \tag{6.2}$$

It is clear that $\left\|h_\mu\psi_{new}\right\|_{2,\sigma} = \|\psi_{new}\|_{2,\sigma} = 1$ and $\left(C_\psi\right)^{2\mu} C_{\psi_{new}} = 1$. This shows that (6.2) is a renormalized continuum Bessel wavelet.

The Bessel wavelet transform (5.2) can be easily expressed in the form of Hankel convolution

$$(B_\psi f)(b,a) = (f\#\psi_a)(b), \tag{6.3}$$

where $\psi_a(t) = \psi(at)$.

We define

$$N(a) = \left(\int_0^\infty \left|(B_\psi f)(b,a)\right|^2 d\sigma(b)\right)^{1/2} = \left\|(B_\psi f)(\cdot\,,a)\right\|_{2,\sigma}. \tag{6.4}$$

Lemma 6.1 *Let $\psi \in L^2_\sigma(I)$ be a renormalized continuum Bessel wavelet and $f \in L^2_\sigma(I)$. Then*

(i)

$$\left|B_\psi f(b,a)\right| \le \|f\|_{2,\sigma}\, a^{\frac{-2\mu-1}{2}}. \tag{6.5}$$

(ii) For $a > 0$, $b \to B_\psi f(b,a)$ is in $L^2_\sigma(I)$ and the norm $N(a)$ satisfies

$$\int_0^\infty \frac{[N(a)]^2}{a^{2\mu+1}} d\sigma(a) = \int_0^\infty \left(\int_0^\infty \left|B_\psi f(b,a)\right|^2 d\sigma(b)\right) \frac{d\sigma(a)}{a^{2\mu+1}} = \|f\|^2_{2,\sigma}. \tag{6.6}$$

Proof From (6.3), we have

$$\begin{aligned}\left|B_\psi f(b,a)\right| &= |(f\#\psi_a)(b)| \\ &\le \|f\#\psi_a\|_{\infty,\sigma}.\end{aligned}$$

From Schwartz inequality [3], above expression yields

$$\begin{aligned}\left|B_\psi f(b,a)\right| &\leq \|f\|_{2,\sigma}\ \|\psi_a\|_{2,\sigma}\\ &= \|f\|_{2,\sigma}\ a^{\frac{-2\mu-1}{2}}\ \|\psi\|_{2,\sigma}\\ &= \|f\|_{2,\sigma}\ a^{\frac{-2\mu-1}{2}}\end{aligned}$$

as $\|\psi\|_{2,\sigma} = 1$.

To prove (ii), we take $f \in L^1_\sigma(I) \cap L^2_\sigma(I)$, then

$$\begin{aligned}[N(a)]^2 &= \int_0^\infty \left|(B_\psi f)(b,a)\right|^2 d\sigma(b)\\ &= \int_0^\infty |(f\#\psi_a)(b)|^2\, d\sigma(b).\end{aligned}$$

From Parseval's relation (4.20), we have further

$$\begin{aligned}[N(a)]^2 &= \int_0^\infty \left|h_\mu(f\#\psi_a)(\xi)\right|^2 d\sigma(\xi)\\ &= \int_0^\infty |(h_\mu f)(\xi)|^2 |(h_\mu\psi_a)(\xi)|^2 d\sigma(\xi)\\ &< \infty.\end{aligned}$$

In particular, $b \to B_\psi f(b,a) \in L^2_\sigma(I)$ for every $a > 0$.
Now

$$\begin{aligned}\int_0^\infty [N(a)]^2 \frac{d\sigma(a)}{a^{2\mu+1}} &= \int_0^\infty \frac{d\sigma(a)}{a^{2\mu+1}} \left(\int_0^\infty |(h_\mu f)(\xi)|^2 |(h_\mu\psi_a)(\xi)|^2 d\sigma(\xi)\right)\\ &= \int_0^\infty |(h_\mu f)(\xi)|^2 \left(\int_0^\infty \frac{|(h_\mu\psi)(a\xi)|^2}{a^{2\mu+1}} d\sigma(a)\right) d\sigma(\xi)\\ &= \|f\|^2_{2,\sigma}\,.\end{aligned}$$

This proves (6.6), in case $f \in L^1_\sigma(I) \cap L^2_\sigma(I)$. In particular, $a \to \left\|B_\psi f\right\|^2_{2,\sigma}$ is finite everywhere.

Now if we take $f \in L^2_\sigma(I)$ and $f_n \in L^1_\sigma(I) \cap L^2_\sigma(I)$ with $\|f - f_n\|_{2,\sigma} \to 0$, then from (6.5), we have the pointwise bound

$$\left|B_\psi f(b,a) - B_\psi f_n(b,a)\right| \leq \|f - f_n\|_{2,\sigma} \to 0. \tag{6.7}$$

This shows that $\{B_\psi f_n\}$ converges uniformly to $B_\psi f$.

On the other hand, applying (6.6) to $\{f_m - f_n\}$, we see that $B_\psi f_n$ is a Cauchy sequence in the Hilbert space $L^2\left(I^2, \frac{d\sigma(b)d\sigma(a)}{a^{2\mu+1}}\right)$.

Hence, there exists a limit F in this space, for which

$$\begin{aligned}\int_0^\infty\int_0^\infty |F(b,a)|^2\frac{d\sigma(b)d\sigma(a)}{a^{2\mu+1}} &= \lim_{n\to\infty}\int_0^\infty\int_0^\infty \left|B_\psi f_n(b,a)\right|^2\frac{d\sigma(b)d\sigma(a)}{a^{2\mu+1}}\\ &= \lim_{n\to\infty}\|f_n\|_{2,\sigma}^2\\ &= \|f\|_{2,\sigma}^2\,.\end{aligned}$$

□

Considering the above facts, take a subsequence that converges almost everywhere. Along this subsequence, there is the uniform convergence to $B_\psi f$. Therefore, $F = B_\psi f$.

By taking $n \longrightarrow \infty$, (6.6) can be obtained.

6.3 Kernel of the Partial Inverse Bessel Wavelet Transform

In this section, from the concept of Pinsky [2], the partial inverse transform associated with the Bessel wavelet transform is introduced and its properties are discussed.

Definition 6.2 The partial inverse Bessel wavelet transform is defined as

$$S_\epsilon f(x) = \int_{a>\epsilon}\left(\int_0^\infty B_\psi f(b,a)\psi_{b,a}(x)d\sigma(b)\right)\frac{d\sigma(a)}{a^{2\mu+1}}, \tag{6.8}$$

for $\epsilon > 0$.

Theorem 6.1 *The partial inverse Bessel wavelet transform (6.8) can be expressed as*

$$S_\epsilon f(x) = \int_{a>\epsilon}\left(B_\psi f\#\psi_a\right)(x)\frac{d\sigma(a)}{a^{2\mu+1}}. \tag{6.9}$$

Proof We write

$$\begin{aligned}&\int_0^\infty B_\psi f(b,a)\psi_{b,a}(x)d\sigma(b)\\ &= a^{-2\mu-1}\int_0^\infty B_\psi f(b,a)\left\{\int_0^\infty \psi(z)D(\frac{b}{a},\frac{x}{a},z)d\sigma(z)\right\}d\sigma(b)\\ &= a^{-2\mu-1}\int_0^\infty B_\psi f(b,a)\left\{\int_0^\infty \psi(z)\left(\int_0^\infty j_\mu(\frac{b\xi}{a})j_\mu(\frac{x\xi}{a})j_\mu(z\xi)d\sigma(\xi)\right)d\sigma(z)\right\}d\sigma(b).\end{aligned}$$

By applying Fubini's Theorem, we have

$$\begin{aligned}
&\int_0^\infty B_\psi f(b,a)\psi_{b,a}(x)d\sigma(b)\\
&= a^{-2\mu-1}\int_0^\infty B_\psi f(b,a)\left\{\int_0^\infty (h_\mu\psi)(\xi)j_\mu(\frac{b\xi}{a})j_\mu(\frac{x\xi}{a})d\sigma(\xi)\right\}d\sigma(b)\\
&= a^{-2\mu-1}\left(\int_0^\infty B_\psi f(b,a)j_\mu(\frac{b\xi}{a})d\sigma(b)\right)\left(\int_0^\infty (h_\mu\psi)(\xi)j_\mu(\frac{x\xi}{a})d\sigma(\xi)\right)\\
&= a^{-2\mu-1}\int_0^\infty h_\mu[B_\psi f(b,a)](\frac{\xi}{a})(h_\mu\psi)(\xi)j_\mu(\frac{x\xi}{a})d\sigma(\xi).
\end{aligned}$$

Putting $\frac{\xi}{a}=\omega$, we get

$$\begin{aligned}
\int_0^\infty B_\psi f(b,a)\psi_{b,a}(x)d\sigma(b) &= \int_0^\infty h_\mu[B_\psi f(b,a)\#\psi_a](\omega)j_\mu(x\omega)d\sigma(\omega)\\
&= h_\mu^{-1}\left\{h_\mu[B_\psi f(b,a)\#\psi_a]\right\}(x)\\
&= \left(B_\psi f(b,a)\#\psi_a\right)(x).
\end{aligned}$$

Thus, from (6.8) we have

$$S_\epsilon f(x) = \int_{a>\epsilon}\left(B_\psi f\#\psi_a\right)(x)\frac{d\sigma(a)}{a^{2\mu+1}}.$$

Theorem 6.2 *Let $\psi \in L^2_\sigma(I)$, be a renormalized continuum wavelet and $\epsilon > 0$, $f \in L^2_\sigma(I)$ for $x \in I$. Then the integral (6.8) converges absolutely and has the pointwise bound*

$$|S_\epsilon f(x)| \le A_\epsilon \|f\|_{2,\sigma} \tag{6.10}$$

where

$$A_\epsilon = \left(\int_{a>\epsilon}\frac{1}{a^{2\mu+2}2^{\mu-\frac{1}{2}}\Gamma(\mu+\frac{1}{2})}da\right)^{1/2}. \tag{6.11}$$

Furthermore, $S_\epsilon f \in L^2_\sigma(I)$ and $\|S_\epsilon f - f\|_{2,\sigma} \to 0$ as $\epsilon \to 0$.

Proof From Cauchy-Schwarz inequality, we have the following pointwise bound

$$\begin{aligned}
\left|B_\psi f\#\psi_{a,0}(x)\right| &\le \left\|B_\psi f(\cdot\,,a)\right\|_{2,\sigma}\left\|\psi_{a,0}\right\|_{2,\sigma}\\
&= N(a)\frac{\|\psi\|_{2,\sigma}}{(a^{2\mu+1})^{1/2}}\\
&= \frac{N(a)}{(a^{2\mu+1})^{1/2}}.
\end{aligned}$$

Then,

$$
\begin{aligned}
|S_\epsilon f(x)| &\leq \int_{a>\epsilon} \frac{N(a)}{(a^{2\mu+1})^{1/2}} \frac{d\sigma(a)}{a^{2\mu+1}} \\
&\leq \left(\int_{a>\epsilon} \frac{|N(a)|^2}{a^{2\mu+1}} d\sigma(a) \right)^{1/2} \left(\int_{a>\epsilon} \frac{1}{(a^{2\mu+1})^2} d\sigma(a) \right)^{1/2} \\
&\leq \|f\|_{2,\sigma} \left(\int_{a>\epsilon} \frac{1}{(a^{2\mu+1})^2} d\sigma(a) \right)^{1/2} \\
&\leq \|f\|_{2,\sigma} \left(\int_{a>\epsilon} \frac{1}{a^{2\mu+2} 2^{\mu-\frac{1}{2}} \Gamma(\mu+\frac{1}{2})} da \right)^{1/2}.
\end{aligned}
$$

Therefore, by (6.11),

$$
|S_\epsilon f(x)| \leq \|f\|_{2,\sigma} A_\epsilon. \tag{6.12}
$$

Here, A_ϵ is convergent for each $\epsilon > 0$ and $\mu > -1/2$.

To prove that $S_\epsilon f \in L^2_\sigma(I)$, we take $f \in L^1_\sigma(I) \cap L^2_\sigma(I)$. Then from the properties of Hankel convolution [3], we have

$$
\begin{aligned}
\left\| B_\psi f \# \psi_a \right\|_{2,\sigma} &\leq \left\| B_\psi f \right\|_{1,\sigma} \|\psi_a\|_{2,\sigma} \\
&\leq \frac{\left\| B_\psi f \right\|_{1,\sigma}}{(a^{2\mu+1})^{1/2}} \qquad (\because \|\psi\|_{2,\sigma} = 1) \\
&= \frac{\| f \# \psi_a \|_{1,\sigma}}{(a^{2\mu+1})^{1/2}}.
\end{aligned}
$$

Using the argument of [2, p. 1732], we have

$$
\left\| B_\psi f \# \psi_a \right\|_{2,\sigma} \leq \frac{\|f\|_{1,\sigma}}{a^{2\mu+1}}.
$$

Applying the generalized Minkowski inequality to (6.8), we get

$$
\begin{aligned}
\|S_\epsilon f\|_{2,\sigma} &\leq \|f\|_{1,\sigma} \int_{a>\epsilon} \frac{d\sigma(a)}{a^{4\mu+2}} \\
&\leq \|f\|_{1,\sigma} \int_{a>\epsilon} \frac{da}{a^{2\mu+2} 2^{\mu-\frac{1}{2}} \Gamma(\mu+\frac{1}{2})} \\
&= \|f\|_{1,\sigma} A_\epsilon^2 \\
&< \infty.
\end{aligned}
$$

For $g \in L^2_\sigma(I)$, we obtain

$$\langle S_\epsilon f, g\rangle = \int_0^\infty S_\epsilon f(x)\overline{g(x)}d\sigma(x).$$

In view of (6.8),

$$\langle S_\epsilon f, g\rangle = \int_{a>\epsilon}\int_0^\infty B_\psi f(b,a)\overline{B_\psi g(b,a)}\,\frac{d\sigma(b)d\sigma(a)}{a^{2\mu+1}},$$

and

$$\begin{aligned}\|S_\epsilon f\|_{2,\sigma} &= \sup_{g\neq 0}\frac{|\langle S_\epsilon f, g\rangle|}{\|g\|_{2,\sigma}}\\ &\leq \left(\int_{a>\epsilon}\int_0^\infty \left|B_\psi f(b,a)\right|^2 \frac{d\sigma(b)d\sigma(a)}{a^{2\mu+1}}\right)^{1/2}\\ &\leq \|f\|_{2,\sigma}\,. \end{aligned} \tag{6.13}$$

For $f \in L^2_\sigma(I)$, let $f_n \in L^1_\sigma(I)\cap L^2_\sigma(I)$ with $\|f - f_n\|_{2,\sigma} \to 0$. Then using (6.13), we find that

$$\|S_\epsilon f_n - S_\epsilon f_m\|_{2,\sigma} \leq \|f_n - f_m\|_{2,\sigma} \to 0. \tag{6.14}$$

Hence, (6.14) shows that $S_\epsilon f_n$ is a Cauchy sequence in $L^2_\sigma(I)$ and in particular a subsequence converges pointwise a.e. In view of (6.12), we have, $|S_\epsilon f(x) - S_\epsilon f_n(x)| \leq A_\epsilon\,\|f - f_n\|_{2,\sigma} \to 0$, as $n\to\infty$ with fixed $\epsilon > 0$. This shows that $\{S_\epsilon f_n(x)\}$ converges to $S_\epsilon f(x)$ uniformly in $L^2_\sigma(I)$ when $n\to\infty$ with fixed ϵ. Hence, $S_\epsilon f \in L^2_\sigma(I)$ with bounds $\|S_\epsilon f\|_{2,\sigma} \leq \|f\|_{2,\sigma}$.

To prove the L^2_σ convergence when $\epsilon \to 0$, with help of Lemma 6.1(ii), we can write

$$\langle f, g\rangle = \int_0^\infty\int_0^\infty B_\psi f(b,a)\overline{B_\psi g(b,a)}\frac{d\sigma(b)d\sigma(a)}{a^{2\mu+1}}.$$

Hence,

$$\langle f - S_\epsilon f, g\rangle = \int_{a<\epsilon}\int_0^\infty B_\psi f(b,a)\overline{B_\psi g(b,a)}\frac{d\sigma(b)d\sigma(a)}{a^{2\mu+1}}.$$

Therefore,

$$|\langle f - S_\epsilon f, g\rangle| \leq \left(\int_{a<\epsilon}\int_0^\infty \left|B_\psi f\right|^2 \frac{d\sigma(b)d\sigma(a)}{a^{2\mu+1}}\right)^{1/2} \|g\|_{2,\sigma}\,.$$

Now,

$$\|f - S_\epsilon f\|_{2,\sigma} = \sup_{g\neq 0} \frac{|\langle f - S_\epsilon f, g\rangle|}{\|g\|_{2,\sigma}} \leq \left(\int_{a<\epsilon} \int_0^\infty \left|B_\psi f\right|^2 \frac{d\sigma(b)d\sigma(a)}{a^{2\mu+1}} \right)^{1/2},$$

which tends to zero by the Dominated Convergence Theorem. □

Theorem 6.3 *Let* $\psi \in L^2_\sigma(I)$ *and*

$$K_\epsilon(x, y) = \int_0^\infty \frac{1}{z^{2\mu+1}} \left\{ \int_0^z (\psi \# \overline{\psi})(\xi) d\sigma(\xi) \right\} D(x, y, z) d\sigma(z), \tag{6.15}$$

be the kernel of the partial inverse Bessel wavelet transform. Then $K_\epsilon(x, y)$ *is bounded.*

Proof From (6.15), we get

$$\begin{aligned} |K_\epsilon(x, y)| &\leq \int_0^\infty \frac{1}{z^{2\mu+1}} \left\{ \int_0^z \left|(\psi \# \overline{\psi})(\xi)\right| d\sigma(\xi) \right\} D(x, y, z) d\sigma(z) \\ &\leq \sup_\xi \left|\psi \# \overline{\psi}(\xi)\right| \int_0^\infty \frac{1}{z^{2\mu+1}} \left\{ \int_0^z d\sigma(\xi) \right\} D(x, y, z) d\sigma(z). \end{aligned}$$

Since $\psi \# \overline{\psi}(\xi) \in L^\infty_\sigma(I)$, then the above expression becomes

$$\begin{aligned} |K_\epsilon(x, y)| &\leq A \int_0^\infty \frac{1}{z^{2\mu+1}} \left(\int_0^z d\sigma(\xi) \right) D(x, y, z) d\sigma(z) \\ &= A \int_0^\infty \frac{1}{z^{2\mu+1}} \left(\int_0^z \frac{\xi^{2\mu}}{2^{\mu-1/2}\,\Gamma(\mu + 1/2)} d\xi \right) D(x, y, z) d\sigma(z) \\ &= A \int_0^\infty \frac{1}{z^{2\mu+1}} \left(\frac{z^{2\mu+1}}{2^{\mu-1/2}\,\Gamma(\mu + 1/2)\, 2\mu + 1} \right) D(x, y, z) d\sigma(z) \\ &= \frac{A}{2^{\mu-1/2}\,\Gamma(\mu + 1/2)\, 2\mu + 1} \int_0^\infty D(x, y, z) d\sigma(z). \end{aligned}$$

We get after using (4.9),

$$|K_\epsilon(x, y)| \leq \frac{A}{2^{\mu-1/2}\,\Gamma(\mu + 1/2)\, 2\mu + 1}.$$

This implies that $K_\epsilon(x, y)$ is bounded. □

Theorem 6.4 *If $\psi \in L^2_\sigma(I)$ then we have*

$$\hat{\boldsymbol{K}}(\xi) = h_\mu K(\xi) = \int_{a>1} \frac{|(h_\mu \psi)(a\xi)|^2}{a^{2\mu+1}} d\sigma(a). \tag{6.16}$$

Further, $S_\epsilon f(x)$ can be expressed in the following form

$$S_\epsilon f(x) = \int_0^\infty K_\epsilon(x, y) f(y) d\sigma(y), \tag{6.17}$$

where $K_\epsilon(x, y)$ is defined in (6.15).

Proof We have

$$\begin{aligned}
\int_{a>1} \frac{|(h_\mu \psi)(a\xi)|^2}{a^{2\mu+1}} d\sigma(a) &= \int_{u>\xi} \frac{|(h_\mu \psi)(u)|^2}{u^{2\mu+1}} d\sigma(u) \\
&= \int_{u>\xi} \frac{(h_\mu \psi)(u)\overline{(h_\mu \psi)(u)}}{u^{2\mu+1}} d\sigma(u) \\
&= \int_{u>\xi} \frac{h_\mu(\psi \# \overline{\psi})(u)}{u^{2\mu+1}} d\sigma(u) \\
&= \int_{u>\xi} \frac{1}{u^{2\mu+1}} \left(\int_0^\infty j_\mu(u\xi)(\psi \# \overline{\psi})(\xi) d\sigma(\xi) \right) d\sigma(u).
\end{aligned}$$

Changing the order of integration, the above expression yields

$$\int_{a>1} \frac{|(h_\mu \psi)(a\xi)|^2}{a^{2\mu+1}} d\sigma(a) = \int_0^\infty \left(\frac{1}{u^{2\mu+1}} \int_{u>\xi} (\psi \# \overline{\psi})(\xi) d\sigma(\xi) \right) j_\mu(u\xi) d\sigma(u).$$

Consider $K(u) = \frac{1}{u^{2\mu+1}} \int_0^u (\psi \# \overline{\psi})(\xi) d\sigma(\xi)$, then

$$\int_{a>1} \frac{|(h_\mu \psi)(a\xi)|^2}{a^{2\mu+1}} d\sigma(a) = \int_0^\infty K(u) j_\mu(u\xi) d\sigma(u) = h_\mu K(\xi) = \hat{\mathbf{K}}(\xi).$$

Further, using the fact of (4.6), we have

$$\begin{aligned}
K_\epsilon(x, y) &= \int_0^\infty K(z) D(x, y, z) d\sigma(z) \\
&= \int_0^\infty \frac{1}{z^{2\mu+1}} \left\{ \int_0^z (\psi \# \overline{\psi})(\xi) d\sigma(\xi) \right\} D(x, y, z) d\sigma(z).
\end{aligned}$$

Therefore,

$$
\begin{aligned}
&\int_0^\infty K_\epsilon(x,y)f(y)d\sigma(y)\\
&=\int_0^\infty \left\{\int_0^\infty \frac{1}{z^{2\mu+1}}\left(\int_0^z (\psi\#\overline{\psi})(\xi)d\sigma(\xi)\right)D(x,y,z)d\sigma(z)\right\} f(y)d\sigma(y)\\
&=S_\epsilon f(x).
\end{aligned}
$$

This completes the proof of (6.17). □

6.4 Properties of the Continuum Bessel Wavelet Kernel

In this section, various properties of the Bessel wavelet kernel are obtained exploiting (6.16).

Proposition 6.1 *Let ψ be a renormalized continuum wavelet. Then $\hat{\mathbb{K}} \in L^1_\sigma(I)$, $\hat{\mathbb{K}}$ is continuous with $\hat{\mathbb{K}}(0) = 1$ and $\hat{\mathbb{K}}(\xi) \to 0$ when $\xi \to \infty$ where $\hat{\mathbb{K}}$ is defined in (6.16).*

Proof From (6.16), we have

$$
\begin{aligned}
\int_0^\infty \left|\hat{\mathbb{K}}(\xi)\right| d\sigma(\xi) &= \int_0^\infty \left|\int_{\nu>\xi} \frac{|(h_\mu\psi)(\nu)|^2}{\nu^{2\mu+1}} d\sigma(\nu)\right| d\sigma(\xi)\\
&= \int_0^\infty \frac{|(h_\mu\psi)(\nu)|^2}{\nu^{2\mu+1}} \left(\int_{\xi<\nu} d\sigma(\xi)\right) d\sigma(\nu)\\
&= \int_0^\infty \frac{|(h_\mu\psi)(\nu)|^2}{\nu^{2\mu+1}} \left(\int_{\xi<\nu} \frac{\xi^{2\mu}}{2^{\mu-1/2}\,\Gamma(\mu+1/2)} d\xi\right) d\sigma(\nu)\\
&= \int_0^\infty \frac{|(h_\mu\psi)(\nu)|^2}{2^{\mu-1/2}\,\Gamma(\mu+1/2)} d\sigma(\nu)\\
&= \frac{1}{2^{\mu-1/2}\,\Gamma(\mu+1/2)} \left\|h_\mu\psi\right\|^2_{2,\sigma}\\
&= \frac{1}{2^{\mu-1/2}\,\Gamma(\mu+1/2)} \|\psi\|^2_{2,\sigma}\\
&< \infty.
\end{aligned}
$$

The above expression implies that $\Psi \in L^1_\sigma(I)$. By (6.16), it is clear that Ψ is continuous with

$$
\hat{\mathbb{K}}(0) = h_\mu K(0) = \int_{u>0} \frac{|(h_\mu\psi)(u)|^2}{u^{2\mu+1}} d\sigma(u) = 1. \tag{6.18}
$$

For $\xi \to \infty$, we get $\left|h_\mu \psi(u)\right|^2 \in L^1_\sigma(I)$. From the Dominated Convergence Theorem, we find that $\hat{\mathbb{K}}(\xi) \to 0$ as $\xi \to \infty$. □

The following theorems give sufficient conditions for the integrability of the Bessel wavelet kernel.

Theorem 6.5 *Suppose that* ψ *is a renormalized continuum Bessel wavelet for which the associated wavelet kernel is nonnegative:* $K(x) \geq 0$ *for* $x \in I$. *Then* $\int_0^\infty K(x)d\sigma(x) = 1$; *in particular,* $K(x) \in L^1_\sigma(I)$. *Hence, for any bounded uniformly continuous f, we have* $\|S_\epsilon f - f\|_{\infty,\sigma} \to 0$ *when* $\epsilon \to 0$. *If* $f \in L^p_\sigma(I), 1 \leq p < \infty$, *then* $\|S_\epsilon f - f\|_{p,\sigma} \to 0$.

Proof Applying Parseval's identity to the Fejér kernel, we have

$$\int_0^M \left(1 - \frac{x}{M}\right) K(x)d\sigma(x) = \int_0^\infty h_\mu \left(1 - \frac{x}{M}\right)(\xi)\,(h_\mu K)(\xi)d\sigma(\xi).$$

From simple calculation, the R.H.S of the above integral becomes

$$\int_0^M \left(1 - \frac{x}{M}\right) K(x)d\sigma(x) \leq M^{2\mu+1} \int_0^\infty \frac{1}{(2\mu+2)(2\mu+3)} \hat{\mathbb{K}}(\xi)d\sigma(\xi),$$

which is bounded for $\mu > -1/2$ as $\hat{\mathbb{K}}$ is bounded and continuous at $\xi = 0$ with $\hat{\mathbb{K}}(0) = 1$. With the help of Fatou's Lemma and the Fejér kernel, we find

$$\int_0^\infty K(x)d\sigma(x) \leq \lim_{M\to\infty} \int_0^M \left(1 - \frac{x}{M}\right) K(x)d\sigma(x) = 1.$$

After making the use of the Dominated Convergence Theorem, we can prove the theorem. □

Theorem 6.6 *Let* ψ *be a renormalized continuum Bessel wavelet with* $\int_{x>1} log(x)\left|\psi\#\overline{\psi}(x)\right| d\sigma(x) < \infty$. *Then* $K \in L^1_\sigma(I)$ *and* $\int_0^\infty K(x)d\sigma(x) = 1$. *Hence for any bounded uniformly continuous f, we have* $\|S_\epsilon f - f\|_{\infty,\sigma} \to 0$ *when* $\epsilon \to 0$. *If* $f \in L^p_\sigma(I), 1 \leq p < \infty$, *then* $\|S_\epsilon f - f\|_{p,\sigma} \to 0$.

Proof The integrability condition implies that $\psi\#\overline{\psi}(x) \in L^1_\sigma(I)$, in particular that $\psi \in L^1_\sigma(I)$ by Fubini's Theorem. But $\psi \in L^1_\sigma(I)$ implies that $\int_0^\infty (\psi\#\overline{\psi})(x)d\sigma(x) = 0$. Thus, we use this to write the equivalent formula

$$\begin{aligned} K(x) &= \frac{1}{x^{2\mu+1}} \int_0^x (\psi\#\overline{\psi})(z)d\sigma(z) \\ &= \frac{1}{x^{2\mu+1}} \int_0^\infty (\psi\#\overline{\psi})(z)d\sigma(z) - \frac{1}{x^{2\mu+1}} \int_x^\infty (\psi\#\overline{\psi})(z)d\sigma(z) \\ &= -\frac{1}{x^{2\mu+1}} \int_x^\infty (\psi\#\overline{\psi})(z)d\sigma(z). \end{aligned} \tag{6.19}$$

Since K is continuous, we have that $\int_{x\le 1} |K(x)|\, d\sigma(x) < \infty$.

With the help of (6.19), we get

$$\begin{aligned}
\int_{x\ge 1} |K(x)|\, d\sigma(x) &\le \int_{x\ge 1} \left(\frac{1}{x^{2\mu+1}} \int_x^\infty \left|\psi\#\overline{\psi}(z)\right| d\sigma(z) \right) d\sigma(x) \\
&= \int_{z\ge 1} \left|(\psi\#\overline{\psi})(z)\right| d\sigma(z) \int_1^z \frac{d\sigma(x)}{x^{2\mu+1}} \\
&= \int_{z\ge 1} \frac{log(z)}{2^{\mu-1/2}\,\Gamma(\mu+1/2)} \left|(\psi\#\overline{\psi})(z)\right| d\sigma(z) \\
&< \infty.
\end{aligned}$$

Therefore, $K \in L^1_\sigma(I)$.

From (6.18), it follows that

$$\int_0^\infty K(x) d\sigma(x) = \hat{\mathbb{K}}(0) = 1.$$

References

1. Pinsky, M.A.: Introduction to fourier analysis and wavelets. Contemp. Math. **191**, 139–152 (1995)
2. Pinsky, M.A.: Integrability of the continuum wavelet kernel. Proc. Amer. Math. Soc. **132**, 1729–1737 (2004)
3. Pathak, R.S., Upadhyay, S.K., Pandey, R.S.: The bessel wavelet convolution product. Rend. Semin. Mat. Univ. Politec. Torino **3**(69), 267–279

Chapter 7
The Continuous Bessel Wavelet Transform of Distributions

7.1 Introduction

The Hankel transform played an important role to solve many problems of physics, engineering, and mathematical sciences. Zemanian [1–4], Koh [5, 6], Pathak et al. [7–10], Lee [11], Dube and Pandey [12], Betancor [13–16] explored the theory of Hankel transform on various function spaces and characterized many results. Betancor and Marrero [17–21], Betancor and González [22], Betancor and Rodríguez-Mesa [23, 24] studied properties of functional spaces by taking the theory of Hankel transform and Hankel convolution. Aforesaid tools are also very effective in the problems of wavelet theory.

In 2003, Pathak and Dixit [25] introduced the continuous Bessel wavelet transform and studied its properties by exploiting the theory of Haimo [26], Hirschman [27], and Cholewinski [28]. Later on, considering Zemanian theory of Hankel transform, Upadhyay et al. [29–34] investigated continuous Bessel wavelet transform and their properties.

Motivated from the results of [29, 30, 35], our main concern in the present chapter is to find the continuous Bessel wavelet transform in $H'_\mu(I)$ by exploiting the Hankel transform and the Hankel convolution. Later on, we shall obtain the boundedness properties of continuous Bessel wavelet transform in L^p-Sobolev type space.

7.2 The Continuous Bessel Wavelet Transform of Distributions

In this section, the properties of continuous Bessel wavelet transform in distributional sense are discussed by using the Hankel transform technique.

The test function space $\widetilde{H}_\mu(I \times I)$ is defined to be the space of all functions $\phi \in C^\infty(I \times I)$ such that for $l, k, \alpha, \beta \in \mathbb{N}_0$ and $\mu \geq -\frac{1}{2}$,

S. K. Upadhyay and J. S. Maurya, *The Bessel Wavelet Transform*,
Industrial and Applied Mathematics,
https://doi.org/10.1007/978-981-96-9938-4_7

$$\gamma^{\mu}_{k,l,\alpha,\beta}(\phi) = \sup_{\substack{(b,a)\in I\times I\\ k+\alpha\le 2\left(l+\beta+\mu+\frac{1}{2}\right)}} \left| a^k b^\alpha \left(a^{-1}D_a\right)^l \left(b^{-1}D_b\right)^\beta (ab)^{-\mu-\frac{1}{2}}\phi(b,a)\right| < \infty. \tag{7.1}$$

Lemma 7.1 *If $\psi \in H_\mu(I)$ and $k, l, \delta \in \mathbb{N}_0$, $\mu \ge -\frac{1}{2}$, then the relation*

$$\begin{aligned} &a^k \left(a^{-1}D_a\right)^l \left(\omega^{-1}D_\omega\right)^\delta (a\omega)^{-\mu-\frac{1}{2}} \left(h_\mu\psi\right)(a\omega) \\ &= (-1)^{l+k+2\delta}\omega^{2l-2\delta-k} \\ &\quad\times \int_0^\infty \left\{(a\omega y)^{-\mu-l} J_{\mu+l+k+2\delta}(a\omega y)\, y^{2\mu+2l+2\delta+k+1}\left(y^{-1}D_y\right)^{k+\delta} y^{-\mu-\frac{1}{2}}\psi(y)\right\}dy \end{aligned}$$

holds for $a, \omega \in I$.

Proof By substituting $t = a\omega$ and with help of change of variable, we get the differentiation

$$\begin{aligned} &a^k \left(a^{-1}D_a\right)^l \left(\omega^{-1}D_\omega\right)^\delta (a\omega)^{-\mu-\frac{1}{2}} \left(h_\mu\psi\right)(a\omega) \\ &= a^k a^{2\delta}\omega^{2l}\left(t^{-1}D_t\right)^{l+\delta} t^{-\mu-\frac{1}{2}}\left(h_\mu\psi\right)(t) \\ &= a^{k+2\delta}\omega^{2l}\int_0^\infty \left(t^{-1}D_t\right)^{l+\delta} t^{-\mu}J_\mu(yt)y^{\frac{1}{2}}\psi(y)dy \\ &= a^{k+2\delta}\omega^{2l}\int_0^\infty t^{-\mu-l-\delta}J_{\mu+l+\delta}(yt)(-1)^{l+\delta}y^{l+\delta+\frac{1}{2}}\psi(y)dy \\ &= \omega^{2l-2\delta-k}(-1)^{l+\delta}\int_0^\infty t^{-\mu-l+k+\delta}y^{\mu+l+\delta}J_{\mu+l+\delta}(yt)y^{-\mu+\frac{1}{2}}\psi(y)dy. \end{aligned}$$

Using (1.120) and integrating by parts, we find

$$\begin{aligned} &a^k \left(a^{-1}D_a\right)^l \left(\omega^{-1}D_\omega\right)^\delta (a\omega)^{-\mu-\frac{1}{2}} \left(h_\mu\psi\right)(a\omega) \\ &= \omega^{2l-2\delta-k}(-1)^{l+\delta}\int_0^\infty t^{-\mu-l}\left\{\left(y^{-1}D_y\right)^{k+\delta} y^{\mu+l+k+2\delta}J_{\mu+l+k+2\delta}(yt)\right\}y^{-\mu+\frac{1}{2}}\psi(y)dy \\ &= \omega^{2l-2\delta-k}(-1)^{l+k+2\delta}\int_0^\infty t^{-\mu-l}y^{\mu+l+k+2\delta+1}J_{\mu+l+k+2\delta}(yt)\left(y^{-1}D_y\right)^{k+\delta}y^{-\mu-\frac{1}{2}}\psi(y)dy \\ &= \omega^{2l-2\delta-k}(-1)^{l+k+2\delta} \\ &\quad\times\int_0^\infty (yt)^{-\mu-l}J_{\mu+l+k+2\delta}(yt)\,y^{2\mu+2l+2\delta+k+1}\left(y^{-1}D_y\right)^{k+\delta}y^{-\mu-\frac{1}{2}}\psi(y)dy. \end{aligned}$$

Theorem 7.1 *Let $\psi \in H_\mu(I)$, then the continuous Bessel wavelet transform $\left(B_\psi f\right)(b,a)$ is a continuous linear map from $H_\mu(I)$ into $\widetilde{H}_\mu(I\times I)$ for $\mu \ge -\frac{1}{2}$.*

Proof For $f \in H_\mu(I)$ and $k, l, \alpha, \beta \in \mathbb{N}_0$ and from (1.128), we get

$$\begin{aligned}
&a^k b^\alpha \left(a^{-1}D_a\right)^l \left(b^{-1}D_b\right)^\beta (ab)^{-\mu-\frac{1}{2}} \left(B_\psi f\right)(b,a) \\
&= a^k b^\alpha \left(a^{-1}D_a\right)^l \left(b^{-1}D_b\right)^\beta (ab)^{-\mu-\frac{1}{2}} \int_0^\infty (b\omega)^{\frac{1}{2}} J_\mu(b\omega)\omega^{-\mu-\frac{1}{2}} \left(h_\mu f\right)(\omega) \left(h_\mu \psi\right)(a\omega) d\omega \\
&= a^k \left(a^{-1}D_a\right)^l a^{-\mu-\frac{1}{2}} \int_0^\infty b^\alpha \left(b^{-1}D_b\right)^\beta b^{-\mu} J_\mu(b\omega)\omega^{-\mu} \left(h_\mu f\right)(\omega) \left(h_\mu \psi\right)(a\omega) d\omega \\
&= a^k \left(a^{-1}D_a\right)^l a^{-\mu-\frac{1}{2}} \int_0^\infty b^\alpha b^{-\mu-\beta} J_{\mu+\beta}(b\omega)(-1)^\beta \omega^{\beta-\mu} \left(h_\mu f\right)(\omega) \left(h_\mu \psi\right)(a\omega) d\omega \\
&= a^k \left(a^{-1}D_a\right)^l a^{-\mu-\frac{1}{2}} \int_0^\infty (-1)^\beta b^{-\mu-\beta+\alpha} \omega^{\mu+\beta} J_{\mu+\beta}(b\omega)\omega^{-2\mu} \left(h_\mu f\right)(\omega) \left(h_\mu \psi\right)(a\omega) d\omega.
\end{aligned}$$

Using (1.120) and integrating by parts, we have

$$\begin{aligned}
&a^k b^\alpha \left(a^{-1}D_a\right)^l \left(b^{-1}D_b\right)^\beta (ab)^{-\mu-\frac{1}{2}} \left(B_\psi f\right)(b,a) \\
&= a^k \left(a^{-1}D_a\right)^l a^{-\mu-\frac{1}{2}} \\
&\times \int_0^\infty (-1)^\beta b^{-\mu-\beta} \left\{\left(\omega^{-1}D_\omega\right)^\alpha \omega^{\mu+\beta+\alpha} J_{\mu+\beta+\alpha}(b\omega)\right\} \omega^{-2\mu} \left(h_\mu f\right)(\omega) \left(h_\mu \psi\right)(a\omega) d\omega \\
&= a^k \left(a^{-1}D_a\right)^l a^{-\mu-\frac{1}{2}} \\
&\times \int_0^\infty (-1)^{\alpha+\beta} b^{-\mu-\beta} \omega^{\mu+\beta+\alpha+1} J_{\mu+\beta+\alpha}(b\omega) \left(\omega^{-1}D_\omega\right)^\alpha \omega^{-2\mu-1} \left(h_\mu f\right)(\omega) \left(h_\mu \psi\right)(a\omega) d\omega \\
&= a^k \left(a^{-1}D_a\right)^l a^{-\mu-\frac{1}{2}} \int_0^\infty (-1)^{\alpha+\beta} \omega^{2\mu+2\beta+\alpha+1} (b\omega)^{-\mu-\beta} J_{\mu+\beta+\alpha}(b\omega) \\
&\times \sum_{\delta=0}^{\alpha} \binom{\alpha}{\delta} \left\{ \left(\omega^{-1}D_\omega\right)^{\alpha-\delta} \omega^{-\mu-\frac{1}{2}} \left(h_\mu f\right)(\omega) \left(\omega^{-1}D_\omega\right)^\delta \omega^{-\mu-\frac{1}{2}} \left(h_\mu \psi\right)(a\omega) \right\} d\omega \\
&= \int_0^\infty (-1)^{\alpha+\beta} \omega^{2\mu+2\beta+\alpha+1} (b\omega)^{-\mu-\beta} J_{\mu+\beta+\alpha}(b\omega) \sum_{\delta=0}^{\alpha} \binom{\alpha}{\delta} \left\{ \left(\omega^{-1}D_\omega\right)^{\alpha-\delta} \omega^{-\mu-\frac{1}{2}} \left(h_\mu f\right)(\omega) \right. \\
&\left. \times a^k \left(a^{-1}D_a\right)^l \left(\omega^{-1}D_\omega\right)^\delta (a\omega)^{-\mu-\frac{1}{2}} \left(h_\mu \psi\right)(a\omega) \right\} d\omega.
\end{aligned}$$

Taking Lemma 7.1, we get

$$\begin{aligned}
&a^k b^\alpha \left(a^{-1}D_a\right)^l \left(b^{-1}D_b\right)^\beta (ab)^{-\mu-\frac{1}{2}} \left(B_\psi f\right)(b,a) \\
&= \int_0^\infty \left[(-1)^{\alpha+\beta} \omega^{2\mu+2\beta+\alpha+1} (b\omega)^{-\mu-\beta} J_{\mu+\beta+\alpha}(b\omega) \right. \\
&\times \sum_{\delta=0}^{\alpha} \binom{\alpha}{\delta} \left\{ \left(\omega^{-1}D_\omega\right)^{\alpha-\delta} \omega^{-\mu-\frac{1}{2}} \left(h_\mu f\right)(\omega) \right\} \omega^{2l-2\delta-k} (-1)^{l+k+2\delta} \\
&\left. \times \int_0^\infty \left\{ (yt)^{-\mu-l} J_{\mu+l+k+2\delta}(yt) \right\}_{t=a\omega} y^{2\mu+2l+2\delta+k+1} \left(y^{-1}D_y\right)^{k+\delta} y^{-\mu-\frac{1}{2}} \psi(y) dy \right] d\omega
\end{aligned}$$

$$
\begin{aligned}
&= \sum_{\delta=0}^{\alpha} \binom{\alpha}{\delta} (-1)^{\alpha+\beta+l+k+2\delta} \\
&\times \int_0^\infty \Big[(b\omega)^{-\mu-\beta} J_{\mu+\beta+\alpha}(b\omega) \omega^{2\mu+2\beta+2l+\alpha-k-2\delta+1} \Big\{ \left(\omega^{-1} D_\omega\right)^{\alpha-\delta} \omega^{-\mu-\frac{1}{2}} \left(h_\mu f\right)(\omega) \Big\} \\
&\times \int_0^\infty (a\omega y)^{-\mu-l} J_{\mu+l+k+2\delta}(a\omega y) y^{2\mu+2l+2\delta+k+1} \left(y^{-1} D_y\right)^{k+\delta} y^{-\mu-\frac{1}{2}} \psi(y) dy \Big] d\omega.
\end{aligned}
$$

Therefore

$$
\begin{aligned}
&\left| a^k b^\alpha \left(a^{-1} D_a\right)^l \left(b^{-1} D_b\right)^\beta (ab)^{-\mu-\frac{1}{2}} \left(B_\psi f\right)(b,a) \right| \\
&\le \sum_{\delta=0}^{\alpha} \binom{\alpha}{\delta} \int_0^\infty \Big[\left| (b\omega)^{-\mu-\beta} J_{\mu+\beta+\alpha}(b\omega) \right| \omega^{2\mu+2\beta+2l+\alpha-k-2\delta+1} \\
&\times \left| \left(\omega^{-1} D_\omega\right)^{\alpha-\delta} \omega^{-\mu-\frac{1}{2}} \left(h_\mu f\right)(\omega) \right| \int_0^\infty \left| (a\omega y)^{-\mu-l} J_{\mu+l+k+2\delta}(a\omega y) \right| \\
&\times \left| y^{2\mu+2l+2\delta+k+1} \left(y^{-1} D_y\right)^{k+\delta} y^{-\mu-\frac{1}{2}} \psi(y) \right| dy \Big] d\omega \\
&\le \sum_{\delta=0}^{\alpha} \binom{\alpha}{\delta} A_{\mu,\alpha,\beta} \int_0^\infty \Big[\left| \omega^{2\mu+2\beta+2l+\alpha-k-2\delta+1} \left(\omega^{-1} D_\omega\right)^{\alpha-\delta} \omega^{-\mu-\frac{1}{2}} \left(h_\mu f\right)(\omega) \right| B_{\mu,l,k,\delta} \\
&\times \int_0^\infty \left| y^{2\mu+2l+2\delta+k+1} \left(y^{-1} D_y\right)^{k+\delta} y^{-\mu-\frac{1}{2}} \psi(y) \right| dy \Big] d\omega,
\end{aligned}
$$

where $A_{\mu,\alpha,\beta}$ and $B_{\mu,l,k,\delta}$ are positive constants such that

$$
\left| (b\omega)^{-\mu-\beta} J_{\mu+\beta+\alpha}(b\omega) \right| \le A_{\mu,\alpha,\beta} \quad \text{and} \quad \left| (a\omega y)^{-\mu-l} J_{\mu+l+k+2\delta}(a\omega y) \right| \le B_{\mu,l,k,\delta}.
$$

Now, for

$$
\begin{aligned}
&k+\alpha \le 2\left(l+\beta+\mu+\frac{1}{2}\right), \ \rho_1 = E\left(\mu+\beta+l-\delta+\frac{\alpha-k+1}{2}\right) \text{ and} \\
&\rho_2 = E\left(\mu+l+\delta+\frac{k+1}{2}\right),
\end{aligned}
$$

we have

$$
\begin{aligned}
&\left| a^k b^\alpha \left(a^{-1} D_a\right)^l \left(b^{-1} D_b\right)^\beta (ab)^{-\mu-\frac{1}{2}} \left(B_\psi f\right)(b,a) \right| \\
&\le \sum_{\delta=0}^{\alpha} \binom{\alpha}{\delta} \Big[A_{\mu,\alpha,\beta} B_{\mu,l,k,\delta} \int_0^\infty \left| \left(1+\omega^2\right)^{\rho_1+1} \left(\omega^{-1} D_\omega\right)^{\alpha-\delta} \omega^{-\mu-\frac{1}{2}} \left(h_\mu f\right)(\omega) \right| d\omega \\
&\times \int_0^\infty \left| \left(1+y^2\right)^{\rho_2+1} \left(y^{-1} D_y\right)^{k+\delta} y^{-\mu-\frac{1}{2}} \psi(y) \right| dy \Big]
\end{aligned}
$$

$$\leq \sum_{\delta=0}^{\alpha} \binom{\alpha}{\delta} \Big[A_{\mu,\alpha,\beta} B_{\mu,l,k,\delta} \sum_{m=0}^{\rho_1+2} \binom{\rho_1+2}{m} \gamma^{\mu}_{2m,\alpha-\delta}(h_\mu f) \int_0^\infty \frac{1}{1+\omega^2} d\omega$$

$$\times \sum_{r=0}^{\rho_2+2} \binom{\rho_2+2}{r} \gamma^{\mu}_{2r,k+\delta}(\psi) \int_0^\infty \frac{1}{1+y^2} dy \Big]$$

$$\leq \sum_{\delta=0}^{\alpha} \binom{\alpha}{\delta} \sum_{m=0}^{\rho_1+2} \binom{\rho_1+2}{m} \sum_{r=0}^{\rho_2+2} \binom{\rho_2+2}{r} \left(\frac{\pi}{2}\right)^2 A_{\mu,\alpha,\beta} B_{\mu,l,k,\delta} \gamma^{\mu}_{2m,\alpha-\delta}(h_\mu f) \gamma^{\mu}_{2r,k+\delta}(\psi).$$

In view of (7.1), we get

$$\gamma^{\mu}_{k,l,\alpha,\beta}(B_\psi f) \leq \sum_{\delta=0}^{\alpha} \binom{\alpha}{\delta} \sum_{m=0}^{\rho_1+2} \binom{\rho_1+2}{m} \sum_{r=0}^{\rho_2+2} \binom{\rho_2+2}{r} \left(\frac{\pi}{2}\right)^2 A_{\mu,\alpha,\delta} B_{\mu,l,k,\delta}$$
$$\times \gamma^{\mu}_{2m,\alpha-\delta}(h_\mu f) \gamma^{\mu}_{2r,k+\delta}(\psi). \tag{7.2}$$

This shows that $B_\psi f(b,a) \in \widetilde{H}_\mu(I \times I)$. The continuity of $B_\psi f$ follows from (7.2). □

Definition 7.1 Let $\widetilde{H}'_\mu(I \times I)$ be the dual of $\widetilde{H}_\mu(I \times I)$, then the generalized Bessel wavelet transform $B'_\psi T$ of $T \in \widetilde{H}'_\mu(I \times I)$ is defined by

$$\langle B'_\psi T, \phi \rangle = \langle T, B_\psi \phi \rangle, \qquad \phi \in H_\mu(I). \tag{7.3}$$

Theorem 7.2 *Let $\psi \in H_\mu(I)$, then the generalized Bessel wavelet transform B'_ψ is a continuous linear map from $\widetilde{H}'_\mu(I \times I)$ into $H'_\mu(I)$ for $\mu \geq -\frac{1}{2}$.*

Proof From (7.1), we have

$$\langle B'_\psi T, \phi \rangle = \langle T, B_\psi \phi \rangle \qquad \forall\, \phi \in H_\mu(I), \tag{7.4}$$

where $T \in \widetilde{H}'_\mu(I \times I)$ and $\phi \in H_\mu(I)$. From (7.4), $B'_\psi T$ is that functional on $H_\mu(I)$ which assigns to each $\phi \in H_\mu(I)$ the same number that $T \in \widetilde{H}'_\mu(I \times I)$ assigns to $B_\psi \phi \in \widetilde{H}_\mu(I \times I)$.

We see that $B'_\psi T \in H'_\mu(I)$. For any $\phi, \theta \in H_\mu(I)$ and $\alpha, \beta \in \mathbb{C}$,

$$\langle B'_\psi T, \alpha\phi + \beta\theta \rangle = \langle T, B_\psi(\alpha\phi + \beta\theta) \rangle = \langle T, \alpha B_\psi \phi + \beta B_\psi \theta \rangle$$
$$= \alpha \langle B'_\psi T, \phi \rangle + \beta \langle B'_\psi T, \theta \rangle.$$

This implies that $B'_\psi T$ is a linear functional on $H_\mu(I)$. Further, let $\{\phi_n\}_{n=1}^{\infty}$ converges to zero in $H_\mu(I)$. Then by Theorem 7.1, as $n \to \infty$, $B_\psi \phi_n \to 0$ in $\widetilde{H}_\mu(I \times I)$. Therefore

$$\langle B'_\psi T, \phi_n \rangle = \langle T, B_\psi \phi_n \rangle \to 0, \text{ as } n \to \infty.$$

Hence, the above expression shows that $B'_\psi T$ is a linear continuous functional on $H_\mu(I)$.

Thus B'_ψ is a mapping from $\widetilde{H}'_\mu(I \times I)$ into $H'_\mu(I)$. We now prove that B'_ψ is linear and continuous. Let $T_1, T_2 \in \widetilde{H}'_\mu(I \times I), \phi \in H_\mu(I)$, and $\alpha, \beta \in \mathbb{C}$. Then

$$\begin{aligned}\left\langle B'_\psi\left(\alpha T_1+\beta T_2\right), \phi\right\rangle &= \left\langle \alpha T_1+\beta T_2, B_\psi \phi\right\rangle \\ &= \alpha\left\langle T_1, B_\psi \phi\right\rangle+\beta\left\langle T_2, B_\psi \phi\right\rangle \\ &= \alpha\left\langle B'_\psi T_1, \phi\right\rangle+\beta\left\langle B'_\psi T_2, \phi\right\rangle \\ &= \left\langle \alpha B'_\psi T_1, \phi\right\rangle+\left\langle \beta B'_\psi T_2, \phi\right\rangle .\end{aligned}$$

The last expression implies that B'_ψ is linear. For continuity of B'_ψ, let $\{T_n\}_{n=1}^{\infty} \in \widetilde{H}'_\mu(I \times I)$ such that $T_n \to 0$ in $\widetilde{H}'_\mu(I \times I)$. Then for every $\phi \in H_\mu(I)$

$$\left\langle B'_\psi T_n, \phi\right\rangle = \left\langle T_n, B_\psi \phi\right\rangle \to 0, \text{ as } n \to \infty,$$

so that

$$B'_\psi T_n \to 0 \text{ in } H'_\mu(I).$$

Hence, B'_ψ is continuous. □

Definition 7.2 Let $\psi \in H_\mu(I)$ be Bessel wavelet. Assume that $h_\mu \psi \in C^\infty(I)$ such that

$$\left\|h_\mu \psi\right\|_{\mu,\alpha}^{m,\rho} = \sup_{\omega \in I}(1+\omega)^{-m+\rho\alpha}\left|\left(\omega^{-1} D_\omega\right)^\alpha \omega^{-\mu-\frac{1}{2}}\left(h_\mu \psi\right)(\omega)\right| < \infty, \tag{7.5}$$

where $m \in \mathbb{R}, 0 \le \rho \le 1$ and $\alpha \in \mathbb{N}_0$.

Consider the test function space $H^1_\mu(I \times I)$, defined to be the space of all functions $\phi \in C^\infty(I \times I)$ such that for $l, k, \alpha, \beta \in \mathbb{N}_0$ and $\mu \ge -\frac{1}{2}$,

$$\gamma^{\mu}_{k,l,\alpha,\beta}(\phi) = \sup_{\substack{(b,a)\in I\times I \\ k+\alpha \le 2\left(l+\beta+\mu+\frac{1}{2}\right) \\ k+2\alpha \le m}} \left|a^k b^\alpha\left(a^{-1} D_a\right)^l\left(b^{-1} D_b\right)^\beta (ab)^{-\mu-\frac{1}{2}} \phi(b, a)\right| < \infty. \tag{7.6}$$

Theorem 7.3 *Let $\psi \in H_\mu(I)$ and (7.5) is satisfied, then the continuous Bessel wavelet transform $\left(B_\psi f\right)(b, a)$ is a continuous linear map from $H_\mu(I)$ into $H^1_\mu(I \times I)$ for $\mu \ge -\frac{1}{2}$.*

Proof Proceeding as in the proof of Theorem 7.1, for $f \in H_\mu(I)$ and $k, l, \alpha, \beta \in \mathbb{N}_0$, we have

$$
\begin{aligned}
&a^k b^\alpha \left(a^{-1}D_a\right)^l \left(b^{-1}D_b\right)^\beta (ab)^{-\mu-\frac{1}{2}} \left(B_\psi f\right)(b,a) \\
&= \sum_{\delta=0}^{\alpha} \binom{\alpha}{\delta} (-1)^{\alpha+\beta} \\
&\times \int_0^\infty \Big[(b\omega)^{-\mu-\beta} J_{\mu+\beta+\alpha}(b\omega) \left\{\omega^{2\mu+2\beta+\alpha+1} \left(\omega^{-1}D_\omega\right)^{\alpha-\delta} \omega^{-\mu-\frac{1}{2}} \left(h_\mu f\right)(\omega)\right\} \\
&\times a^k \left(a^{-1}D_a\right)^l \left(\omega^{-1}D_\omega\right)^\delta (a\omega)^{-\mu-\frac{1}{2}} \left(h_\mu \psi\right)(a\omega)\Big] d\omega \\
&= \sum_{\delta=0}^{\alpha} \binom{\alpha}{\delta} (-1)^{\alpha+\beta} \\
&\times \int_0^\infty \Big[(b\omega)^{-\mu-\beta} J_{\mu+\beta+\alpha}(b\omega) \left\{\omega^{2\mu+2l+2\beta+\alpha+1-k-2\delta} \left(\omega^{-1}D_\omega\right)^{\alpha-\delta} \omega^{-\mu-\frac{1}{2}} \left(h_\mu f\right)(\omega)\right\} \\
&\times \left\{t^{k+2\delta} \left(t^{-1}D_t\right)^{l+\delta} t^{-\mu-\frac{1}{2}} \left(h_\mu \psi\right)(t)\right\}_{t=a\omega} \Big] d\omega.
\end{aligned}
$$

Therefore

$$
\begin{aligned}
&\left|a^k b^\alpha \left(a^{-1}D_a\right)^l \left(b^{-1}D_b\right)^\beta (ab)^{-\mu-\frac{1}{2}} \left(B_\psi f\right)(b,a)\right| \\
&\leq \sum_{\delta=0}^{\alpha} \binom{\alpha}{\delta} \int_0^\infty \Big[\left|(b\omega)^{-\mu-\beta} J_{\mu+\beta+\alpha}(b\omega)\right| \omega^{2\mu+2l+2\beta+\alpha+1-k-2\delta} \\
&\times \left|\left(\omega^{-1}D_\omega\right)^{\alpha-\delta} \omega^{-\mu-\frac{1}{2}} \left(h_\mu f\right)(\omega)\right| \left|t^{k+2\delta} \left(t^{-1}D_t\right)^{l+\delta} t^{-\mu-\frac{1}{2}} \left(h_\mu \psi\right)(t)\right|_{t=a\omega} \Big] d\omega.
\end{aligned}
$$

Using (7.5), we get

$$
\begin{aligned}
&\left|a^k b^\alpha \left(a^{-1}D_a\right)^l \left(b^{-1}D_b\right)^\beta (ab)^{-\mu-\frac{1}{2}} \left(B_\psi f\right)(b,a)\right| \\
&\leq \sum_{\delta=0}^{\alpha} \binom{\alpha}{\delta} \left\|h_\mu \psi\right\|_{\mu,l+\delta}^{m,\rho} D_{\mu,\alpha,\beta} \\
&\times \int_0^\infty \left|\omega^{2\mu+2l+2\beta+\alpha+1-k-2\delta} \left(\omega^{-1}D_\omega\right)^{\alpha-\delta} \omega^{-\mu-\frac{1}{2}} \left(h_\mu f\right)(\omega)\right| (1+a\omega)^{k+2\delta+m-\rho(l+\delta)} d\omega,
\end{aligned}
$$

where $D_{\mu,\alpha,\beta}$ is positive constant such that $\left|(b\omega)^{-\mu-\beta} J_{\mu+\beta+\alpha}(b\omega)\right| \leq D_{\mu,\alpha,\beta}$.

For $2\mu + 2l + 2\beta + \alpha + 1 - k - 2\delta \geq 0$ and $k + 2\delta + m - \rho(l+\delta) \leq 0$, the last expression can be written as

$$\left|a^k b^\alpha \left(a^{-1}D_a\right)^l \left(b^{-1}D_b\right)^\beta (ab)^{-\mu-\frac{1}{2}} \left(B_\psi f\right)(b,a)\right|$$

$$\leq D_{\mu,\alpha,\beta} \sum_{\delta=0}^{\alpha} \binom{\alpha}{\delta} \|h_\mu \psi\|_{\mu,l+\delta}^{m,\rho}$$

$$\times \int_0^\infty \left|\left(1+\omega^2\right)^{\mu+l+\beta+\frac{\alpha+1-k}{2}-\delta} \left(\omega^{-1}D_\omega\right)^{\alpha-\delta} \omega^{-\mu-\frac{1}{2}} \left(h_\mu f\right)(\omega)\right| d\omega$$

$$\leq D_{\mu,\alpha,\beta} \sum_{\delta=0}^{\alpha} \binom{\alpha}{\delta} \|h_\mu \psi\|_{\mu,l+\delta}^{m,\rho}$$

$$\times \int_0^\infty \left|\left(1+\omega^2\right)^{\rho_1+2} \left(\omega^{-1}D_\omega\right)^{\alpha-\delta} \omega^{-\mu-\frac{1}{2}} \left(h_\mu f\right)(\omega)\right| \frac{1}{1+\omega^2} d\omega$$

$$\leq D_{\mu,\alpha,\beta} \sum_{\delta=0}^{\alpha} \binom{\alpha}{\delta} \|h_\mu \psi\|_{\mu,l+\delta}^{m,\rho} \sum_{r=0}^{\rho_1+2} \binom{\rho_1+2}{r} \gamma_{2r,\alpha-\delta}^{\mu}(h_\mu f) \int_0^\infty \frac{1}{1+\omega^2} d\omega$$

$$\leq D_{\mu,\alpha,\beta} \sum_{\delta=0}^{\alpha} \binom{\alpha}{\delta} \|h_\mu \psi\|_{\mu,l+\delta}^{m,\rho} \sum_{r=0}^{\rho_1+2} \binom{\rho_1+2}{r} \frac{\pi}{2} \gamma_{2r,\alpha-\delta}^{\mu} \left(h_\mu f\right),$$

where $\rho_1 = E\left(\mu + l + \beta + \frac{\alpha+1-k}{2} - \delta\right)$.

Thus, we have

$$\gamma_{k,l,\alpha,\beta}^{\mu} \left(B_\psi f\right) \leq \frac{\pi}{2} D_{\mu,\alpha,\beta} \sum_{\delta=0}^{\alpha} \binom{\alpha}{\delta} \sum_{r=0}^{\rho_1+2} \binom{\rho_1+2}{r} \|h_\mu \psi\|_{\mu,l+\delta}^{m,\rho} \gamma_{2r,\alpha-\delta}^{\mu} \left(h_\mu f\right).$$

Hence, for $m \leq -k - 2\alpha$ and $k + \alpha \leq 2\left(l + \beta + \mu + \frac{1}{2}\right)$, $B_\psi f(b,a) \in H_\mu^1(I \times I)$ and continuity of $B_\psi f$ follows from the above inequality. □

Definition 7.3 Let $(H_\mu^1)'(I \times I)$ be the dual of $H_\mu^1(I \times I)$, then for $T \in (H_\mu^1)'(I \times I)$ the generalized Bessel wavelet transform B'_ψ is defined by

$$\left\langle B'_\psi T, \phi \right\rangle = \left\langle T, B_\psi \phi \right\rangle, \qquad \phi \in H_\mu(I). \tag{7.7}$$

Theorem 7.4 *Let $\psi \in H_\mu(I)$, then the generalized Bessel wavelet transform B'_ψ is a continuous linear map from $(H_\mu^1)'(I \times I)$ into $H'_\mu(I)$ for $\mu \geq -\frac{1}{2}$.*

Proof From (7.7), we have

$$\left\langle B'_\psi T, \phi \right\rangle = \left\langle T, B_\psi \phi \right\rangle, \qquad \phi \in H_\mu(I), \tag{7.8}$$

where $T \in (H_\mu^1)'(I \times I)$, and $\phi \in H_\mu(I)$. From (7.8), $B'_\psi T$ is that functional on $H_\mu(I)$ which assigns to each $\phi \in H_\mu(I)$ the same number that $T \in (H_\mu^1)'(I \times I)$ assigns to $B_\psi \phi \in H_\mu^1(I \times I)$.

We see that $B'_\psi T \in H'_\mu(I)$. For any $\phi, \theta \in H_\mu(I)$, and $\alpha, \beta \in \mathbb{C}$

$$\left\langle B'_\psi T, \alpha\phi + \beta\theta \right\rangle = \langle T, B_\psi(\alpha\phi + \beta\theta)\rangle = \langle T, \alpha B_\psi\phi + \beta B_\psi\theta\rangle = \alpha\left\langle B'_\psi T, \phi\right\rangle + \beta\left\langle B'_\psi T, \theta\right\rangle.$$

This implies that $B'_\psi T$ is a linear functional on $H_\mu(I)$.

Let $\{\phi_n\}_{n=1}^\infty$ converges to zero in $H_\mu(I)$. Then by Theorem 7.3, as $n \to \infty$, $B_\psi\phi_n \to 0$ in $H^1_\mu(I \times I)$. Therefore,

$$\langle B'_\psi T, \phi_n\rangle = \langle T, B_\psi\phi_n\rangle \to 0.$$

Hence, $B'_\psi T$ is a linear continuous functional on $H_\mu(I)$.

Thus B'_ψ is a mapping from $(H^1_\mu)'(I \times I)$ into $H'_\mu(I)$. We now prove that B'_ψ is linear and continuous. Now, we take $\phi \in H_\mu(I)$, $T_1, T_2 \in (H^1_\mu)'(I \times I)$, and $\alpha, \beta \in \mathbb{C}$. Then

$$\begin{aligned}\langle B'_\psi(\alpha T_1 + \beta T_2), \phi\rangle = \langle \alpha T_1 + \beta T_2, B_\psi\phi\rangle &= \alpha\langle T_1, B_\psi\phi\rangle + \beta\langle T_2, B_\psi\phi\rangle \\ &= \alpha\langle B'_\psi T_1, \phi\rangle + \beta\langle B'_\psi T_2, \phi\rangle \\ &= \langle \alpha B'_\psi T_1, \phi\rangle + \langle \beta B'_\psi T_2, \phi\rangle.\end{aligned}$$

This shows that B'_ψ is linear.

For continuity of B'_ψ, let $\{T_n\}_{n=1}^\infty \in (H^1_\mu)'(I \times I)$ such that $T_n \to 0$ in $(H^1_\mu)'(I \times I)$. Then for every $\phi \in H_\mu(I)$

$$\langle B'_\psi T_n, \phi\rangle = \langle T_n, B_\psi\phi\rangle \to 0, \text{ as } n \to \infty,$$

so that

$$B'_\psi T_n \to 0 \text{ in } H'_\mu(I).$$

Hence, B'_ψ is continuous. □

7.3 The Bessel Wavelet Transform on L^p-Sobolev Space

In this section, we study continuous Bessel wavelet transform on the L^p- Sobolev type space.

Definition 7.4 For $-\infty < s < \infty$, $\mu \geq -\frac{1}{2}$ and $1 \leq p < \infty$, then L^p-Sobolev space $H^{s,p}_\mu$ is defined to be set of all $f \in H'_\mu(I)$ such that

$$\|f\|_{H^{s,p}_\mu} = \left\|\omega^{\frac{s}{p}-\mu-\frac{1}{2}} h_\mu f\right\|_{L^p}, \qquad \omega \in I. \tag{7.9}$$

For $1 \leq p, p' < \infty$ and $-\infty < s < \infty$, the space $W_p^{s,p'}$ of all measurable functions g on $I \times I$ such that

$$\|g(b,a)\|_{W_p^{s,p'}} = \left(\int_0^\infty \left(\int_0^\infty |g(b,a)|^p \, db\right)^{\frac{p'}{p}} a^{-s-1} da\right)^{\frac{1}{p'}} < \infty. \tag{7.10}$$

Lemma 7.2 *Let $\psi \in H_\mu(I)$ be the Bessel wavelet and $f \in H'_\mu(I)$ then for $1 \leq p < \infty$, we have*

$$\int_0^\infty \int_0^\infty \left|\omega^{-\mu-\frac{1}{2}}(h_\mu\psi)(a\omega)(h_\mu f)(\omega)\right|^p d\omega\, a^{-s-1} da = C_{\mu,\psi}^{s,p} \int_0^\infty \left|\omega^{\frac{s}{p}-\mu-\frac{1}{2}}(h_\mu f)(\omega)\right|^p d\omega, \tag{7.11}$$

where

$$C_{\mu,\psi}^{s,p} = \int_0^\infty \left|(h_\mu\psi)(a\omega)\right|^p (a\omega)^{-s} \frac{da}{a}, \qquad a > 0. \tag{7.12}$$

Proof By Fubini's theorem, we have

$$\begin{aligned}
&\int_0^\infty \int_0^\infty \left|\omega^{-\mu-\frac{1}{2}}(h_\mu\psi)(a\omega)(h_\mu f)(\omega)\right|^p d\omega\, a^{-s-1} da \\
&= \int_0^\infty \int_0^\infty \left|\omega^{-\mu-\frac{1}{2}}(h_\mu\psi)(a\omega)(h_\mu f)(\omega)\right|^p a^{-s-1} da d\omega \\
&= \int_0^\infty \int_0^\infty \left|\omega^{\frac{s}{p}} \omega^{-\frac{s}{p}} \omega^{-\mu-\frac{1}{2}}(h_\mu\psi)(a\omega)(h_\mu f)(\omega)\right|^p a^{-s-1} da d\omega \\
&= \int_0^\infty \left(\int_0^\infty \left|(h_\mu\psi)(a\omega)\right|^p (a\omega)^{-s} a^{-1} da\right) \left|\omega^{\frac{s}{p}-\mu-\frac{1}{2}}(h_\mu f)(\omega)\right|^p d\omega \\
&= C_{\mu,\psi}^{s,p} \int_0^\infty \left|\omega^{\frac{s}{p}-\mu-\frac{1}{2}}(h_\mu f)(\omega)\right|^p d\omega,
\end{aligned}$$

where

$$C_{\mu,\psi}^{s,p} = \int_0^\infty \left|(h_\mu\psi)(a\omega)\right|^p (a\omega)^{-s} \frac{da}{a} > 0.$$

Theorem 7.5 *Let the Bessel wavelet ψ satisfies the admissibility condition (7.12). Then the continuous Bessel wavelet transform is a bounded linear operator from $H_\mu^{s,p}(I)$ into $W_p^{s,p'}(I \times I)$ for $1 \leq p \leq 2$, $\frac{1}{p} + \frac{1}{p'} = 1$ and for all $s \in \mathbb{R}$. Also, for all $f \in H_\mu^{s,p}(I)$ we have*

$$\|f\|_{H_\mu^{s,p'}} \cong \left\|B_\psi f(b,a)\right\|_{W_p^{s,p'}},$$

for all $s \in \mathbb{R}$ and $1 \leq p \leq 2$, $\frac{1}{p} + \frac{1}{p'} = 1$.

Proof From (1.128), we have

$$h_\mu \left[B_\psi f(b,a)\right](\omega) = \omega^{-\mu-\frac{1}{2}}(h_\mu \psi)(a\omega)(h_\mu f)(\omega). \tag{7.13}$$

For $1 \le p \le 2$, $\frac{1}{p} + \frac{1}{p'} = 1$, using [36] and (7.13) we get

$$\begin{aligned}\left(\int_0^\infty |B_\psi f(b,a)|^p\, db\right)^{\frac{1}{p}} &= \left(\int_0^\infty \left|h_\mu^{-1}[\omega^{-\mu-\frac{1}{2}}(h_\mu \psi)(a\omega)(h_\mu f)(\omega)](b)\right|^p db\right)^{\frac{1}{p}} \\ &\le D_{p'}\left(\int_0^\infty \left|\omega^{-\mu-\frac{1}{2}}(h_\mu \psi)(a\omega)(h_\mu f)(\omega)\right|^{p'} d\omega\right)^{\frac{1}{p'}},\end{aligned}$$

where $D_{p'} > 0$ is a constant. Multiplying both sides by a^{-s-1} and integrating from 0 to ∞, we find

$$\begin{aligned}&\int_0^\infty \left(\int_0^\infty |B_\psi f(b,a)|^p\, db\right)^{\frac{p'}{p}} a^{-s-1} da \\ &\qquad \le (D_{p'})^{p'} \int_0^\infty \left(\int_0^\infty \left|\omega^{-\mu-\frac{1}{2}}(h_\mu \psi)(a\omega)(h_\mu f)(\omega)\right|^{p'} d\omega\right) a^{-s-1} da.\end{aligned}$$

From Lemma 7.2, we get

$$\int_0^\infty \left(\int_0^\infty |B_\psi f(b,a)|^p\, db\right)^{\frac{p'}{p}} a^{-s-1} da \le (D_{p'})^{p'} C_{\mu,\psi}^{s,p'} \int_0^\infty \left|\omega^{\frac{s}{p'}-\mu-\frac{1}{2}}(h_\mu f)(\omega)\right|^{p'} d\omega.$$

This implies that

$$\left\| B_\psi f(b,a)\right\|_{W_p^{s,p'}} \le D_{p'}(C_{\mu,\psi}^{s,p'})^{\frac{1}{p'}} \left\|f\right\|_{H_\mu^{s,p'}}. \tag{7.14}$$

Further, from [36] and (7.13) for $1 \le p \le 2$, $\frac{1}{p} + \frac{1}{p'} = 1$, we get

$$\begin{aligned}\left(\int_0^\infty \left|\omega^{-\mu-\frac{1}{2}}(h_\mu \psi)(a\omega)(h_\mu f)(\omega)\right|^{p'} d\omega\right)^{\frac{1}{p'}} &= \left(\int_0^\infty |h_\mu[B_\psi f(b,a)](\omega)|^{p'} d\omega\right)^{\frac{1}{p'}} \\ &\le D_p\left(\int_0^\infty |B_\psi f(b,a)|^p\, db\right)^{\frac{1}{p}},\end{aligned}$$

where $D_p > 0$ is a constant. Multiplying both sides by a^{-s-1} and integrating from 0 to ∞, we find

$$\int_0^\infty \left(\int_0^\infty \left| \omega^{-\mu-\frac{1}{2}} (h_\mu \psi)(a\omega)(h_\mu f)(\omega) \right|^{p'} d\omega \right) a^{-s-1} da$$
$$\leq (D_p)^{p'} \int_0^\infty \left(\int_0^\infty |B_\psi f(b,a)|^p \, db \right)^{\frac{p'}{p}} a^{-s-1} da.$$

From Lemma 7.2, we get

$$C_{\mu,\psi}^{s,p'} \int_0^\infty \left| \omega^{\frac{s}{p'}-\mu-\frac{1}{2}} (h_\mu f)(\omega) \right|^{p'} d\omega \leq (D_p)^{p'} \int_0^\infty \left(\int_0^\infty |B_\psi f(b,a)|^p \, db \right)^{\frac{p'}{p}} a^{-s-1} da.$$

This yields

$$\|f\|_{H_\mu^{s,p'}} \leq \frac{D_p}{\left(C_{\mu,\psi}^{s,p'} \right)^{\frac{1}{p'}}} \left\| B_\psi f(b,a) \right\|_{W_p^{s,p'}}. \tag{7.15}$$

From (7.14) and (7.15), we get the results. □

***

References

1. Zemanian, A.H.: A distributional Hankel transformation. SIAM J. Appl. Math. **14**(3), 561–576 (1966)
2. Zemanian, A.H.: Generalized integral transformations. Pure and applied mathematics XVIII. Interscience Publishers, New York (1968)
3. Zemanian, A.H.: The Hankel transformation of certain distributions of rapid growth. SIAM J. Appl. Math. **14**(4), 678–690 (1966)
4. Zemanian, A.H.: Hankel transforms of arbitrary order. Duke Math. J. **34**(4), 761–769 (1967)
5. Koh, E.L.: The Hankel transformation of negative order for distributions of rapid growth. SIAM J. Math. Anal. **1**(3), 322–327 (1970)
6. Koh, E.L.: The n-dimensional distributional Hankel transformation. Canad. J. Math. **27**(2), 423–433 (1975)
7. Pathak, R.S.: Integral transforms of generalized functions and their applications. Gordon and Breach Science Publishers, Amsterdam (1997)
8. Pathak, R.S.: On Hankel transformable spaces and a Cauchy problem. Canad. J. Math. **37**(1), 84–106 (1985)
9. Pathak, R.S., Pandey, A.B.: On Hankel transforms of ultradistributions. Applicable Anal. **20**(3–4), 245–268 (1985)
10. Pathak, R.S., Pandey, P.K.: Sobolev type spaces associated with Bessel operators. J. Math. Anal. Appl. **215**(1), 95–111 (1997)
11. Lee, W.Y.K.: On spaces of type H_μ and their Hankel transformations. SIAM J. Math. Anal. **5**(2), 336–348 (1974)
12. Dube, L.S., Pandey, J.N.: On the Hankel transform of distributions. Tohoku Math. J. **27**(3), 337–354 (1975)
13. Betancor, J.J.: A generalized Hankel convolution on Zemanian spaces. Int. J. Math. Math. Sci. **23**(2), 131–140 (2000)

14. Betancor, J.J.: A new characterization of the bounded operators commuting with Hankel translation. Arch. Math. **69**(5), 403–408 (1997)
15. Betancor, J.J., Jerez, C.: Convolution Hankel transforms on the Zemanian spaces. Acta Math. Hungar. **80**(3), 225–235 (1998)
16. Betancor, J.J.: On Hankel transformable distribution spaces. Publ. Inst. Math. (Beograd)(N.S.) **65**(79), 123–141 (1999)
17. Betancor, J.J., Marrero, I.: The Hankel convolution and the Zemanian spaces β_μ and β'_μ. Math. Nachr. **160**, 277–298 (1993)
18. Betancor, J.J., Marrero, I.: Some properties of Hankel convolution operators. Canad. Math. Bull. **36**(4), 398–406 (1993)
19. Betancor, J.J., Marrero, I.: Structure and convergence in certain spaces of distributions and the generalized Hankel convolution. Math. Japon. **38**(6), 1141–1155 (1993)
20. Betancor, J.J., Marrero, I.: Algebraic characterization of convolution and multiplication operators on Hankel-transformable function and distribution spaces. Rocky Mountain J. Math. **25**(4), 1189–1204 (1995)
21. Marrero, I., Betancor, J.J.: Hankel convolution of generalized functions. Rend. Mat. Appl. **15**(3), 351–380 (1995)
22. Betancor, J.J., González, B.J.: A convolution operation for a distributional Hankel transformation. Studia Math. **117**(1), 57–72 (1995)
23. Betancor, J.J., Rodríguez-Mesa, L.: Hankel convolution on distribution spaces with exponential growth. Studia Math. **121**(1), 35–52 (1996)
24. Betancor, J.J., Rodríguez-Mesa, L.: On Hankel convolution equations in distribution spaces. Rocky Mountain J. Math. **29**(1), 93–114 (1999)
25. Pathak, R.S., Dixit, M.M.: Continuous and discrete Bessel wavelet transforms. J. Comput. Appl. Math. **160**(1–2), 241–250 (2003)
26. Haimo, D.T.: Integral equations associated with Hankel convolutions. Trans. Amer. Math. Soc. **116**, 330–375 (1965)
27. Hirschman, I.: Variation diminishing Hankel transforms. J. Analyse Math. **8**(1), 307–336 (1960–61)
28. Cholewinski, F.M.: A Hankel convolution complex inversion theory. Mem. Amer. Math, Soc (1965)
29. Upadhyay, S.K., Yadav, R.N., Debnath, L.: On continuous Bessel wavelet transformation associated with the Hankel-Hausdorff operator. Integral transforms Spec. Funct. **23**(5), 315–323 (2012)
30. Upadhyay, S.K., Singh, R.: Abelian theorems for the Bessel wavelet transform. J. Anal. **28**(1), 179–190 (2020)
31. Upadhyay, S.K., Singh, R.: Linear time invariant filter associated with Bessel wavelet transform. J. Anal. **26**(2), 323–332 (2018)
32. Upadhyay, S.K., Singh, R.: Bessel wavelet transform on the spaces with exponential growth. Filomat **31**(8), 2459–2466 (2017)
33. Upadhyay, S.K., Singh, R., Tripathi, A.: The relation between Bessel wavelet convolution product and Hankel convolution product involving Hankel transform. Int. J. Wavelets Multiresolut. Inf. Process. **15**(4), 1750030 (2017)
34. Upadhyay, S.K., Singh, R.: Integrability of the continuum Bessel wavelet kernel. Int. J. Wavelets Multiresolut. Inf. Process. **13**(5), 1550032 (2015)
35. Pathak, R.S.: The wavelet transform of distributions. Tohoku Math. J. **56**(3), 411–421 (2004)
36. De Carli, L.: On the $L^p - L^q$ norm of the Hankel transform and related operators. J. Math. Anal. Appl. **348**(1), 366–382 (2008)

Chapter 8
Characterizations of the Bessel Wavelet Transform in Besov and Triebel-Lizorkin Type Spaces

8.1 Introduction

Besov space is an effective tool for measuring regular properties of functions and is a generalization of Sobolev space. Exploiting the results of Fourier analysis, the characterizations of the spaces $B^s_{p,q}(\mathbb{R}^n)$ and $F^s_{p,q}(\mathbb{R}^n)$ were introduced by Triebel [1]. Motivated from the result of multiplier theorem of Triebel [1], boundedness results of the wavelet transform in Besov space $B^s_{p,q}(\mathbb{R}^n)$ and Triebel-Lizorkin space $F^s_{p,q}(\mathbb{R}^n)$ for $s \in \mathbb{R}$ and $0 < p,\ q \leq \infty$ are obtained by Pathak [2] by taking Fourier transform technique. Later on, Betancor et al. [3, 4] introduced Besov-Hankel space $BH^{\alpha,\mu}_{p,q}$ and studied its various properties by taking the Haimo Hankel transform theory [5].

From the aforementioned information, our main goal in this chapter is to introduce the Besov and Triebel-Lizorkin type spaces by using the Zemanian theory of Hankel transformation and to find the boundedness of the Bessel wavelet transform and its associated results.

The results of the present chapter are organized by the following way:
Section 8.1 is introductory, which provides about the historical backgrounds of Besov space and Triebel-Lizorkin type space in Hankel setting. In Sect. 8.2, various definitions and properties of Besov space and Triebel-Lizorkin space associated with Hankel transform and Hankel convolution are given. Section 8.3 describes that the boundedness of the Bessel wavelet transform in Besov space and Triebel-Lizorkin space are proved by exploiting the Hankel transform theory.

S. K. Upadhyay and J. S. Maurya, *The Bessel Wavelet Transform*,
Industrial and Applied Mathematics,
https://doi.org/10.1007/978-981-96-9938-4_8

8.2 Properties of the Besov Space and Triebel-Lizorkin Type Space

In this section, definitions and results of Triebel [1] in Hankel setting by using Zemanian space H_μ are constructed and useful inequalities in the same setting are derived.

From Hardy et al. [6, Theorem 201], for $p > 1$, the Minkowski integral inequality is given by

$$\left[\sum_{k=0}^{\infty}\left\{\int_0^{\infty} f_k(x)dx\right\}^p\right]^{\frac{1}{p}} \leq \int_0^{\infty}\left\{\sum_{k=0}^{\infty} f_k^p(x)\right\}^{\frac{1}{p}}dx. \tag{8.1}$$

From [1], for $1 \leq p < \infty, 1 \leq q \leq \infty$ and if $\{f_k(x)\}_{k=0}^{\infty}$ is a sequence of complex-valued Borel measurable function on I, then

$$\| f_k \|_{L_p^\mu(l_q)} = \left(\int_0^{\infty} x^{2\mu+1}\left(\sum_{k=0}^{\infty} |f_k(x)|^q\right)^{\frac{p}{q}}dx\right)^{\frac{1}{p}}, \tag{8.2}$$

$$\| f_k \|_{l_q(L_p^\mu)} = \left(\sum_{k=0}^{\infty}\left(\int_0^{\infty} x^{2\mu+1}\, |f_k(x)|^p\, dx\right)^{\frac{q}{p}}\right)^{\frac{1}{q}}, \tag{8.3}$$

with

$$\| f_k(x) \|_{l_\infty} = \sup_k |f_k(x)|\,, \tag{8.4}$$

and $f(x) = (f_0(x), f_1(x), \ldots, f_k(x), \ldots) \equiv \{f_k(x)\}_{k=0}^{\infty} \in l_q$ then

$$\|f(x)\|_{l_q} = \left(\sum_{k=0}^{\infty} |f_k(x)|^q\right)^{\frac{1}{q}}, \quad \|f_k\|_{L_p^\mu} = \left(\int_0^{\infty} x^{2\mu+1}\, |f_k(x)|^p\, dx\right)^{\frac{1}{p}}. \tag{8.5}$$

Definition 8.1 If N is a natural number then $A_\mu^N(I)$ is the collection of all systems $\phi = \{\phi_j(x)\}_{j=0}^{\infty} \subset H_\mu(I),\ \mu \geq -\frac{1}{2}$ of functions with compact supports such that

$$C_\mu(\phi) = \sup_{x\in I} x^N \sum_{\alpha=0}^{N}\left|\left(x^{-1}D_x\right)^{\alpha} x^{-\mu-\frac{1}{2}}\phi_0(x)\right| + \sup_{\substack{x\in I\\ j=1,2,3,\ldots}} \left(x^N + x^{-N}\right)\sum_{\alpha=0}^{N}\left|\left(x^{-1}D_x\right)^{\alpha} x^{-\mu-\frac{1}{2}}\phi_j(2^j x)\right| < \infty. \tag{8.6}$$

Definition 8.2 If N is a natural number, $\phi = \{\phi_j(x)\}_{j=0}^{\infty} \in A_{\mu}^{N}(I)$, $f \in H'_{\mu}(I)$ and $d > 0$ then

$$\left(\phi_j^* f\right)(x) = \sup_{y \in I} \frac{\left|\left(\left(h_{\mu}^{-1}\phi_j\right) \# f\right)(x, y)\right|}{1 + \left(2^j y\right)^{2d}}, \quad x \in I, \quad j = 0, 1, 2, 3, \ldots \tag{8.7}$$

is called maximal function.

From (8.7), we get

$$\left|\left(\left(h_{\mu}^{-1}\phi_j\right) \# f\right)(x, y)\right| \leq \left(1 + \left(2^j y\right)^{2d}\right) \left(\phi_j^* f\right)(x). \tag{8.8}$$

Definition 8.3 Let $\Phi(I)$ be the collection of all systems $\phi = \{\phi_j(x)\}_{j=0}^{\infty} \subset H_{\mu}(I)$ such that

$$\begin{cases} \operatorname{supp} x^{-\mu-\frac{1}{2}}\phi_0 \subset \{x : 0 \leq x \leq 2\}, \\ \operatorname{supp} x^{-\mu-\frac{1}{2}}\phi_j \subset \{x : 2^{j-1} \leq x \leq 2^{j+1}\}, \quad j = 1, 2, 3, \ldots \end{cases} \tag{8.9}$$

For every $\alpha \in \mathbb{N}_0$, there exists a positive number C_{α} such that

$$2^{j\alpha} \left|\left(x^{-1}D_x\right)^{\alpha} x^{-\mu-\frac{1}{2}}\phi_j(x)\right| \leq C_{\alpha} \qquad \forall j = 0, 1, 2, 3, \ldots, \quad x \in I \tag{8.10}$$

and

$$\sum_{j=0}^{\infty} x^{-\mu-\frac{1}{2}}\phi_j(x) = 1, \qquad \forall\, x \in I. \tag{8.11}$$

Definition 8.4 Let $-\infty < s < \infty$ and $1 \leq q \leq \infty$. Assume that $\{\phi_j(x)\}_{j=0}^{\infty} \in H_{\mu}(I)$ and $\mu \geq -\frac{1}{2}$, then we define the following spaces:

$$\text{(i) } F_{p,q}^{\mu,s} = \left\{f : f \in H'_{\mu}(I), \|f\|_{F_{p,q}^{\mu,s}} = \left\|2^{sj} x^{-\mu-\frac{1}{2}} \left(h_{\mu}^{-1}\phi_j\right) \# f\right\|_{L_p^{\mu}(l_q)} < \infty\right\}$$

for $1 \leq p < \infty$.

$$\text{(ii) } B_{p,q}^{\mu,s} = \left\{f : f \in H'_{\mu}(I), \|f\|_{B_{p,q}^{\mu,s}} = \left\|2^{sj} x^{-\mu-\frac{1}{2}} \left(h_{\mu}^{-1}\phi_j\right) \# f\right\|_{l_q(L_p^{\mu})} < \infty\right\}$$

for $1 \leq p < \infty$.

Definition 8.5 Let $1 \le p < \infty$, and $1 \le q \le \infty$. If $E = \{E_k\}_{k=0}^{\infty}$ is a sequence of compact subsets of I, then

$$L^E_{p,\mu}(l_q) = \Big\{ f : f = \{f_k\}_{k=0}^{\infty} \subset H'_\mu(I),\ \ \text{supp}\,(h_\mu f_k) \subset E_k \ \text{ if } k = 0, 1, 2, \ldots \\ \text{and } \left\| x^{-\mu-\frac{1}{2}} f_k \right\|_{L^\mu_p(l_q)} < \infty \Big\}.$$

Lemma 8.1 *Let $\phi, \psi \in L^1(I)$, and $h_\mu^{-1}\phi, h_\mu^{-1}\psi \in L^1(I)$. Then*

$$\left(h_\mu^{-1}\phi \# h_\mu^{-1}\psi\right)\left(2^{-k}y\right) = 2^{k-k(\mu+\frac{1}{2})}\left(h_\mu^{-1}\left(\phi(2^k\cdot)\right) \# h_\mu^{-1}\left(\psi(2^k\cdot)\right)\right)(y).$$

Proof For $\phi \in L^1(I)$, by the definition of inverse Hankel transformation

$$h_\mu^{-1}\left(\phi\left(2^k\cdot\right)\right)(y) = \int_0^\infty (xy)^{\frac{1}{2}} J_\mu(xy)\phi(2^k x)dx.$$

Putting $x = 2^{-k}t$ in the above expression, we get

$$\begin{aligned} h_\mu^{-1}\left(\phi\left(2^k\cdot\right)\right)(y) &= 2^{-k}\int_0^\infty (2^{-k}ty)^{\frac{1}{2}} J_\mu(2^{-k}ty)\phi(t)dt \\ &= 2^{-k}\left(h_\mu^{-1}\phi\right)\left(2^{-k}y\right). \end{aligned} \tag{8.12}$$

Using (1.85), we find

$$\begin{aligned} &h_\mu\left\{\left(h_\mu^{-1}\left(\phi(2^k\cdot)\right) \# h_\mu^{-1}\left(\psi(2^k\cdot)\right)\right)(y)\right\}(\eta) \\ &= \eta^{-\mu-\frac{1}{2}} h_\mu\left\{h_\mu^{-1}\left(\phi(2^k\cdot)\right)\right\}(\eta)\, h_\mu\left\{h_\mu^{-1}\left(\psi(2^k\cdot)\right)(y)\right\}(\eta) = \eta^{-\mu-\frac{1}{2}}\phi(2^k\eta)\psi(2^k\eta). \end{aligned}$$

This implies that

$$\begin{aligned} \left(h_\mu^{-1}\left(\phi(2^k\cdot)\right) \# h_\mu^{-1}\left(\psi(2^k\cdot)\right)\right)(y) &= h_\mu^{-1}\left(\eta^{-\mu-\frac{1}{2}}\phi(2^k\eta)\psi(2^k\eta)\right)(y) \\ &= 2^{k(\mu+\frac{1}{2})} h_\mu^{-1}\left(\left(2^k\eta\right)^{-\mu-\frac{1}{2}}\phi(2^k\eta)\psi(2^k\eta)\right)(y). \end{aligned}$$

Therefore, from (8.12) we get

$$\begin{aligned} \left(h_\mu^{-1}\left(\phi(2^k\cdot)\right) \# h_\mu^{-1}\left(\psi(2^k\cdot)\right)\right)(y) &= 2^{k(\mu+\frac{1}{2})}2^{-k} h_\mu^{-1}\left(\eta^{-\mu-\frac{1}{2}}\phi(\eta)\psi(\eta)\right)(2^{-k}y) \\ &= 2^{-k+k(\mu+\frac{1}{2})}\left\{\left(h_\mu^{-1}\phi \# h_\mu^{-1}\psi\right)\left(2^{-k}y\right)\right\}. \end{aligned}$$

Thus, we have

$$\left(h_\mu^{-1}\phi\#h_\mu^{-1}\psi\right)\left(2^{-k}y\right)=2^{k-k(\mu+\frac{1}{2})}\left(h_\mu^{-1}\left(\phi(2^k\cdot)\right)\#h_\mu^{-1}\left(\psi(2^k\cdot)\right)\right)(y).$$

Theorem 8.1 *Let* $1\le p<\infty$, $1\le q\le\infty$ *and* $d>0$. *Let* $E=\{E_k\}_{k=0}^{\infty}$ *is a sequence of compact subsets of* I *, then*

$$\left\|2^{ks}x^{-\mu-\frac{1}{2}}\sup_{y\in I}\frac{|f_k(x,y)|}{1+\left(2^k y\right)^{2d}}\right\|_{L_p^\mu(l_q)}\le c_\mu^{-1}\left\|2^{ks}x^{-\mu-\frac{1}{2}}f_k(x)\right\|_{L_p^\mu(l_q)}$$

holds for all $f\in L_{p,\mu}^E(l_q)$, *where* $f=\{f_k\}_{k=0}^{\infty}$, $\mu\ge-\frac{1}{2}$, $c_\mu=2^\mu\Gamma(\mu+1)$, *and*

$$f_k(x,y)=\int_0^\infty f_k(z)D_\mu(x,y,z)dz$$

is the Hankel translation of $f_k(x)$.

Proof From (1.80), we take

$$f_k(x,y)=\int_0^\infty f_k(z)D_\mu(x,y,z)dz. \tag{8.13}$$

Multiplying by 2^{ks} and taking l_q-norm on both sides, we get

$$\Big(\sum_{k=0}^{\infty}2^{ksq}\,|f_k(x,y)|^q\Big)^{\frac{1}{q}}=\Big(\sum_{k=0}^{\infty}\Big|\int_0^\infty 2^{ks}f_k(z)D_\mu(x,y,z)dz\Big|^q\Big)^{\frac{1}{q}}.$$

Using Minkowski's integral inequality (8.1), we obtain

$$\begin{aligned}&\Big(\sum_{k=0}^{\infty}2^{ksq}\,|f_k(x,y)|^q\Big)^{\frac{1}{q}}\\&\le\int_0^\infty\Big(\sum_{k=0}^{\infty}2^{ksq}\,|f_k(z)D_\mu(x,y,z)|^q\Big)^{\frac{1}{q}}dz\\&=\int_0^\infty\Big(\sum_{k=0}^{\infty}2^{ksq}\left|z^{-\mu-\frac{1}{2}}f_k(z)\right|^q\Big)^{\frac{1}{q}}\left(z^{\mu+\frac{1}{2}}D_\mu(x,y,z)\right)^{\frac{1}{p}}\left(z^{\mu+\frac{1}{2}}D_\mu(x,y,z)\right)^{\frac{1}{p'}}dz,\end{aligned}$$

where $\frac{1}{p}+\frac{1}{p'}=1$. Now applying Holder's inequality, we get

$$\Big(\sum_{k=0}^{\infty} 2^{ksq}\,|f_k(x,y)|^q\Big)^{\frac{1}{q}}$$
$$\leq \Big(\int_0^\infty \Big(\sum_{k=0}^{\infty} 2^{ksq}\,\Big|z^{-\mu-\frac{1}{2}} f_k(z)\Big|^q\Big)^{\frac{1}{q}\times p} z^{\mu+\frac{1}{2}} D_\mu(x,y,z)dz\Big)^{\frac{1}{p}}$$
$$\times \Big(\int_0^\infty z^{\mu+\frac{1}{2}} D_\mu(x,y,z)dz\Big)^{\frac{1}{p'}}$$
$$= \Big(\int_0^\infty \Big(\sum_{k=0}^{\infty} 2^{ksq}\,\Big|z^{-\mu-\frac{1}{2}} f_k(z)\Big|^q\Big)^{\frac{1}{q}\times p} z^{\mu+\frac{1}{2}} D_\mu(x,y,z)dz\Big)^{\frac{1}{p}} \Big(c_\mu^{-1}(xy)^{\mu+\frac{1}{2}}\Big)^{\frac{1}{p'}},$$

since $\int_0^\infty z^{\mu+\frac{1}{2}} D_\mu(x,y,z)dz = c_\mu^{-1}(xy)^{\mu+\frac{1}{2}},\ c_\mu = 2^\mu\Gamma(\mu+1)$ (1.84).

This implies that

$$(xy)^{(\mu+\frac{1}{2})(-\frac{p}{p'})}\Big(\sum_{k=0}^{\infty} 2^{ksq}\,|f_k(x,y)|^q\Big)^{\frac{p}{q}}$$
$$\leq (c_\mu^{-1})^{\frac{p}{p'}} \int_0^\infty \Big(\sum_{k=0}^{\infty} 2^{ksq}\,\Big|z^{-\mu-\frac{1}{2}} f_k(z)\Big|^q\Big)^{\frac{p}{q}} z^{\mu+\frac{1}{2}} D_\mu(x,y,z)dz.$$

Now, multiplying by $x^{\mu+\frac{1}{2}}$ and taking integration with respect to x, we get

$$\int_0^\infty y^{(\mu+\frac{1}{2})(-\frac{p}{p'})} x^{(\mu+\frac{1}{2})(1-\frac{p}{p'})}\Big(\sum_{k=0}^{\infty} 2^{ksq}\,|f_k(x,y)|^q\Big)^{\frac{p}{q}} dx$$
$$\leq (c_\mu^{-1})^{\frac{p}{p'}} \int_0^\infty\int_0^\infty \Big(\sum_{k=0}^{\infty} 2^{ksq}\,\Big|z^{-\mu-\frac{1}{2}} f_k(z)\Big|^q\Big)^{\frac{p}{q}} z^{\mu+\frac{1}{2}} x^{\mu+\frac{1}{2}} D_\mu(x,y,z)dzdx.$$

By Fubini's theorem, the above expression yields

$$\int_0^\infty y^{(\mu+\frac{1}{2})(1-p)} x^{(\mu+\frac{1}{2})(2-p)}\Big(\sum_{k=0}^{\infty} 2^{ksq}\,|f_k(x,y)|^q\Big)^{\frac{p}{q}} dx$$
$$\leq (c_\mu^{-1})^{\frac{p}{p'}} \int_0^\infty \Big(\sum_{k=0}^{\infty} 2^{ksq}\,\Big|z^{-\mu-\frac{1}{2}} f_k(z)\Big|^q\Big)^{\frac{p}{q}} z^{\mu+\frac{1}{2}} \int_0^\infty x^{\mu+\frac{1}{2}} D_\mu(x,y,z)dxdz$$
$$\leq (c_\mu^{-1})^{\frac{p}{p'}} \int_0^\infty \Big(\sum_{k=0}^{\infty} 2^{ksq}\,\Big|z^{-\mu-\frac{1}{2}} f_k(z)\Big|^q\Big)^{\frac{p}{q}} z^{\mu+\frac{1}{2}} \Big(c_\mu^{-1}(yz)^{\mu+\frac{1}{2}}\Big) dz$$
$$\leq (c_\mu^{-1})^{(1+\frac{p}{p'})} \int_0^\infty \Big(\sum_{k=0}^{\infty} 2^{ksq}\,\Big|z^{-\mu-\frac{1}{2}} f_k(z)\Big|^q\Big)^{\frac{p}{q}} z^{\mu+\frac{1}{2}} \Big((yz)^{\mu+\frac{1}{2}}\Big) dz.$$

Therefore

$$\int_0^\infty x^{2\mu+1}\Big(\sum_{k=0}^\infty 2^{ksq}x^{-\mu-\frac{1}{2}}\Big|\frac{f_k(x,y)}{y^{\mu+\frac{1}{2}}}\Big|^q\Big)^{\frac{p}{q}}dx$$
$$\leq (c_\mu^{-1})^p\int_0^\infty\Big(\sum_{k=0}^\infty 2^{ksq}\left|z^{-\mu-\frac{1}{2}}f_k(z)\right|^q\Big)^{\frac{p}{q}}z^{2\mu+1}dz.$$

Now, for $y\in I$

$$\Big(\int_0^\infty x^{2\mu+1}\Big(\sum_{k=0}^\infty 2^{ksq}x^{-\mu-\frac{1}{2}}\sup_{y\in I}\Big|\frac{f_k(x,y)}{1+(2^ky)^{\mu+\frac{1}{2}}}\Big|^q\Big)^{\frac{p}{q}}dx\Big)^{\frac{1}{p}}$$
$$\leq c_\mu^{-1}\Big(\int_0^\infty z^{2\mu+1}\Big(\sum_{k=0}^\infty 2^{ksq}\left|z^{-\mu-\frac{1}{2}}f_k(z)\right|^q\Big)^{\frac{p}{q}}dz\Big)^{\frac{1}{p}}.$$

Thus, we get

$$\left\|2^{ks}x^{-\mu-\frac{1}{2}}\sup_{y\in I}\frac{|f_k(x,y)|}{1+(2^ky)^{\mu+\frac{1}{2}}}\right\|_{L_p^\mu(l_q)}\leq c_\mu^{-1}\left\|2^{ks}x^{-\mu-\frac{1}{2}}f_k(x)\right\|_{L_p^\mu(l_q)}$$

for $1\leq p<\infty$ and $1\leq q<\infty$. Taking $\mu+\frac{1}{2}=2d$, we get

$$\left\|2^{ks}x^{-\mu-\frac{1}{2}}\sup_{y\in I}\frac{|f_k(x,y)|}{1+(2^ky)^{2d}}\right\|_{L_p^\mu(l_q)}\leq c_\mu^{-1}\left\|2^{ks}x^{-\mu-\frac{1}{2}}f_k(x)\right\|_{L_p^\mu(l_q)}.$$

For $q=\infty$, from (8.13), we have

$$\sup_k 2^{ks}|f_k(x,y)|=\sup_k\left|\int_0^\infty 2^{ks}f_k(z)D_\mu(x,y,z)dz\right|$$
$$\leq\int_0^\infty 2^{ks}\sup_k\left|z^{-\mu-\frac{1}{2}}f_k(z)\right|z^{\mu+\frac{1}{2}}D_\mu(x,y,z)dz.$$

Now, proceeding as in the case of $1\leq q<\infty$ we get

$$\left\|2^{ks}x^{-\mu-\frac{1}{2}}\sup_{y\in I}\frac{|f_k(x,y)|}{1+(2^ky)^{2d}}\right\|_{L_p^\mu(l_\infty)}\leq c_\mu^{-1}\left\|2^{ks}x^{-\mu-\frac{1}{2}}f_k(x)\right\|_{L_p^\mu(l_\infty)}.$$

Theorem 8.2 *Let $1 \leq p < \infty$, $1 \leq q \leq \infty$ and $d > 0$. Let $E = \{E_k\}_{k=0}^{\infty}$ is a sequence of compact subsets of I, then*

$$\left\| 2^{ks} x^{-\mu-\frac{1}{2}} \sup_{y \in I} \frac{|f_k(x, y)|}{1 + (2^k y)^{2d}} \right\|_{l_q(L_p^\mu)} \leq c_\mu^{-1} \left\| 2^{ks} x^{-\mu-\frac{1}{2}} f_k(x) \right\|_{l_q(L_p^\mu)}$$

holds for all $f_k \in L_{p,\mu}^{E_k}$, where $f = \{f_k\}_{k=0}^{\infty}$, $c_\mu = 2^\mu \Gamma(\mu + 1)$ and for $\mu \geq -\frac{1}{2}$

$$f_k(x, y) = \int_0^\infty f_k(z) D_\mu(x, y, z) dz$$

is the Hankel translation of $f_k(x)$.

Proof From (1.80), we have

$$f_k(x, y) = \int_0^\infty f_k(z) D_\mu(x, y, z) dz. \tag{8.14}$$

Therefore

$$2^{ks} |f_k(x, y)| \leq \int_0^\infty \left| 2^{ks} z^{-\mu-\frac{1}{2}} f_k(z) \left(z^{\mu+\frac{1}{2}} D_\mu(x, y, z) \right)^{\frac{1}{p}} \left(z^{\mu+\frac{1}{2}} D_\mu(x, y, z) \right)^{\frac{1}{p'}} \right| dz$$

for $\frac{1}{p} + \frac{1}{p'} = 1$. Applying Holder's inequality, we get

$$2^{ks} |f_k(x, y)| \leq \left(\int_0^\infty \left| 2^{ks} z^{-\mu-\frac{1}{2}} f_k(z) \right|^p z^{\mu+\frac{1}{2}} D_\mu(x, y, z) dz \right)^{\frac{1}{p}} \left(\int_0^\infty z^{\mu+\frac{1}{2}} D_\mu(x, y, z) dz \right)^{\frac{1}{p'}}.$$

From (1.84), we find

$$2^{ks} |f_k(x, y)| \leq \left(\int_0^\infty \left| 2^{ks} z^{-\mu-\frac{1}{2}} f_k(z) \right|^p z^{\mu+\frac{1}{2}} D_\mu(x, y, z) dz \right)^{\frac{1}{p}} \left(c_\mu^{-1} (xy)^{\mu+\frac{1}{2}} \right)^{\frac{1}{p'}}.$$

This implies that

$$2^{ks} (xy)^{(\mu+\frac{1}{2})(-\frac{p}{p'})} |f_k(x, y)| \leq \left(c_\mu^{-1} \right)^{\frac{p}{p'}} \int_0^\infty \left| 2^{ks} z^{-\mu-\frac{1}{2}} f_k(z) \right|^p z^{\mu+\frac{1}{2}} D_\mu(x, y, z) dz.$$

Therefore, we have

$$\int_0^\infty 2^{ksp} y^{\left(\mu+\frac{1}{2}\right)\left(-\frac{p}{p'}\right)} x^{\left(\mu+\frac{1}{2}\right)\left(1-\frac{p}{p'}\right)} |f_k(x,y)|^p\, dx$$
$$\leq \left(c_\mu^{-1}\right)^{\frac{p}{p'}} \int_0^\infty \int_0^\infty \left|2^{ks} z^{-\mu-\frac{1}{2}} f_k(z)\right|^p z^{\mu+\frac{1}{2}} x^{\mu+\frac{1}{2}} D_\mu(x,y,z)\,dz\,dx.$$

In view of the Fubini's theorem, we find

$$\int_0^\infty 2^{ksp} y^{(\mu+\frac{1}{2})(1-p)} x^{(\mu+\frac{1}{2})(2-p)} |f_k(x,y)|^p\, dx$$
$$\leq \left(c_\mu^{-1}\right)^{\frac{p}{p'}} \int_0^\infty \left|2^{ks} z^{-\mu-\frac{1}{2}} f_k(z)\right|^p z^{\mu+\frac{1}{2}} \int_0^\infty x^{\mu+\frac{1}{2}} D_\mu(x,y,z)\,dx\,dz$$
$$\leq \left(c_\mu^{-1}\right)^{\frac{p}{p'}} \int_0^\infty \left|2^{ks} z^{-\mu-\frac{1}{2}} f_k(z)\right|^p z^{\mu+\frac{1}{2}} c_\mu^{-1} (yz)^{\mu+\frac{1}{2}}\,dz$$
$$\leq \left(c_\mu^{-1}\right)^{\left(1+\frac{p}{p'}\right)} \int_0^\infty \left|2^{ks} z^{-\mu-\frac{1}{2}} f_k(z)\right|^p z^{2\mu+1} y^{\mu+\frac{1}{2}}\,dz.$$

Therefore

$$\int_0^\infty x^{2\mu+1} 2^{ksp} \left(x^{-\mu-\frac{1}{2}} \left|\frac{f_k(x,y)}{y^{\mu+\frac{1}{2}}}\right|\right)^p dx \leq \left(c_\mu^{-1}\right)^p \int_0^\infty z^{2\mu+1} 2^{ksp} \left|z^{-\mu-\frac{1}{2}} f_k(z)\right|^p dz,$$

so that, for $y \in I$

$$\left(\int_0^\infty x^{2\mu+1} 2^{ksp} \left(x^{-\mu-\frac{1}{2}} \sup_{y\in I} \left|\frac{f_k(x,y)}{1+(2^k y)^{\mu+\frac{1}{2}}}\right|\right)^p dx\right)^{\frac{1}{p}}$$
$$\leq c_\mu^{-1} \left(\int_0^\infty z^{2\mu+1} 2^{ksp} \left|z^{-\mu-\frac{1}{2}} f_k(z)\right|^p dz\right)^{\frac{1}{p}}.$$

Applying l_q-norm (8.4) and (8.5), we obtain

$$\left\|2^{ks} x^{-\mu-\frac{1}{2}} \sup_{y\in I} \frac{|f_k(x,y)|}{1+(2^k y)^{\mu+\frac{1}{2}}}\right\|_{l_q(L_p^\mu)} \leq c_\mu^{-1} \left\|2^{ks} x^{-\mu-\frac{1}{2}} f_k(x)\right\|_{l_q(L_p^\mu)}$$

for $1 \leq p < \infty$ and $1 \leq q \leq \infty$. Taking $\mu + \frac{1}{2} = 2d$, we get

$$\left\|2^{ks} x^{-\mu-\frac{1}{2}} \sup_{y\in I} \frac{|f_k(x,y)|}{1+(2^k y)^{2d}}\right\|_{l_q(L_p^\mu)} \leq c_\mu^{-1} \left\|2^{ks} x^{-\mu-\frac{1}{2}} f_k(x)\right\|_{l_q(L_p^\mu)}.$$

8.3 Boundedness of the Bessel Wavelet Transform in Triebel-Lizorkin and Besov Type Spaces

In this section, a multiplier theorem and other results are discussed by exploiting the Hankel transform theory. Using the multiplier theorem and other results, boundedness of the continuous Bessel wavelet transform in the Besov space $B_{p,q}^{\mu,s}$ and the Triebel-Lizorkin space $F_{p,q}^{\mu,s}$ are investigated.

Theorem 8.3 *Let $a > 0$ be fixed. Let $-\infty < s < \infty$ and N be a natural number*

(i) If $1 \leq q \leq \infty$, and $1 \leq p < \infty$ then there exists a positive number D such that

$$\left\| 2^{ks} x^{-\mu-\frac{1}{2}} \left(h_\mu^{-1}\theta_k\right) \# f \right\|_{L_p^\mu(l_q)} \leq DC_\mu(\theta) \left\| 2^{ks} x^{-\mu-\frac{1}{2}} \left(\phi_k^* f\right) \right\|_{L_p^\mu(l_q)} \leq c_\mu^{-1} DC_\mu(\theta) \left\| f \right\|_{F_{p,q}^{\mu,s}}$$

holds for all $\phi = \{\phi_k(x)\}_{k=0}^{\infty} \in \Phi(I)$, $\theta = \{\theta_k(x)\}_{k=0}^{\infty} \in A_\mu^N(I)$ and $f \in H_\mu'(I)$.

(ii) If $1 \leq q \leq \infty$ and $1 \leq p < \infty$, then there exists a positive number D such that

$$\left\| 2^{ks} x^{-\mu-\frac{1}{2}} \left(h_\mu^{-1}\theta_k\right) \# f \right\|_{l_q(L_p^\mu)} \leq DC_\mu(\theta) \left\| 2^{ks} x^{-\mu-\frac{1}{2}} \left(\phi_k^* f\right) \right\|_{l_q(L_p^\mu)} \leq c_\mu^{-1} DC_\mu(\theta) \left\| f \right\|_{B_{p,q}^{\mu,s}}$$

holds for all $\phi = \{\phi_k(x)\}_{k=0}^{\infty} \in \Phi(I)$, $\theta = \{\theta_k(x)\}_{k=0}^{\infty} \in A_\mu^N(I)$ and $f \in H_\mu'(I)$.

Proof Let $\{\psi_k(x)\}_{k=0}^{\infty} \in A_\mu^N(I)$ with

$$\begin{cases} \operatorname{supp} x^{-\mu-\frac{1}{2}} \psi_0(x) \subset \{x : 0 \leq x \leq 4\}, \\ \operatorname{supp} x^{-\mu-\frac{1}{2}} \psi_k(x) \subset \{x : 2^{k-2} \leq x \leq 2^{k+2}\}, \quad k = 1, 2, 3, \ldots \end{cases} \tag{8.15}$$

and

$$x^{-\mu-\frac{1}{2}} \psi_k(x) = 1, \text{ if } x \in \operatorname{supp}\left(x^{-\mu-\frac{1}{2}} \phi_k\right), \quad k = 0, 1, 2, 3, \ldots. \tag{8.16}$$

Now for $\phi = \{\phi_k(x)\}_{k=0}^{\infty} \in \Phi(I)$, $\theta = \{\theta_k(x)\}_{k=0}^{\infty} \in A_\mu^N(I)$ and $f \in H_\mu'(I)$, we have

$$h_\mu\left[\left(h_\mu^{-1}\theta_k\right) \# f\right] = \eta^{-\mu-\frac{1}{2}} \theta_k h_\mu f.$$

This implies that

$$\left(h_\mu^{-1}\theta_k\right) \# f = h_\mu^{-1}\left[\eta^{-\mu-\frac{1}{2}} \theta_k h_\mu f\right].$$

From (8.11) and (8.16), we find

$$\begin{aligned}
(h_\mu^{-1}\theta_k)\#f &= h_\mu^{-1}\Big[\eta^{-\mu-\frac{1}{2}}\theta_k\Big(\sum_{l=0}^{\infty}\eta^{-\mu-\frac{1}{2}}\psi_l\ \eta^{-\mu-\frac{1}{2}}\phi_l\Big)h_\mu f\Big] \\
&= \sum_{l=0}^{\infty} h_\mu^{-1}\Big[\eta^{-\mu-\frac{1}{2}}\eta^{-\mu-\frac{1}{2}}h_\mu h_\mu^{-1}\theta_k h_\mu h_\mu^{-1}\psi_l\ \eta^{-\mu-\frac{1}{2}}h_\mu h_\mu^{-1}\phi_l h_\mu f\Big] \\
&= \sum_{l=0}^{\infty} h_\mu^{-1}\Big[\eta^{-\mu-\frac{1}{2}}h_\mu\left(h_\mu^{-1}\theta_k\#h_\mu^{-1}\psi_l\right)h_\mu\left(h_\mu^{-1}\phi_l\#f\right)\Big] \\
&= \sum_{l=0}^{\infty} h_\mu^{-1}\left[h_\mu\left(\left(h_\mu^{-1}\theta_k\#h_\mu^{-1}\psi_l\right)\#\left(h_\mu^{-1}\phi_l\#f\right)\right)\right] \\
&= \sum_{l=0}^{\infty}\left[\left(h_\mu^{-1}\theta_k\#h_\mu^{-1}\psi_l\right)\#\left(h_\mu^{-1}\phi_l\#f\right)\right].
\end{aligned}$$

By multiplying 2^{ks} and taking absolute value, the above expression becomes

$$\begin{aligned}
\left|2^{ks}\left(h_\mu^{-1}\theta_k\#f\right)(x)\right| &\le \sum_{l=0}^{\infty}2^{ks}\left|\left(h_\mu^{-1}\theta_k\#h_\mu^{-1}\psi_l\right)\#\left(h_\mu^{-1}\phi_l\#f\right)(x)\right| \\
&\le \sum_{l=0}^{\infty}2^{ks}\int_0^\infty\left|\left(h_\mu^{-1}\theta_k\#h_\mu^{-1}\psi_l\right)(y)\right|\left|\left(h_\mu^{-1}\phi_l\#f\right)(x,y)\right|dy.
\end{aligned}$$

From (8.8), we have

$$\begin{aligned}
\left|2^{ks}\left(h_\mu^{-1}\theta_k\#f\right)(x)\right| &\le \sum_{l=0}^{\infty}2^{ks}\int_0^\infty\left|\left(h_\mu^{-1}\theta_k\#h_\mu^{-1}\psi_l\right)(y)\right|\left|\left(1+\left(2^l y\right)^{2d}\right)\left(\phi_l^* f\right)(x)\right|dy \\
&= \sum_{l=0}^{\infty}2^{ks}\left(\phi_l^* f\right)(x)\int_0^\infty\left|\left(h_\mu^{-1}\theta_k\#h_\mu^{-1}\psi_l\right)(y)\right|\left(1+\left(2^l y\right)^{2d}\right)dy.
\end{aligned}$$

This implies that

$$\left|2^{ks}\left(h_\mu^{-1}\theta_k\#f\right)(x)\right| \le \sum_{l=0}^{\infty}2^{ks}\left(\phi_l^* f\right)(x)\int_0^\infty\left|\left(h_\mu^{-1}\theta_k\#h_\mu^{-1}\psi_l\right)(y)\right|\left(1+\left(2^l y\right)^{2d}\right)dy. \tag{8.17}$$

Now, we take

$$I_{k,l} = \int_0^\infty\left|\left(h_\mu^{-1}\theta_k\#h_\mu^{-1}\psi_l\right)(y)\right|\left(1+\left(2^l y\right)^{2d}\right)dy.$$

Putting $y = 2^{-k}z$ in the above expression, we get

$$\begin{aligned} I_{k,l} &= 2^{-k} \int_0^\infty \left|\left(h_\mu^{-1}\theta_k \# h_\mu^{-1}\psi_l\right)(2^{-k}z)\right| \left(1 + \left(2^{l-k}z\right)^{2d}\right) dz \\ &\leq 2^{-k+2d|l-k|} \int_0^\infty \left|\left(h_\mu^{-1}\theta_k \# h_\mu^{-1}\psi_l\right)(2^{-k}z)\right| \left(1 + z^{2d}\right) dz \\ &\leq 2^{-k+2d|l-k|} \int_0^\infty \left|\left(h_\mu^{-1}\theta_k \# h_\mu^{-1}\psi_l\right)(2^{-k}z)\right| \left(1 + z^2\right)^d dz. \end{aligned}$$

Using Holder's inequality, we obtain

$$I_{k,l} \leq 2^{-k+2d|l-k|} \left\| \left(1 + z^2\right)^{d+\frac{1}{2}} \left(h_\mu^{-1}\theta_k \# h_\mu^{-1}\psi_l\right)(2^{-k}z) \right\|_2 \left\| \left(1 + z^2\right)^{-\frac{1}{2}} \right\|_2 .$$

In view of Lemma 8.1 and putting $\rho = E\left(d + \frac{1}{2}\right) + 1$, we find

$$I_{k,l} \leq \sqrt{\frac{\pi}{2}}\, 2^{-k+2d|l-k|} 2^k 2^{-k(\mu+\frac{1}{2})} \left\| \left(1 + z^2\right)^\rho \left(h_\mu^{-1}\left(\theta_k(2^k\cdot)\right) \# h_\mu^{-1}\left(\psi_l(2^k\cdot)\right)\right) \right\|_2 .$$

From (1.85) and (1.77), the above expression can be written as

$$I_{k,l} \leq \sqrt{\frac{\pi}{2}}\, 2^{2d|l-k|-k(\mu+\frac{1}{2})} \left\| h_\mu \left\{ \left(1 + z^2\right)^\rho h_\mu^{-1} \left(\eta^{-\mu-\frac{1}{2}}\theta_k(2^k\eta)\psi_l(2^k\eta)\right) \right\} \right\|_2 .$$

From (1.114), we have

$$I_{k,l} \leq \sqrt{\frac{\pi}{2}}\, 2^{2d|l-k|-k(\mu+\frac{1}{2})} \left\| \left(1 - S_{\mu,\eta}\right)^\rho \left(\eta^{-\mu-\frac{1}{2}}\theta_k(2^k\eta)\psi_l(2^k\eta)\right) \right\|_2 . \tag{8.18}$$

The expression in the norm on R.H.S of (8.18) will be

$$\begin{aligned} &\left\| \left(1 - S_{\mu,\eta}\right)^\rho \left(\eta^{-\mu-\frac{1}{2}}\theta_k(2^k\eta)\psi_l(2^k\eta)\right) \right\|_2 \\ &= \left\| \sum_{r=0}^{\rho} \binom{\rho}{r} (-1)^r S_{\mu,\eta}^r \left(\eta^{-\mu-\frac{1}{2}}\theta_k(2^k\eta)\psi_l(2^k\eta)\right) \right\|_2 \\ &= \left\| \sum_{r=0}^{\rho} \binom{\rho}{r} \sum_{j=0}^{r} A_j \eta^{2j+\mu+\frac{1}{2}} \left(\eta^{-1}D_\eta\right)^{r+j} \left(\eta^{-\mu-\frac{1}{2}}\theta_k(2^k\eta)\eta^{-\mu-\frac{1}{2}}\psi_l(2^k\eta)\right) \right\|_2 \\ &= \left\| \sum_{r=0}^{\rho} \binom{\rho}{r} \sum_{j=0}^{r} A_j \sum_{m=0}^{r+j} \binom{r+j}{m} \eta^{2j+\mu+\frac{1}{2}} \left(\eta^{-1}D_\eta\right)^m \left(\eta^{-\mu-\frac{1}{2}}\theta_k(2^k\eta)\right) \right. \\ &\quad \left. \times \left(\eta^{-1}D_\eta\right)^{r+j-m} \left(\eta^{-\mu-\frac{1}{2}}\psi_l(2^k\eta)\right) \right\|_2 \end{aligned}$$

$$\leq \sum_{r=0}^{\rho} \binom{\rho}{r} \sum_{j=0}^{r} A_j \sum_{m=0}^{r+j} \binom{r+j}{m} \left\| \left(\eta^{-1} D_\eta\right)^m \left(\eta^{-\mu-\frac{1}{2}} \theta_k(2^k \eta)\right) \eta^{2j+\mu+\frac{1}{2}} \right.$$
$$\left. \times \left(\eta^{-1} D_\eta\right)^{r+j-m} \left(\eta^{-\mu-\frac{1}{2}} \psi_l(2^k \eta)\right) \right\|_2$$
$$= \sum_{r=0}^{\rho} \binom{\rho}{r} \sum_{j=0}^{r} A_j \sum_{m=0}^{r+j} \binom{r+j}{m} \Big(\int_0^\infty \left| \left(\eta^{-1} D_\eta\right)^m \left(\eta^{-\mu-\frac{1}{2}} \theta_k(2^k \eta)\right) \right|^2$$
$$\times \left| \eta^{2j+\mu+\frac{1}{2}} \left(\eta^{-1} D_\eta\right)^{r+j-m} \left(\eta^{-\mu-\frac{1}{2}} \psi_l(2^k \eta)\right) \right|^2 d\eta \Big)^{\frac{1}{2}}.$$

From (8.15), $\psi_l(2^k\eta)$ vanishes outside the set

$$\left\{\eta : 2^{l-k-2} \leq \eta \leq 2^{l-k+2}\right\},$$

and $\psi_0(2^k\eta)$ vanishes outside the set

$$\left\{\eta : 0 \leq \eta \leq 2^{-k+2}\right\}.$$

So, if η belongs to that set then from (8.6), we have

$$\left| \left(\eta^{-1} D_\eta\right)^m \left(\eta^{-\mu-\frac{1}{2}} \theta_k(2^k \eta)\right) \right| \leq C_1 2^{-N|l-k|} C_\mu(\theta), \tag{8.19}$$

where C_1 is a constant and N is a natural number.

Using (8.19) and for $N \geq 2\rho$, we find that

$$\left\| (1 - S_{\mu,\eta})^\rho \left(\eta^{-\mu-\frac{1}{2}} \theta_k(2^k \eta) \psi_l(2^k \eta)\right) \right\|_2$$
$$\leq C_1 2^{-N|l-k|} C_\mu(\theta) \sum_{r=0}^{\rho} \binom{\rho}{r} \sum_{j=0}^{r} A_j \sum_{m=0}^{r+j} \binom{r+j}{m}$$
$$\times \left(\int_0^\infty \left| \eta^{2j+\mu+\frac{1}{2}} \left(\eta^{-1} D_\eta\right)^{r+j-m} \left(\eta^{-\mu-\frac{1}{2}} \psi_l(2^k \eta)\right) \right|^2 d\eta \right)^{\frac{1}{2}}.$$

Now, putting $\eta = 2^{l-k} t$ we get

$$\left\| (1 - S_{\mu,\eta})^\rho \left(\eta^{-\mu-\frac{1}{2}} \theta_k(2^k \eta) \psi_l(2^k \eta)\right) \right\|_2$$
$$\leq C_1 2^{-N|l-k|} C_\mu(\theta) \sum_{r=0}^{\rho} \binom{\rho}{r} \sum_{j=0}^{r} A_j \sum_{m=0}^{r+j} \binom{r+j}{m} 2^{(l-k)(2m-2r+\frac{1}{2})}$$
$$\times \left(\int_0^\infty \left| t^{2j+\mu+\frac{1}{2}} \left(t^{-1} D_t\right)^{r+j-m} \left(t^{-\mu-\frac{1}{2}} \psi_l(2^l t)\right) \right|^2 dt \right)^{\frac{1}{2}}$$

$$\leq C_1 2^{-N|l-k|} C_\mu(\theta) 2^{(2\rho+\frac{1}{2})|l-k|}$$
$$\times \sum_{r=0}^{\rho} \binom{\rho}{r} \sum_{j=0}^{r} A_j \sum_{m=0}^{r+j} \binom{r+j}{m} \left\| t^{2j+\mu+\frac{1}{2}} \left(t^{-1} D_t\right)^{r+j-m} \left(t^{-\mu-\frac{1}{2}} \psi_l(2^l t)\right) \right\|_2.$$

Exploiting (8.15), we have

$$\begin{aligned}\left\| \left(1 - S_{\mu,\eta}\right)^\rho \left(\eta^{-\mu-\frac{1}{2}} \theta_k(2^k \eta) \psi_l(2^k \eta)\right) \right\|_2 &\leq C_1 2^{(-N+2\rho+\frac{1}{2})|l-k|} C_\mu(\theta) C_2 C_3 \\ &\leq C_1 C_2 C_3 2^{(-N+2\rho+\frac{1}{2})|l-k|} C_\mu(\theta).\end{aligned} \tag{8.20}$$

Using (8.18) and (8.20), we find the estimate of $I_{k,l}$

$$I_{k,l} \leq \sqrt{\frac{\pi}{2}}\, C_1 C_2 C_3 C_\mu(\theta) 2^{(2d+2\rho+\frac{1}{2}-N)|l-k|-k(\mu+\frac{1}{2})}. \tag{8.21}$$

From (8.17) and (8.21), finally we get

$$\begin{aligned}&\left|2^{ks} \left(h_\mu^{-1} \theta_k \# f\right)(x)\right| \\ &\quad\leq \sum_{l=0}^{\infty} 2^{s(k-l)} 2^{ls} \left(\phi_l^* f\right)(x) \sqrt{\frac{\pi}{2}}\, C_1 C_2 C_3 C_\mu(\theta) 2^{(2d+2\rho+\frac{1}{2}-N)|l-k|-k(\mu+\frac{1}{2})} \\ &\quad\leq \sqrt{\frac{\pi}{2}}\, C_1 C_2 C_3 C_\mu(\theta) \sum_{l=0}^{\infty} 2^{(|s|+2d+2\rho+\frac{1}{2}-N)|l-k|-k(\mu+\frac{1}{2})} 2^{ls} \left(\phi_l^* f\right)(x) \\ &\quad\leq C C_\mu(\theta) \sum_{l=0}^{\infty} 2^{(|s|+2d+2\rho+\frac{1}{2}+\mu+\frac{1}{2}-N)|l-k|} 2^{-l(\mu+\frac{1}{2})} 2^{ls} \left(\phi_l^* f\right)(x),\end{aligned}$$

where $C = \sqrt{\frac{\pi}{2}}\, C_1 C_2 C_3$ is independent of k, l, x, f, θ and ϕ.

Taking $\sigma = |s| + 2d + 2\rho + \mu + 1$, we have

$$\left|2^{ks} \left(h_\mu^{-1} \theta_k \# f\right)(x)\right| \leq C C_\mu(\theta) \sum_{l=0}^{\infty} 2^{(\sigma-N)|l-k|} 2^{-l(\mu+\frac{1}{2})} 2^{ls} \left(\phi_l^* f\right)(x). \tag{8.22}$$

For $N > \sigma$, from (8.22)

$$\left|2^{ks} \left(h_\mu^{-1} \theta_k \# f\right)(x)\right| \leq C C_\mu(\theta) C' \Big(\sum_{l=0}^{\infty} 2^{(\sigma+\epsilon-N)|l-k|q} 2^{-l(\mu+\frac{1}{2})q} 2^{lsq} \left(\phi_l^* f\right)^q(x) \Big)^{\frac{1}{q}}$$

with $\epsilon > 0$ and $N > \sigma + \epsilon$. On taking l_q- norm on both sides, we obtain

$$\begin{aligned}
&\Big(\sum_{k=0}^{\infty} \left|2^{ks}\left(h_\mu^{-1}\theta_k \# f\right)(x)\right|^q\Big)^{\frac{1}{q}} \\
&\leq C C_\mu(\theta) C' \Big(\sum_{k=0}^{\infty}\Big|\sum_{l=0}^{\infty} 2^{(\sigma+\epsilon-N)|l-k|q} 2^{-l(\mu+\frac{1}{2})q} 2^{lsq}\left(\phi_l^* f\right)^q(x)\Big|^{\frac{1}{q}\times q}\Big)^{\frac{1}{q}} \\
&\leq C C_\mu(\theta) C' \Big(\sum_{k=0}^{\infty}\sum_{l=0}^{\infty} 2^{(\sigma+\epsilon-N)|l-k|q} 2^{-l(\mu+\frac{1}{2})q}\left|2^{ls}\left(\phi_l^* f\right)(x)\right|^q\Big)^{\frac{1}{q}} \\
&\leq C C_\mu(\theta) C' C'' \Big(\sum_{l=0}^{\infty}\left|2^{ls}\left(\phi_l^* f\right)(x)\right|^q\Big)^{\frac{1}{q}}.
\end{aligned}$$

Therefore

$$\left\|2^{ks} x^{-\mu-\frac{1}{2}}\left(h_\mu^{-1}\theta_k \# f\right)(x)\right\|_{L_p^\mu(l_q)} \leq D C_\mu(\theta)\left\|2^{ks} x^{-\mu-\frac{1}{2}}\left(\phi_k^* f\right)(x)\right\|_{L_p^\mu(l_q)}, \tag{8.23}$$

with $N > |s| + \mu + 4d + 4$, $d > 0$ and $D = CC'C''$ for $1 \leq q < \infty$. From Lemma 8.1, taking $f_k = \left(h_\mu^{-1}\phi_k\right) \# f$, we have

$$\left\|2^{ks} x^{-\mu-\frac{1}{2}}\left(\phi_k^* f\right)(x)\right\|_{L_p^\mu(l_q)} \leq c_\mu^{-1}\left\|2^{ks} x^{-\mu-\frac{1}{2}}\left(h_\mu^{-1}\phi_k \# f\right)(x)\right\|_{L_p^\mu(l_q)} = c_\mu^{-1}\|f\|_{F_{p,q}^{\mu,s}}. \tag{8.24}$$

From (8.23) and (8.24), we get the result **(i)** of Theorem 8.3:

$$\begin{aligned}
\left\|2^{ks} x^{-\mu-\frac{1}{2}}\left(h_\mu^{-1}\theta_k \# f\right)(x)\right\|_{L_p^\mu(l_q)} &\leq D C_\mu(\theta)\left\|2^{ks} x^{-\mu-\frac{1}{2}}\left(\phi_k^* f\right)(x)\right\|_{L_p^\mu(l_q)} \\
&\leq c_\mu^{-1} D C_\mu(\theta)\|f\|_{F_{p,q}^{\mu,s}}
\end{aligned}$$

with $N > |s| + \mu + 4d + 4$, $d > 0$.

Remark 8.1 In case of $q = \infty$; for $N > \sigma$, from (8.22) we have

$$\left|2^{ks}\left(h_\mu^{-1}\theta_k \# f\right)(x)\right| \leq C C_\mu(\theta)\Big\{\sup_l 2^{-l(\mu+\frac{1}{2})} 2^{ls}\left(\phi_l^* f\right)(x)\Big\}\sum_{l=0}^{\infty} 2^{(\sigma-N)|l-k|}.$$

Now, taking l_∞-norm, we get

$$\begin{aligned}
\sup_k\left|2^{ks}\left(h_\mu^{-1}\theta_k \# f\right)(x)\right| &\leq C C_\mu(\theta)\Big\{\sup_l 2^{-l(\mu+\frac{1}{2})} 2^{ls}\left(\phi_l^* f\right)(x)\Big\}\sup_k \sum_{l=0}^{\infty} 2^{(\sigma-N)|l-k|} \\
&\leq C C_\mu(\theta)\Big\{\sup_l 2^{ls}\left(\phi_l^* f\right)(x)\Big\} C_1.
\end{aligned}$$

Therefore,

$$\left\| 2^{ks} x^{-\mu-\frac{1}{2}} \left(h_{\mu}^{-1} \theta_k \# f \right)(x) \right\|_{L_p^{\mu}(l_\infty)} \leq DC_{\mu}(\theta) \left\| 2^{ks} x^{-\mu-\frac{1}{2}} \left(\phi_k^* f \right)(x) \right\|_{L_p^{\mu}(l_\infty)} \tag{8.25}$$

with $N > |s| + \mu + 4d + 4,\ d > 0$ and $D = CC_1$. □

Now, to prove Theorem 8.3(**ii**), we take $N > \sigma$. Then from (8.22), we have

$$\left| 2^{ks} x^{-\mu-\frac{1}{2}} \left(h_{\mu}^{-1} \theta_k \# f \right)(x) \right| \leq CC_{\mu}(\theta) \sum_{l=0}^{\infty} 2^{(\sigma-N)|l-k|} 2^{-l(\mu+\frac{1}{2})} 2^{ls} x^{-\mu-\frac{1}{2}} \left(\phi_l^* f \right)(x).$$

Using Minkowski's inequality, we obtain

$$\left\| 2^{ks} x^{-\mu-\frac{1}{2}} \left(h_{\mu}^{-1} \theta_k \# f \right)(x) \right\|_{L_p^{\mu}} \leq CC_{\mu}(\theta) \sum_{l=0}^{\infty} 2^{(\sigma-N)|l-k|} 2^{-l(\mu+\frac{1}{2})} \left\| 2^{ls} x^{-\mu-\frac{1}{2}} \left(\phi_l^* f \right)(x) \right\|_{L_p^{\mu}}. \tag{8.26}$$

From (8.26), we get

$$\begin{aligned} &\left\| 2^{ks} x^{-\mu-\frac{1}{2}} \left(h_{\mu}^{-1} \theta_k \# f \right)(x) \right\|_{L_p^{\mu}} \\ &\leq CC_{\mu}(\theta) C' \Big(\sum_{l=0}^{\infty} 2^{(\sigma+\epsilon-N)|l-k|q} 2^{-l(\mu+\frac{1}{2})q} \left\| 2^{ls} x^{-\mu-\frac{1}{2}} \left(\phi_l^* f \right)(x) \right\|_{L_p^{\mu}}^q \Big)^{\frac{1}{q}} \end{aligned}$$

with $\epsilon > 0$ and $N > \sigma + \epsilon$. Therefore

$$\begin{aligned} &\Big(\sum_{k=0}^{\infty} \left\| 2^{ks} x^{-\mu-\frac{1}{2}} (h_{\mu}^{-1} \theta_k \# f)(x) \right\|_{L_p^{\mu}}^q \Big)^{\frac{1}{q}} \\ &\leq CC_{\mu}(\theta) C' \Big(\sum_{k=0}^{\infty} \Big| \sum_{l=0}^{\infty} 2^{(\sigma+\epsilon-N)|l-k|q} 2^{-l(\mu+\frac{1}{2})q} \left\| 2^{ls} x^{-\mu-\frac{1}{2}} \left(\phi_l^* f \right)(x) \right\|_{L_p^{\mu}}^q \Big|^{\frac{1}{q} \times q} \Big)^{\frac{1}{q}} \\ &\leq CC_{\mu}(\theta) C' \Big(\sum_{k=0}^{\infty} \sum_{l=0}^{\infty} 2^{(\sigma+\epsilon-N)|l-k|q} 2^{-l(\mu+\frac{1}{2})q} \left\| 2^{ls} x^{-\mu-\frac{1}{2}} \left(\phi_l^* f \right)(x) \right\|_{L_p^{\mu}}^q \Big)^{\frac{1}{q}} \\ &\leq CC_{\mu}(\theta) C' C'' \Big(\sum_{l=0}^{\infty} \left\| 2^{ls} x^{-\mu-\frac{1}{2}} \left(\phi_l^* f \right)(x) \right\|_{L_p^{\mu}}^q \Big)^{\frac{1}{q}}. \end{aligned}$$

That is,

$$\left\| 2^{ks} x^{-\mu-\frac{1}{2}} (h_{\mu}^{-1} \theta_k \# f)(x) \right\|_{l_q(L_p^{\mu})} \leq DC_{\mu}(\theta) \left\| 2^{ks} x^{-\mu-\frac{1}{2}} \left(\phi_k^* f \right)(x) \right\|_{l_q(L_p^{\mu})} \tag{8.27}$$

with $N > |s| + \mu + 4d + 4,\ d > 0$ and $D = CC'C''$ for $1 \leq q < \infty$.

From Lemma 8.2, taking $f_k = (h_\mu^{-1}\phi_k)\# f$, we have

$$\left\|2^{ks}x^{-\mu-\frac{1}{2}}(\phi_k^* f)(x)\right\|_{l_q(L_p^\mu)} \le c_\mu^{-1}\left\|2^{ks}x^{-\mu-\frac{1}{2}}(h_\mu^{-1}\phi_k\# f)(x)\right\|_{l_q(L_p^\mu)} = c_\mu^{-1}\left\|f\right\|_{B_{p,q}^{\mu,s}}. \tag{8.28}$$

From (8.27) and (8.28), we get the result **(ii)** of Theorem 8.3:

$$\begin{aligned}\left\|2^{ks}x^{-\mu-\frac{1}{2}}(h_\mu^{-1}\theta_k\# f)(x)\right\|_{l_q(L_p^\mu)} &\le DC_\mu(\theta)\left\|2^{ks}x^{-\mu-\frac{1}{2}}(\phi_k^* f)(x)\right\|_{l_q(L_p^\mu)}\\ &\le c_\mu^{-1}DC_\mu(\theta)\left\|f\right\|_{B_{p,q}^{\mu,s}}\end{aligned}$$

with $N > |s| + \mu + 4d + 4,\ d > 0$. □

Remark 8.2 In case of $q = \infty$; for $N > \sigma$, from (8.26) we find

$$\begin{aligned}&\sup_k\left\|2^{ks}x^{-\mu-\frac{1}{2}}\left(h_\mu^{-1}\theta_k\# f\right)(x)\right\|_{L_p^\mu}\\ &\le CC_\mu(\theta)\left\{\sup_l 2^{-l(\mu+\frac{1}{2})}\left\|2^{ls}x^{-\mu-\frac{1}{2}}\left(\phi_l^* f\right)(x)|\right\|_{L_p^\mu}\right\}\sup_k\sum_{l=0}^{\infty}2^{(\sigma-N)|l-k|}\\ &\le CC_\mu(\theta)\left\{\sup_l\left\|2^{ls}x^{-\mu-\frac{1}{2}}\left(\phi_l^* f\right)(x)|\right\|_{L_p^\mu}\right\}C_1.\end{aligned}$$

Therefore

$$\left\|2^{ks}x^{-\mu-\frac{1}{2}}(h_\mu^{-1}\theta_k\# f)(x)\right\|_{l_\infty(L_p^\mu)} \le DC_\mu(\theta)\left\|2^{ks}x^{-\mu-\frac{1}{2}}\left(\phi_k^* f\right)(x)\right\|_{l_\infty(L_p^\mu)} \tag{8.29}$$

with $N > |s| + \mu + 4d + 4,\ d > 0$ and $D = CC_1$. □

Theorem 8.4 *Let $m(x)$ be a complex-valued function in $C^\infty(I)$ such that*

$$\|m\|_N = \sup_{\alpha\le N}\sup_{x\in I}\left(1+x^2\right)^{\frac{\alpha}{2}}\left|\left(x^{-1}D_x\right)^\alpha x^{-\mu-\frac{1}{2}}m(x)\right| < \infty, \qquad N \in \mathbb{N}_0. \tag{8.30}$$

Let $-\infty < s < \infty$, $1 \le q \le \infty$ and $A(I)$ be either $F_{p,q}^{\mu,s}(I)$ with $1 \le p < \infty$ or $B_{p,q}^{\mu,s}(I)$ with $1 \le p < \infty$. Then there exists a positive number C such that

$$\left\|\left(h_\mu^{-1}m\right)\# f\right\|_A \le C\|m\|_N\|f\|_A$$

for all $m \in C^\infty(I)$ and $f \in A$ with $N > |s| + \mu + 4d + 4,\ d > 0$.

Proof We take $\phi = \{\phi_k(x)\}_{k=0}^{\infty} \in \Phi(I), m \in C^{\infty}(I)$ and $f \in A\big(= F_{p,q}^{\mu,s}(I)$ or $B_{p,q}^{\mu,s}(I)\big)$. From Definition 8.4 (i) and (1.85), we have

$$\begin{aligned}\left\|\left(h_{\mu}^{-1}m\right)\#f\right\|_{F_{p,q}^{\mu,s}} &= \left\|2^{ks}x^{-\mu-\frac{1}{2}}h_{\mu}^{-1}\phi_k\#\left(h_{\mu}^{-1}m\#f\right)\right\|_{L_p^{\mu}(l_q)}\\ &= \left\|2^{ks}x^{-\mu-\frac{1}{2}}\left(h_{\mu}^{-1}\phi_k\#h_{\mu}^{-1}m\right)\#f\right\|_{L_p^{\mu}(l_q)}\\ &= \left\|2^{ks}x^{-\mu-\frac{1}{2}}\left(h_{\mu}^{-1}\left(\eta^{-\mu-\frac{1}{2}}m\phi_k\right)\right)\#f\right\|_{L_p^{\mu}(l_q)}. \end{aligned} \tag{8.31}$$

Similarily, from Definition 8.4 (ii) and (1.85)

$$\left\|\left(h_{\mu}^{-1}m\right)\#f\right\|_{B_{p,q}^{\mu,s}} = \left\|2^{ks}x^{-\mu-\frac{1}{2}}\left(h_{\mu}^{-1}\left(\eta^{-\mu-\frac{1}{2}}m\phi_k\right)\right)\#f\right\|_{l_q(L_p^{\mu})}. \tag{8.32}$$

From (8.31), (8.32) and Theorem 8.3 with $\theta = \{\theta_k(x)\}_{k=0}^{\infty}$ and $\theta_k = \eta^{-\mu-\frac{1}{2}}m\phi_k$, we get

$$\left\|\left(h_{\mu}^{-1}m\right)\#f\right\|_{F_{p,q}^{\mu,s}} \leq c_{\mu}^{-1}DC_{\mu}(\theta)\,\|f\|_{F_{p,q}^{\mu,s}} \text{ and } \left\|\left(h_{\mu}^{-1}m\right)\#f\right\|_{B_{p,q}^{\mu,s}} \leq c_{\mu}^{-1}DC_{\mu}(\theta)\,\|f\|_{B_{p,q}^{\mu,s}},$$

respectively for $N > |s| + \mu + 4d + 4,\ d > 0$. From (8.6) and (8.30), we have

$$C_{\mu}(\theta) \leq C_1\,\|m\|_N\,,$$

where C_1 is a constant.

Thus, for $N > |s| + \mu + 4d + 4,\ d > 0$, we get

$$\left\|\left(h_{\mu}^{-1}m\right)\#f\right\|_A \leq C\,\|m\|_N\,\|f\|_A\,,$$

where $C = c_{\mu}^{-1}DC_1$ and $A\ \big(= F_{p,q}^{\mu,s}(I)$ or $B_{p,q}^{\mu,s}(I)\big)$. □

Theorem 8.5 *Let* $-\infty < s < \infty$, $\mu \geq -\frac{1}{2}$ *and* $1 \leq q \leq \infty$. *Let* $f \in A(I)$, *where* A *denotes* $F_{p,q}^{\mu,s}(I)$ *with* $1 \leq p < \infty$ *or* $B_{p,q}^{\mu,s}(I)$ *with* $1 \leq p < \infty$. *Let* $N \in \mathbb{N}$ *such that* $N > |s| + \mu + 4d + 4,\ d > 0$. *Assume that* $h_{\mu}\psi \in C^{\infty}(I)$ *and (7.5) holds. Then there exists a positive number* C *such that*

$$\left\|B_{\psi}f\right\|_A \leq C\left(1+a^2\right)^N a^{\mu+\frac{1}{2}} \sup_{\alpha\leq N}\left\|h_{\mu}\psi\right\|_{\mu,\alpha}^{m_1,\rho}\|f\|_A \tag{8.33}$$

for $m_1 + (1-\rho)N \leq 0$; $m_1 \in \mathbb{R}$, $\alpha \in \mathbb{N}_0$ *and* $0 \leq \rho \leq 1$.

Proof Assume that

$$m(\omega) = (h_{\mu}\psi)(a\omega)$$

for $\omega \in I$ and $a > 0$. Then

$$\|m\|_N = \sup_{\alpha \le N} \sup_{\omega \in I} \left(1+\omega^2\right)^{\frac{\alpha}{2}} \left| \left(\omega^{-1} D_\omega\right)^\alpha \omega^{-\mu-\frac{1}{2}} \left(h_\mu \psi\right)(a\omega) \right|.$$

Putting $a\omega = u$, we get

$$\begin{aligned}
\|m\|_N &= \sup_{\alpha \le N} \sup_{u \in I} \left(1+\left(\frac{u}{a}\right)^2\right)^{\frac{\alpha}{2}} \left| a^{2\alpha+\mu+\frac{1}{2}} \left(u^{-1}D_u\right)^\alpha u^{-\mu-\frac{1}{2}} \left(h_\mu\psi\right)(u) \right| \\
&= \sup_{\alpha \le N} \sup_{u \in I} \left(a^2+u^2\right)^{\frac{\alpha}{2}} a^{\alpha+\mu+\frac{1}{2}} \left| \left(u^{-1}D_u\right)^\alpha u^{-\mu-\frac{1}{2}} \left(h_\mu\psi\right)(u) \right| \\
&\le \left(1+a^2\right)^{\frac{N}{2}} \left(1+a^2\right)^{\frac{N}{2}} a^{\mu+\frac{1}{2}} \sup_{\alpha \le N} \sup_{u \in I} \left(1+u^2\right)^{\frac{\alpha}{2}} \left| \left(u^{-1}D_u\right)^\alpha u^{-\mu-\frac{1}{2}} \left(h_\mu\psi\right)(u) \right| \\
&\le \left(1+a^2\right)^N a^{\mu+\frac{1}{2}} \\
&\quad \times \sup_{\alpha \le N} \sup_{u \in I} \frac{(1+u)^\alpha}{(1+u)^{-m_1+\rho\alpha}} \left[(1+u)^{-m_1+\rho\alpha} \left| \left(u^{-1}D_u\right)^\alpha u^{-\mu-\frac{1}{2}} \left(h_\mu\psi\right)(u) \right|\right] \\
&\le \left(1+a^2\right)^N a^{\mu+\frac{1}{2}} \sup_{\alpha \le N} \left\| h_\mu \psi \right\|_{\mu,\alpha}^{m_1,\rho}
\end{aligned}$$

for $m_1 + (1-\rho)N \le 0$. From Theorem 8.4 and (1.128), we have

$$\begin{aligned}
\left\| B_\psi f \right\|_A &= \left\| h_\mu^{-1}\{(h_\mu\psi)(a\cdot)\}\# f \right\|_A \\
&= \left\| h_\mu^{-1} m \# f \right\|_A \le C\, \|m\|_N \, \|f\|_A \le C \left(1+a^2\right)^N a^{\mu+\frac{1}{2}} \sup_{\alpha \le N} \left\| h_\mu \psi \right\|_{\mu,\alpha}^{m_1,\rho} \|f\|_A
\end{aligned}$$

for $m_1 + (1-\rho)N \le 0$ and $N > |s| + \mu + 4d + 4,\ d > 0$. □

References

1. Triebel, H.: Theory of function spaces. Monographs in mathematics, Springer Basel (1983)
2. Pathak, R.S.: The wavelet transform of distributions. Tohoku Math. J. **56**(3), 411–421 (2004)
3. Betancor, J.J., Rodríguez-Mesa, L.: On the Besov-Hankel spaces. J. Math. Soc. Japan **50**, 781–788 (1998)
4. Betancor, J.J., Rodríguez-Mesa, L.: On Besov spaces in the Hankel setting. Acta Math. Hungar. **111**(3), 237–262 (2006)
5. Haimo, D.T.: Integral equations associated with Hankel convolutions. Trans. Amer. Math. Soc. **116**, 330–375 (1965)
6. Hardy, G.H., Littlewood, J.E., Pólya, G.: Inequalities. Cambridge University Press, Cambridge (1988)

Chapter 9
Characterizations of the Inversion Formula of the Continuous Bessel Wavelet Transform of Distributions in $H'_\mu(I)$

9.1 Introduction

Hankel transform had considerable effects on the problems of the theory of distributions. Exploiting the theory of distributions, Zemanian [1–4], Koh [5, 6], Lee [7], Dube et al. [8], and Arteaga and Marrero [9] gave significant contributions in this area. Using the Hankel transform approach, Betancor et al. [10–20] and Pathak et al. [21–26] discussed many properties of functional spaces and Hankel convolution. The Hankel convolution made an adequate foundation for the formation of the Bessel wavelet transform. Considering the Zemanian theory of the Hankel transform, Upadhyay et al. [27–32] discussed the continuous Bessel wavelet transform and studied its properties.

Motivated from the aforesaid results, properties of the continuous Bessel wavelet transform in Besov and Triebel-Lizorkin type spaces introduced in Chap. 4 by taking Hankel transform tool. Our main objective in this chapter is to investigate the inversion formula of the Bessel wavelet transform of distributions in $H'_\mu(I)$ by considering the Hankel transform theory.

The present chapter is organized in the following way:

Section 9.1 is introductory, which gives a brief history regarding the development of the inversion formula of the continuous Bessel wavelet transform of distributions in $H'_\mu(I)$. Section 9.2 provides the basic properties of Bessel wavelet and Bessel wavelet transform of distributions in form of Lemmas and Theorem. Section 9.3 deals the structure formula of distributions in $H'_\mu(I)$ and some important results of the continuous Bessel wavelet transform in the classical sense which are useful to find the inversion formula of the continuous Bessel wavelet transform in $H'_\mu(I)$. Section 9.4 is devoted to find some results related to the inversion formula of the continuous Bessel wavelet transform in $H'_\mu(I)$ and finally the inversion formula of the continuous Bessel wavelet transform of distributions is given. In Sect. 9.5, some

S. K. Upadhyay and J. S. Maurya, *The Bessel Wavelet Transform*,
Industrial and Applied Mathematics,
https://doi.org/10.1007/978-981-96-9938-4_9

applications of the inversion formula of the continuous Bessel wavelet transform of distributions in $H'_\mu(I)$ in form of Calderón reproducing formula and heat equation in $H'_\mu(I)$ are given.

9.2 Properties of the Bessel Wavelet and the Bessel Wavelet Transform of Distributions

In this section, properties of the Bessel wavelet and the Bessel wavelet transform of distributions are found in $H'_\mu(I)$-space.

Lemma 9.1 *Let $\psi \in H_\mu(I)$, $\mu \geq -\frac{1}{2}$. Then ψ is a basic Bessel wavelet if and only if $\int_0^\infty x^{\mu+\frac{1}{2}}\psi(x)dx = 0$.*

Proof Let $\psi \in H_\mu(I)$ be the basic Bessel wavelet which satisfies the admissibility condition (2.9).

Since $\omega^{-\mu-\frac{1}{2}}(h_\mu\psi)(\omega)$ continuous on I, therefore

$$\begin{aligned} \omega^{-\mu-\frac{1}{2}}(h_\mu\psi)(\omega) &= \omega^{-\mu-\frac{1}{2}} \int_0^\infty (x\omega)^{\frac{1}{2}} J_\mu(x\omega)\psi(x)dx \\ &= \int_0^\infty (x\omega)^{-\mu} J_\mu(x\omega) x^{\mu+\frac{1}{2}}\psi(x)dx. \end{aligned}$$

If we take $\omega \to 0$, then $(x\omega)^{-\mu}J_\mu(x\omega) \to \frac{1}{2^\mu\Gamma\mu+1}$ and from (2.9) it is clear that $\omega^{-\mu-\frac{1}{2}}(h_\mu\psi)(\omega)$ must goes to zero. Hence from the last expression, we have

$$\frac{1}{2^\mu\Gamma\mu+1}\int_0^\infty x^{\mu+\frac{1}{2}}\psi(x)dx = 0,$$

so that

$$\int_0^\infty x^{\mu+\frac{1}{2}}\psi(x)dx = 0. \tag{9.1}$$

Conversely, for $\psi \in H_\mu(I) \subset L^2(I)$, we can write

$$\int_0^\infty \frac{|(h_\mu\psi)(\omega)|^2}{\omega^{2\mu+2}}d\omega = \int_0^1 \frac{|(h_\mu\psi)(\omega)|^2}{\omega^{2\mu+2}}d\omega + \int_1^\infty \frac{|(h_\mu\psi)(\omega)|^2}{\omega^{2\mu+2}}d\omega. \tag{9.2}$$

The second integral of the R.H.S. of (9.2) can be estimated as

$$\begin{aligned}\int_1^\infty \frac{|(h_\mu\psi)(\omega)|^2}{\omega^{2\mu+2}}d\omega &\le \int_1^\infty |(h_\mu\psi)(\omega)|^2 d\omega\\ &\le \int_0^\infty |(h_\mu\psi)(\omega)|^2 d\omega\\ &= \int_0^\infty |\psi(x)|^2 dx.\end{aligned}$$

Therefore,

$$\int_1^\infty \frac{|(h_\mu\psi)(\omega)|^2}{\omega^{2\mu+2}}d\omega \le \|\psi(x)\|_2^2. \tag{9.3}$$

Next, we can show the bound of the first integral of the R.H.S. of (9.2). Since $\omega^{-\mu-\frac{1}{2}}(h_\mu\psi)(\omega) \to 0$ as $\omega \to 0$. Therefore,

$$\begin{aligned}\left|\omega^{-\mu-\frac{1}{2}}\Big(h_\mu\psi\Big)(\omega)\right| &= \left|\lim_{\epsilon\to 0}\int_\epsilon^\omega \frac{\partial}{\partial y}y^{-\mu-\frac{1}{2}}(h_\mu\psi)(y)dy\right|\\ &\le \lim_{\epsilon\to 0}\int_\epsilon^\omega \left|yy^{-1}\frac{\partial}{\partial y}y^{-\mu-\frac{1}{2}}(h_\mu\psi)(y)\right|dy\\ &\le \lim_{\epsilon\to 0}\int_\epsilon^\omega y^{-\frac{1}{2}}\left|(1+y^2)y^{-1}\frac{\partial}{\partial y}y^{-\mu-\frac{1}{2}}(h_\mu\psi)(y)\right|dy\\ &\le \lim_{\epsilon\to 0}\sup_{x\in I}\left|(1+y^2)y^{-1}\frac{\partial}{\partial y}y^{-\mu-\frac{1}{2}}(h_\mu\psi)(y)\right|\int_\epsilon^\omega y^{-\frac{1}{2}}dy.\end{aligned}$$

Using (1.88), we find

$$\begin{aligned}\left|\omega^{-\mu-\frac{1}{2}}(h_\mu\psi)(\omega)\right| &\le \gamma_{1,1}^\mu(h_\mu\psi)\lim_{\epsilon\to 0}\int_\epsilon^\omega y^{-\frac{1}{2}}dy\\ &\le \gamma_{1,1}^\mu(h_\mu\psi)2\,\omega^{\frac{1}{2}},\end{aligned}$$

so that

$$\left|\omega^{-\mu-1}(h_\mu\psi)(\omega)\right| \le 2\gamma_{1,1}^\mu(h_\mu\psi).$$

Therefore,

$$\int_0^1 \left|\omega^{-\mu-1}(h_\mu\psi)(\omega)\right|^2 d\omega \le 4\Big\{\gamma_{1,1}^\mu(h_\mu\psi)\Big\}^2\int_0^1 1^2\,d\omega.$$

This implies that

$$\int_0^1 \frac{|(h_\mu\psi)(\omega)|^2}{\omega^{2\mu+2}}d\omega \le 4\Big\{\gamma_{1,1}^\mu(h_\mu\psi)\Big\}^2, \tag{9.4}$$

for $\psi \in H_\mu(I)$ and $(h_\mu\psi)(y) \in H_\mu(I)$.

This shows that

$$\int_0^\infty \frac{|(h_\mu \psi)(\omega)|^2}{\omega^{2\mu+2}} d\omega < \infty. \tag{9.5}$$

Definition 9.1 Let $\psi \in H_\mu(I)$ be the Bessel wavelet and $f \in H'_\mu(I)$, then the Bessel wavelet transform of f is defined by

$$(B_\psi f)(a,b) = \left\langle f(x), a^{\mu-\frac{1}{2}} \psi\left(\frac{x}{a}, \frac{b}{a}\right)\right\rangle,$$

where $a > 0, b > 0$ and $\mu > -\frac{1}{2}$.

Lemma 9.2 *For $\mu \geq -\frac{1}{2}$, $Cx^{\mu+\frac{1}{2}}$ belongs to $H'_\mu(I)$.*

Proof We have $f(x) = Cx^{\mu+\frac{1}{2}}$ and $\phi \in H_\mu(I)$, then

$$\begin{aligned}
\langle f, \phi \rangle &= \int_0^\infty f(x)\phi(x)dx \\
&= \int_0^\infty Cx^{\mu+\frac{1}{2}}\phi(x)dx \\
&= C\int_0^\infty x^{2\mu+1}x^{-\mu-\frac{1}{2}}\phi(x)dx.
\end{aligned}$$

Therefore,

$$\begin{aligned}
|\langle f, \phi \rangle| &= \left| C\int_0^\infty \frac{x^{2\mu+1}}{(1+x^2)^m}(1+x^2)^m x^{-\mu-\frac{1}{2}}\phi(x)dx \right| \\
&\leq C\int_0^\infty \frac{x^{2\mu+1}}{(1+x^2)^m}\left|(1+x^2)^m x^{-\mu-\frac{1}{2}}\phi(x)\right|dx \\
&\leq \sup_{x\in I}\left|(1+x^2)^m x^{-\mu-\frac{1}{2}}\phi(x)\right| C\int_0^\infty \frac{x^{2\mu+1}}{(1+x^2)^m}dx.
\end{aligned}$$

By the definition of (1.88), we get

$$|\langle f, \phi \rangle| \leq C\gamma^\mu_{m,0}(\phi)\int_0^\infty \frac{x^{2\mu+1}}{(1+x^2)^m}dx.$$

Putting $(1+x^2) = u,\ 2xdx = du$, then

$$\begin{aligned}
|\langle f, \phi \rangle| &\leq C\gamma^\mu_{m,0}(\phi)\int_1^\infty \frac{(u-1)^{2\mu+1}}{2u^m(u-1)^{\frac{1}{2}}}du \\
&\leq C\gamma^\mu_{m,0}(\phi)\int_1^\infty \frac{(u-1)^{2\mu+1}}{2u^m}du.
\end{aligned}$$

Now, taking $u = \frac{1}{v}$, $du = -\frac{1}{v^2}dv$, then the above expression yields

$$\begin{aligned}|\langle f, \phi\rangle| &\leq \frac{C}{2}\gamma^{\mu}_{m,0}(\phi)\int_0^1 v^m\left(\frac{1}{v}-1\right)^{\mu}\frac{dv}{v^2}dv\\ &\leq \frac{C}{2}\gamma^{\mu}_{m,0}(\phi)\int_0^1 (1-v)^{\mu}v^{m-\mu-2}dv.\end{aligned}$$

By definition of β- function, we get

$$\begin{aligned}|\langle f, \phi\rangle| &\leq \frac{C}{2}\gamma^{\mu}_{m,0}(\phi)\frac{\Gamma(\mu+1)\Gamma(m-\mu-1)}{\Gamma(\mu+1+m-\mu-1)}\\ &\leq \frac{C}{2}\gamma^{\mu}_{m,0}(\phi)\frac{\Gamma(\mu+1)\Gamma(m-\mu-1)}{\Gamma m},\end{aligned}$$

for $m-\mu-1 \geq 0$. □

Theorem 9.1 *Let $\psi \in H_{\mu}(I)$ be the Bessel wavelet, then the Bessel wavelet transform of distributions $Cx^{\mu+\frac{1}{2}}$ is zero, where C is constant.*

Proof From Definition 9.1, we have the Bessel wavelet transform of the distribution $Cx^{\mu+\frac{1}{2}}$ as

$$\begin{aligned}\left(B_{\psi}Cx^{\mu+\frac{1}{2}}\right)(a,b) =&\left\langle Cx^{\mu+\frac{1}{2}}, a^{\mu-\frac{1}{2}}\psi\left(\frac{x}{a},\frac{b}{a}\right)\right\rangle\\ =&\int_0^{\infty} Cx^{\mu+\frac{1}{2}}a^{\mu-\frac{1}{2}}\psi\left(\frac{x}{a},\frac{b}{a}\right)dx\\ =&\int_0^{\infty} Cx^{\mu+\frac{1}{2}}a^{\mu-\frac{1}{2}}\int_0^{\infty}\psi(z)D_{\mu}\left(\frac{x}{a},\frac{b}{a},z\right)dzdx\\ =&\int_0^{\infty}\int_0^{\infty} Cx^{\mu+\frac{1}{2}}a^{\mu-\frac{1}{2}}\psi(z)D_{\mu}\left(\frac{x}{a},\frac{b}{a},z\right)dxdz.\end{aligned}$$

Putting $\frac{x}{a} = t$ and using (1.84), we find

$$\begin{aligned}\left(B_{\psi}Cx^{\mu+\frac{1}{2}}\right)(a,b) =&\int_0^{\infty} Ca^{2\mu+1}\psi(z)\int_0^{\infty} t^{\mu+\frac{1}{2}}D_{\mu}\left(t,\frac{b}{a},z\right)dtdz\\ =&\int_0^{\infty} Ca^{2\mu+1}\psi(z)\frac{\left(\frac{bz}{a}\right)^{\mu+\frac{1}{2}}}{2^{\mu}\Gamma(\mu+1)}dz\\ =&C\frac{(ab)^{\mu+\frac{1}{2}}}{2^{\mu}\Gamma(\mu+1)}\int_0^{\infty} z^{\mu+\frac{1}{2}}\psi(z)dz\\ =&0.\end{aligned}$$

So, Bessel wavelet transform of distributions $Cx^{\mu+\frac{1}{2}}$ will be zero. □

Example 9.2
Let $\psi(x) \in H_\mu(I)$ such that

$$\psi(x) = S_{\mu,x}\{x^{\mu+\frac{1}{2}}e^{-x^2}\},$$

where $S_{\mu,x} = x^{-\mu-\frac{1}{2}}D_x x^{2\mu+1}D_x x^{-\mu-\frac{1}{2}}$ is Bessel operator. Then ψ satisfies the admissibility condition (2.9) and represents a Bessel wavelet in $H_\mu(I)$ whose all the moments weighted by $x^{\mu+\frac{1}{2}}$ are non-zero.

Solution of Example 9.2 is given below stepwise:

Step I: For $\psi(x) = S_{\mu,x}\{x^{\mu+\frac{1}{2}}e^{-x^2}\}$, using (1.114) and the formula [33, p. 30], we get

$$(h_\mu\psi)(y) = h_\mu\{S_{\mu,x}x^{\mu+\frac{1}{2}}e^{-x^2}\}(y) = -y^2 h_\mu\{x^{\mu+\frac{1}{2}}e^{-x^2}\}(y) = -y^2\frac{y^{\mu+\frac{1}{2}}}{2^{\mu+1}}e^{-\frac{y^2}{4}}.$$

Therefore,

$$\begin{aligned}\int_0^\infty \frac{|(h_\mu\psi)(y)|^2}{y^{2\mu+2}}dy = \int_0^\infty \frac{y^{2\mu+5}e^{-\frac{y^2}{2}}}{2^{2\mu+2}y^{2\mu+2}}dy &= \frac{1}{2^{2\mu+2}}\int_0^\infty y^3 e^{-\frac{y^2}{2}}dy \\ &= \frac{2}{2^{2\mu+2}}\int_0^\infty te^{-t}dt, \quad \left(\text{taking } \frac{y^2}{2} = t\right) \\ &= \frac{1}{2^{2\mu+1}}\Gamma(2) = \frac{1}{2^{2\mu+1}} < \infty.\end{aligned}$$

This implies that $\psi(x) \in H_\mu(I) \subset L^2(I)$ satisfies the admissibility condition (2.9).

Step II: Also, for $\psi(x) = S_{\mu,x}\{x^{\mu+\frac{1}{2}}e^{-x^2}\}$, we have

$$\begin{aligned}\int_0^\infty x^{\mu+\frac{1}{2}}\psi(x)dx &= \int_0^\infty x^{\mu+\frac{1}{2}}S_{\mu,x}\{x^{\mu+\frac{1}{2}}e^{-x^2}\}dx \\ &= \int_0^\infty x^{\mu+\frac{1}{2}}x^{-\mu-\frac{1}{2}}D_x x^{2\mu+1}D_x x^{-\mu-\frac{1}{2}}x^{\mu+\frac{1}{2}}e^{-x^2}dx \\ &= \int_0^\infty D_x\{x^{2\mu+1}(-2x)e^{-x^2}\}dx \\ &= \left\{x^{2\mu+1}(-2x)e^{-x^2}\right\}\Big|_{x=0}^{\infty} = 0.\end{aligned}$$

By Lemma 9.1, we conclude that $\psi(x) \in H_\mu(I)$ is a Bessel wavelet.

Step III: Now, the moment of $\psi(x)$ of order $m \in \mathbb{N}$, weighted by $x^{\mu+\frac{1}{2}}$ be

$$\begin{aligned}\int_0^\infty x^m x^{\mu+\frac{1}{2}} \psi(x)dx &= \int_0^\infty x^m x^{\mu+\frac{1}{2}} S_{\mu,x} x^{\mu+\frac{1}{2}} e^{-x^2} dx \\ &= \int_0^\infty x^m x^{\mu+\frac{1}{2}} x^{-\mu-\frac{1}{2}} D_x x^{2\mu+1} D_x x^{-\mu-\frac{1}{2}} x^{\mu+\frac{1}{2}} e^{-x^2} dx \\ &= \int_0^\infty x^m D_x x^{2\mu+1} D_x e^{-x^2} dx \\ &= \left\{ x^m x^{2\mu+1} D_x e^{-x^2} \right\} \Big|_{x=0}^\infty - \int_0^\infty m x^{m-1} x^{2\mu+1} D_x e^{-x^2} dx \\ &= -m \int_1^2 x^{m-1} x^{2\mu+1} (-2x) e^{-x^2} dx \\ &= 2m \int_1^2 x^{m+2\mu+1} e^{-x^2} dx \neq 0.\end{aligned}$$

This implies that moments of all orders weighted by $x^{\mu+\frac{1}{2}}$ of $\psi(x)$ are non-zero.

From the aforesaid Lemma 9.2 and Theorem 9.1, it is clear that the continuous Bessel wavelet transform of the distribution of type $Cx^{\mu+\frac{1}{2}}$ will be zero. Therefore, the inversion formula of the continuous Bessel wavelet transform in $H'_\mu(I)$ cannot be defined. So the inversion formula of the continuous Bessel wavelet transform will be valid for modulo a $Cx^{\mu+\frac{1}{2}}$ distributions.

For investigating the inversion formula of the continuous Bessel wavelet transform of distributions, our observations will be based on the following points:

(A) Inversion formula of the continuous Bessel wavelet transform of distribution will be found on $H'_{\mu,F}(I)$ which can be obtained by filtering

  (i) all the non-zero $Cx^{\mu+\frac{1}{2}}$ distributions from $H'_\mu(I)$.
  (ii) all non-zero $Cx^{\mu+\frac{1}{2}}$ that appear with a distribution as a union. For example, in the distribution $\frac{x^{\mu+\frac{5}{2}}}{1+x^2} = x^{\mu+\frac{1}{2}} - \frac{x^{\mu+\frac{1}{2}}}{1+x^2}$, we would omit $x^{\mu+\frac{1}{2}}$ and retain only $-\frac{x^{\mu+\frac{1}{2}}}{1+x^2}$.

(B) The Bessel wavelet kernel under consideration for determining the continuous Bessel wavelet transform are those Bessel wavelets whose all the moments weighted by $x^{\mu+\frac{1}{2}}$ are non-zero.

9.3 Properties of the Continuous Bessel Wavelet Transform in $L^2(I)$ and Structure Formula in $H'_\mu(I)$

In this section, the various properties of the continuous Bessel wavelet transform in $L^2(I)$ and the structure formula in $H'_\mu(I)$ are discussed by taking the theory of Hankel transform.

Note: If $f \in L^1(I)$, the integral in $1 - dimension$ can be expressed as

$$\int_0^\infty f(x)dx = \int_0^N f(x)dx + \int_N^\infty f(x)dx, \quad N \in (0, \infty), \tag{9.6}$$

provided the integral is convergent. Then, we have

$$\int_0^\infty f(x)dx = \int_0^N f(x)dx + R(N), \tag{9.7}$$

where $R(N)$ is the remainder term. If f is integrable, then $R(N) \to 0$ as $N \to \infty$. We use this technique in the following theorem.

Lemma 9.3 *Let $\psi \in L^2(I), a > 0$ and $b > 0$ with $\mu \geq -\frac{1}{2}$. Then $\psi\left(\frac{x}{a}, \frac{b}{a}\right)$ belongs to $L_b^2(I)$ as well as in $L_x^2(I)$ and its Hankel transform with respect to x and b will be*

$$h_\mu^x \psi\left(\frac{x}{a}, \frac{b}{a}\right)(y) = a^{-\mu+\frac{1}{2}} y^{-\mu-\frac{1}{2}} (by)^{\frac{1}{2}} J_\mu(by)(h_\mu \psi)(ay), \tag{9.8}$$

and

$$h_\mu^b \psi\left(\frac{x}{a}, \frac{b}{a}\right)(y) = a^{-\mu+\frac{1}{2}} y^{-\mu-\frac{1}{2}} (xy)^{\frac{1}{2}} J_\mu(xy)(h_\mu \psi)(ay). \tag{9.9}$$

Proof From Upadhyay et al. [32], we have

$$\psi\left(\frac{x}{a}, \frac{b}{a}\right) = a^{-\mu+\frac{1}{2}} \int_0^\infty y^{-\mu-\frac{1}{2}} (xy)^{\frac{1}{2}} J_\mu(xy)(by)^{\frac{1}{2}} J_\mu(by)(h_\mu \psi)(ay)dy. \tag{9.10}$$

Since $t^{-\mu} J_\mu(t)$ uniformly bounded on I and $h_\mu \psi \in H_\mu(I) \subset L^2(I)$. This implies that $y^{-\mu-\frac{1}{2}}(xy)^{\frac{1}{2}} J_\mu(xy)(h_\mu\psi)(ay)$ and $y^{-\mu-\frac{1}{2}}(by)^{\frac{1}{2}} J_\mu(by)(h_\mu\psi)(ay)$ be in $L^2(I)$. Hence, (9.8) and (9.9) both exist. □

Theorem 9.2 *Let $\psi \in H_\mu(I)$ be the Bessel wavelet, $f \in L^2(I)$ and $(B_\psi f)(a, b)$ be the continuous Bessel wavelet transform of f. Then the Hankel transform of $(B_\psi f)(a, b)$ with respect to variable b can be written as*

$$h_\mu^b\{(B_\psi f)(a, b)\}(y) = a^{\mu-\frac{1}{2}} \left\langle f(x), h_\mu^b \psi\left(\frac{x}{a}, \frac{b}{a}\right)\right\rangle. \tag{9.11}$$

Proof First, we prove that $(B_\psi f)(a,b) \in L^2_b(I)$. The Bessel wavelet transform of function $f \in L^2(I)$ with respect to the Bessel wavelet $\psi \in H_\mu(I)$ be

$$(B_\psi f)(a,b) = a^{\mu-\frac{1}{2}}\Big\langle f(x), \psi\Big(\frac{x}{a}, \frac{b}{a}\Big)\Big\rangle.$$

Since $f \in L^2(I)$ and $\psi\left(\frac{x}{a}, \frac{b}{a}\right) \in L^2_x(I)$, then by the Parseval formula and Lemma 9.3,

$$\begin{aligned}(B_\psi f)(a,b) &= a^{\mu-\frac{1}{2}}\Big\langle (h_\mu f)(y), h^x_\mu \psi\Big(\frac{x}{a}, \frac{b}{a}\Big)(y)\Big\rangle \\ &= a^{\mu-\frac{1}{2}}\int_0^\infty (h_\mu f)(y) a^{-\mu+\frac{1}{2}} y^{-\mu-\frac{1}{2}} (by)^{\frac{1}{2}} J_\mu(by)(h_\mu \psi)(ay)dy \\ &= \int_0^\infty (by)^{\frac{1}{2}} J_\mu(by)(h_\mu f)(y) y^{-\mu-\frac{1}{2}}(h_\mu \psi)(ay)dy.\end{aligned}$$

Since $\psi \in H_\mu(I)$, so $y^{-\mu-\frac{1}{2}}(h_\mu\psi)(ay)$ uniformly bounded on I for fix $a > 0$ and $h_\mu f \in L^2(I)$. Therefore, $y^{-\mu-\frac{1}{2}}(h_\mu\psi)(ay)(h_\mu f)(y) \in L^2_y(I)$ and by the inverse Hankel transformation, $(B_\psi f)(a,b)$ belongs to $L^2_y(I)$. Now, let

$$\begin{aligned}I &= \int_0^\infty f(x)\psi\Big(\frac{x}{a}, \frac{b}{a}\Big)dx \\ &= \int_0^N f(x)\psi\Big(\frac{x}{a}, \frac{b}{a}\Big)dx + \int_N^\infty f(x)\psi\Big(\frac{x}{a}, \frac{b}{a}\Big)dx \\ &= I(N,b) + R(N,b).\end{aligned}$$

So,

$$\begin{aligned}h^b_\mu(I) &= h^b_\mu(I(N,b)) + h^b_\mu(R(N,b)) \\ &= \int_0^N f(x) h^b_\mu \psi\Big(\frac{x}{a}, \frac{b}{a}\Big)dx + \int_N^\infty f(x) h^b_\mu \psi\Big(\frac{x}{a}, \frac{b}{a}\Big)dx,\end{aligned}$$

where $R(N,b)$ as a function of b goes to zero in $L^2(I)$ as $N \to \infty$, therefore $h^b_\mu R(N,b) \to 0$ in $L^2(I)$ as a function of y. Hence letting $N \to \infty$, we get the result (9.11). Since integrals

$$\int_0^\infty \int_0^\infty (by)^{\frac{1}{2}} J_\mu(by) f(x)\psi\Big(\frac{x}{a}, \frac{b}{a}\Big)dxdb,$$

and

$$\int_0^\infty \int_0^\infty (by)^{\frac{1}{2}} J_\mu(by) f(x) \psi\Big(\frac{x}{a}, \frac{b}{a}\Big) db dx,$$

are not absolutely convergent and no way of proving that the above integrals exist. So, we are unable to switch the order of integration directly that is we cannot apply Fubini's theorem. □

Theorem 9.3 *Let $f \in L^2(I)$ be continuous at a point $x = x_0$, then*

$$\lim_{\epsilon \to 0} \int_0^\infty f(x)\phi_\epsilon(x) dx = f(x_0), \tag{9.12}$$

where the function $\phi_\epsilon(x) \in D(I)$ and is defined by

$$\phi_\epsilon(x) = \begin{cases} C_\epsilon \exp\Big(-\frac{\epsilon}{x-x_0} - \frac{\epsilon}{x_0+\epsilon-x}\Big), & x_0 < x < x_0 + \epsilon \\ 0\ , & x \le x_0 \text{ and } x \ge x_0 + \epsilon \end{cases} \tag{9.13}$$

the constant C_ϵ chosen so that

$$\int_0^\infty \phi_\epsilon(x) dx = 1.$$

Proof Since the integral of $\phi_\epsilon(x)$ over I is 1, therefore we choose C_ϵ in such way that

$$\int_{x_0}^{x_0+\epsilon} C_\epsilon \exp\Big(-\frac{\epsilon}{x-x_0} - \frac{\epsilon}{x_0+\epsilon-x}\Big) dx = 1. \tag{9.14}$$

Putting $\frac{x-x_0}{\epsilon} = t$ in (9.14), we get

$$\epsilon\ C_\epsilon \int_0^1 \exp\Big(-\frac{1}{t(1-t)}\Big) dt = 1.$$

Now,

$$\begin{aligned} \int_0^\infty f(x)\phi_\epsilon(x) dx &= \epsilon\ C_\epsilon \int_0^1 f(x_0 + \epsilon t) \exp\Big(-\frac{1}{t(1-t)}\Big) dt \\ &= \epsilon\ C_\epsilon \int_0^1 [f(x_0 + \epsilon t) - f(x_0)] \exp\Big(-\frac{1}{t(1-t)}\Big) dt \\ &\quad + f(x_0)\epsilon\ C_\epsilon \int_0^1 \exp\Big(-\frac{1}{t(1-t)}\Big) dt. \end{aligned}$$

This implies,

$$\int_0^\infty f(x)\phi_\epsilon(x)dx = \epsilon\, C_\epsilon \int_0^1 [f(x_0+\epsilon t) - f(x_0)] \exp\Big(-\frac{1}{t(1-t)}\Big)dt + f(x_0). \tag{9.15}$$

Since f is continuous at $x = x_0$ and $0 < t < 1$, we can choose sufficiently small $\epsilon > 0$ corresponding to δ, so that $\Big|f(x_0+\epsilon t) - f(x_0)\Big| < \delta$, where $\delta > 0$ is arbitrarily chosen small positive number.

Therefore, using continuity property of f, we get

$$\begin{aligned}\Big|\epsilon\, C_\epsilon \int_0^1 [f(x_0+\epsilon t) - f(x_0)] \exp\Big(-\frac{1}{t(1-t)}\Big)dt\Big| \\ &\leq \epsilon\, C_\epsilon \int_0^1 \Big|[f(x_0+\epsilon t) - f(x_0)]\Big| \exp\Big(-\frac{1}{t(1-t)}\Big)dt \\ &< \delta\, \epsilon\, C_\epsilon \int_0^1 \exp\Big(-\frac{1}{t(1-t)}\Big)dt = \delta.\end{aligned}$$

Since δ is an arbitrarily chosen small positive number, we have

$$\lim_{\epsilon\to 0} \epsilon\, C_\epsilon \int_0^1 [f(x_0+\epsilon t) - f(x_0)] \exp\Big(-\frac{1}{t(1-t)}\Big)dt = 0. \tag{9.16}$$

From (9.15) and (9.16), we get

$$\lim_{\epsilon\to 0} \int_0^\infty f(x)\phi_\epsilon(x)dx = f(x_0). \tag{9.17}$$

Theorem 9.4 *Let $f \in L^2(I)$ be continuous function at $x = x_0$ and $h_\mu f$ be its Hankel transform. Let $\phi_\epsilon(x)$ be the function which is defined in Theorem 9.3; then we prove the following:*

$$(i)\quad \lim_{\epsilon\to 0} \int_0^\infty \int_0^\infty (xy)^{\frac{1}{2}} J_\mu(xy)(h_\mu f)(y)\phi_\epsilon(x)dydx = \int_0^\infty (yx_0)^{\frac{1}{2}} J_\mu(yx_0)(h_\mu f)(y)dy. \tag{9.18}$$

$$(ii)\quad \int_0^\infty (yx_0)^{\frac{1}{2}} J_\mu(yx_0)(h_\mu f)(y)dy = f(x_0), \tag{9.19}$$

converges in a pointwise sense. This is called the inverse Hankel transform in the sense of pointwise convergence.

Proof From Theorem 9.3, we have

$$\phi_\epsilon(x) = \begin{cases} C_\epsilon \exp\Big(-\frac{\epsilon}{x-x_0} - \frac{\epsilon}{x_0+\epsilon-x}\Big), & x_0 < x < x_0+\epsilon \\ 0\ , & x \le x_0 \text{ and } x \ge x_0+\epsilon \end{cases}. \tag{9.20}$$

It is easy to see that $\phi_\epsilon^2(x) \le \phi_\epsilon(x)$. Then, we can find

$$\|\phi_\epsilon\|_2^2 = \int_0^\infty \phi_\epsilon^2(x)dx \le \int_0^\infty \phi_\epsilon(x)dx = 1.$$

We have

$$\Big\langle \int_0^\infty (xy)^{\frac{1}{2}} J_\mu(xy)(h_\mu f)(y)dy, \phi_\epsilon(x)\Big\rangle = \Big\langle \int_0^N (xy)^{\frac{1}{2}} J_\mu(xy)(h_\mu f)(y)dy, \phi_\epsilon(x)\Big\rangle + \Big\langle \int_N^\infty (xy)^{\frac{1}{2}} J_\mu(xy)(h_\mu f)(y)dy, \phi_\epsilon(x)\Big\rangle. \tag{9.21}$$

Since $\int_0^N (xy)^{\frac{1}{2}} J_\mu(xy)(h_\mu f)(y)dy$ is a continuous function of x, for all $x \in I$ therefore using Theorem 9.3, we find

$$\lim_{\epsilon\to 0}\Big\langle \int_0^N (xy)^{\frac{1}{2}} J_\mu(xy)(h_\mu f)(y)dy, \phi_\epsilon(x)\Big\rangle = \int_0^N (yx_0)^{\frac{1}{2}} J_\mu(yx_0)(h_\mu f)(y)dy. \tag{9.22}$$

This implies that after taking the certain limit

$$\lim_{N\to\infty}\lim_{\epsilon\to 0}\Big\langle \int_0^N (xy)^{\frac{1}{2}} J_\mu(xy)(h_\mu f)(y)dy, \phi_\epsilon(x)\Big\rangle = \int_0^\infty (yx_0)^{\frac{1}{2}} J_\mu(yx_0)(h_\mu f)(y)dy.$$

In view of Holder's inequality, the second term on the R.H.S. of (9.21) can be obtained as

$$\begin{aligned}\Big|\Big\langle \int_N^\infty (xy)^{\frac{1}{2}} J_\mu(xy)(h_\mu f)(y)dy, \phi_\epsilon(x)\Big\rangle\Big| &\le \Big\| \int_N^\infty (xy)^{\frac{1}{2}} J_\mu(xy)(h_\mu f)(y)dy\Big\|_2 \|\phi_\epsilon(x)\|_2 \\ &\le \Big\| \int_N^\infty (xy)^{\frac{1}{2}} J_\mu(xy)(h_\mu f)(y)dy\Big\|_2.\end{aligned}$$

Since, $\Big\| \int_N^\infty (xy)^{\frac{1}{2}} J_\mu(xy)(h_\mu f)(y)dy\Big\|_2 \to 0$ as $N \to \infty$. Therefore,

$$\lim_{N\to\infty}\lim_{\epsilon\to 0}\Big\langle \int_N^\infty (xy)^{\frac{1}{2}} J_\mu(xy)(h_\mu f)(y)dy, \phi_\epsilon(x)\Big\rangle = 0. \tag{9.23}$$

Thus,

$$\lim_{\epsilon\to 0}\Big\langle \int_0^\infty (xy)^{\frac{1}{2}} J_\mu(xy)(h_\mu f)(y)dy, \phi_\epsilon(x)\Big\rangle = \int_0^\infty (yx_0)^{\frac{1}{2}} J_\mu(yx_0)(h_\mu f)(y)dy. \tag{9.24}$$

Next, we prove (ii), the pointwise convergence of the inverse Hankel transformation by using Parseval's formula

$$\Big\langle h_\mu f, h_\mu \phi_\epsilon\Big\rangle = \Big\langle f, \phi_\epsilon\Big\rangle,$$

for $f \in L^2(I)$ and $\phi_\epsilon \in D(I) \subset L^2(I)$.

Letting $\epsilon \to 0$,

$$\lim_{\epsilon\to 0}\Big\langle h_\mu f, h_\mu \phi_\epsilon\Big\rangle = \lim_{\epsilon\to 0}\Big\langle f, \phi_\epsilon\Big\rangle. \tag{9.25}$$

From (9.24) and (9.25) and Theorem 9.3, we get

$$\int_0^\infty (yx_0)^{\frac{1}{2}} J_\mu(yx_0)(h_\mu f)(y)dy = f(x_0), \tag{9.26}$$

for pointwise convergence. □

Theorem 9.5 *Let $\phi \in H_\mu(I)$ be a Bessel wavelet and $f \in L^2(I)$. Then the following classical inversion formula holds:*

$$f(x) = \frac{1}{C_{\mu,\psi}} \int_0^\infty \int_0^\infty (B_\psi f)(a,b) a^{\mu-\frac{1}{2}} \psi\Big(\frac{x}{a}, \frac{b}{a}\Big) \frac{dbda}{a^{2\mu+2}},$$

where $(B_\psi f)(a,b)$ is defined to be the integral Bessel wavelet transform of $f \in L^2(I)$ by

$$(B_\psi f)(a,b) = \int_0^\infty f(x) a^{\mu-\frac{1}{2}} \psi\Big(\frac{x}{a}, \frac{b}{a}\Big)dx,$$

in duality notation, we write it in the form

$$(B_\psi f)(a,b) = \Big\langle f(x), a^{\mu-\frac{1}{2}} \psi\Big(\frac{x}{a}, \frac{b}{a}\Big)\Big\rangle,$$

where

$$C_{\mu,\psi} = \int_0^\infty \frac{|(h_\mu \psi)(t)|^2}{t^{2\mu+2}} dt < \infty.$$

Proof From Lemma 9.3 and Theorem 9.2, we have

$$h_\mu^b \psi\Big(\frac{x}{a}, \frac{b}{a}\Big)(y) = a^{-\mu+\frac{1}{2}} y^{-\mu-\frac{1}{2}} (xy)^{\frac{1}{2}} J_\mu(xy)(h_\mu \psi)(ay),$$

and

$$h_\mu^b\{(B_\psi f)(a,b)\}(y) = a^{\mu-\frac{1}{2}}\Big\langle f(x), h_\mu^b \psi\Big(\frac{x}{a},\frac{b}{a}\Big)\Big\rangle.$$

Therefore,

$$\begin{aligned}
h_\mu^b\{(B_\psi f)(a,b)\}(y) &= \int_0^\infty f(x) y^{-\mu-\frac{1}{2}}(xy)^{\frac{1}{2}} J_\mu(xy)(h_\mu\psi)(ay)dx \\
&= y^{-\mu-\frac{1}{2}}(h_\mu\psi)(ay)\int_0^\infty (xy)^{\frac{1}{2}} J_\mu(xy) f(x)dx \\
&= y^{-\mu-\frac{1}{2}}(h_\mu\psi)(ay)(h_\mu f)(y).
\end{aligned}$$

Let us consider that

$$F(x) = \frac{1}{C_{\mu,\psi}}\int_0^\infty\int_0^\infty (B_\psi f)(a,b) a^{\mu-\frac{1}{2}}\psi\Big(\frac{x}{a},\frac{b}{a}\Big)\frac{dbda}{a^{2\mu+2}}.$$

Now using Parseval's formula of the Hankel transform with respect to variable b, we get

$$\begin{aligned}
F(x) &= \frac{1}{C_{\mu,\psi}}\int_0^\infty a^{\mu-\frac{1}{2}}\Big[\int_0^\infty h_\mu^b\{(B_\psi f)(a,b)\}(y)\, h_\mu^b\Big\{\psi\Big(\frac{x}{a},\frac{b}{a}\Big)\Big\}(y)dy\Big]\frac{da}{a^{2\mu+2}} \\
&= \frac{1}{C_{\mu,\psi}}\int_0^\infty a^{\mu-\frac{1}{2}}\Big[\int_0^\infty y^{-\mu-\frac{1}{2}}(h_\mu\psi)(ay)(h_\mu f)(y) \\
&\quad \times a^{-\mu+\frac{1}{2}} y^{-\mu-\frac{1}{2}}(xy)^{\frac{1}{2}} J_\mu(xy)(h_\mu\psi)(ay)dy\Big]\frac{da}{a^{2\mu+2}} \\
&= \frac{1}{C_{\mu,\psi}}\int_0^\infty (xy)^{\frac{1}{2}} J_\mu(xy)(h_\mu f)(y)\Big[\int_0^\infty \frac{|(h_\mu\psi)(ay)|^2}{(ay)^{2\mu+1}}\frac{da}{a}\Big]dy \\
&= \frac{C_{\mu,\psi}}{C_{\mu,\psi}}\int_0^\infty (xy)^{\frac{1}{2}} J_\mu(xy)(h_\mu f)(y)dy \\
&= \int_0^\infty (xy)^{\frac{1}{2}} J_\mu(xy)(h_\mu f)(y)dy \\
&= f(x),
\end{aligned}$$

where putting $ay = t$ in $\int_0^\infty \frac{|(h_\mu\psi)(ay)|^2}{(ay)^{2\mu+1}}\frac{da}{a}$, it will be $\int_0^\infty \frac{|(h_\mu\psi)(t)|^2}{t^{2\mu+2}}dt = C_{\mu,\psi}$. Here convergence is in $L^2(I)$ sense. □

Theorem 9.6 *Let $\psi \in H_\mu(I)$ be a Bessel wavelet and $f \in L^2(I)$ be continuous at $x = x_0$, then*

$$\frac{1}{C_{\mu,\psi}}\int_0^\infty\int_0^\infty\int_0^\infty f(t)\psi\Big(\frac{t}{a},\frac{b}{a}\Big)\psi\Big(\frac{x_0}{a},\frac{b}{a}\Big)\frac{dtdbda}{a^3} = f(x_0),$$

in the pointwise sense.

Proof Applying the same technique, as in the proof of Theorem 9.5, at $x = x_0$

$$\frac{1}{C_{\mu,\psi}}\int_0^\infty\int_0^\infty\int_0^\infty f(t)\psi\Big(\frac{t}{a},\frac{b}{a}\Big)\psi\Big(\frac{x_0}{a},\frac{b}{a}\Big)\frac{dtdbda}{a^3} = \int_0^\infty (yx_0)^{\frac{1}{2}}J_\mu(yx_0)(h_\mu f)(y)dy. \tag{9.27}$$

In view of Theorem 9.4 (ii), at the point of continuity $x = x_0$ of f, we have

$$\int_0^\infty (yx_0)^{\frac{1}{2}}J_\mu(yx_0)(h_\mu f)(y)dy = f(x_0), \tag{9.28}$$

in the sense of pointwise convergence. From (9.27) and (9.28), we get the required result. □

Theorem 9.7 *Let $\mu \geq -\frac{1}{2}$. A functional $f \in H'_\mu(I)$, then there exists $r \in \mathbb{N}_0$ and $f_k \in L^q(I)$, $(1 < q \leq \infty)$ $k = 0, 1, 2, \dots, r$; such that*

$$f = \sum_{k=0}^{r} S_{\mu,x}^k(1+x^2)^r x^{-\mu-\frac{1}{2}} f_k, \tag{9.29}$$

where $S_{\mu,x} = x^{-\mu-\frac{1}{2}}D_x x^{2\mu+1}D_x x^{-\mu-\frac{1}{2}}$ is a Bessel operator.

Proof From Marrero and Arteaga [9, p. 8], we have

$$f = \sum_{k=0}^{r} S_{\mu,x}^k(1+x^2)^r x^{-\mu-\frac{1}{2}} f_k, \tag{9.30}$$

Therefore,

$$\begin{aligned}\langle f,\phi\rangle &= \Big\langle \sum_{k=0}^{r} S_{\mu,x}^k(1+x^2)^r x^{-\mu-\frac{1}{2}} f_k(x), \phi(x)\Big\rangle\\ &= \sum_{k=0}^{r}\Big\langle S_{\mu,x}^k(1+x^2)^r x^{-\mu-\frac{1}{2}} f_k(x), \phi(x)\Big\rangle.\end{aligned}$$

Using (1.124) and distributional differentiation, we find

$$\begin{aligned}\langle f,\phi\rangle &= \sum_{k=0}^{r}\Big\langle f_k(x), (1+x^2)^r x^{-\mu-\frac{1}{2}} S_{\mu,x}^k\phi(x)\Big\rangle\\ &= \sum_{k=0}^{r}\Big\langle f_k(x), (1+x^2)^r x^{-\mu-\frac{1}{2}}\sum_{j=0}^{k} b_j x^{2j+\mu+\frac{1}{2}}\Big(x^{-1}\frac{\partial}{\partial x}\Big)^{k+j}x^{-\mu-\frac{1}{2}}\phi(x)\Big\rangle\\ &= \sum_{k=0}^{r}\sum_{j=0}^{k}\Big\langle f_k(x), (1+x^2)^r x^{-\mu-\frac{1}{2}} b_j x^{2j+\mu+\frac{1}{2}}\Big(x^{-1}\frac{\partial}{\partial x}\Big)^{k+j}x^{-\mu-\frac{1}{2}}\phi(x)\Big\rangle.\end{aligned}$$

So that the above expression can be written as

$$
\begin{aligned}
&|\langle f, \phi\rangle| \\
&\leq \sum_{k=0}^{r}\sum_{j=0}^{k}\left|\left\langle f_k(x), (1+x^2)^r x^{-\mu-\frac{1}{2}} b_j x^{2j+\mu+\frac{1}{2}}\left(x^{-1}\frac{\partial}{\partial x}\right)^{k+j} x^{-\mu-\frac{1}{2}}\phi(x)\right\rangle\right| \\
&\leq \sum_{k=0}^{r}\sum_{j=0}^{k}\int_0^\infty \left|f_k(x)(1+x^2)^r x^{-\mu-\frac{1}{2}} b_j x^{2j+\mu+\frac{1}{2}}\left(x^{-1}\frac{\partial}{\partial x}\right)^{k+j} x^{-\mu-\frac{1}{2}}\phi(x)\right| dx \\
&\leq \sum_{k=0}^{r}\sum_{j=0}^{k}\int_0^\infty \left|f_k(x)(1+x^2)^r b_j x^{2j}\left(x^{-1}\frac{\partial}{\partial x}\right)^{k+j} x^{-\mu-\frac{1}{2}}\phi(x)\right| dx \\
&\leq \sum_{k=0}^{r}\sum_{j=0}^{k}\int_0^\infty \left|f_k(x)(1+x^2)^{r+j} b_j \left(x^{-1}\frac{\partial}{\partial x}\right)^{k+j} x^{-\mu-\frac{1}{2}}\phi(x)\right| dx \\
&\leq \sum_{k=0}^{r}\sum_{j=0}^{k} b_j \gamma^{\mu}_{r+j+1,k+j}(\phi)\int_0^\infty \frac{|f_k(x)|}{1+x^2} dx.
\end{aligned}
$$

Let q be a conjugate exponent of p $(1 \leq p \leq \infty)$ such that $\frac{1}{p}+\frac{1}{q}=1$; then using Holder's inequality, we get

$$
\begin{aligned}
|\langle f, \phi\rangle| &\leq \sum_{k=0}^{r}\sum_{j=0}^{k} b_j \gamma^{\mu}_{r+j+1,k+j}(\phi)\left(\int_0^\infty |f_k(x)|^q dx\right)^{\frac{1}{q}}\left(\int_0^\infty \frac{1}{(1+x^2)^p} dx\right)^{\frac{1}{p}} \\
&\leq \sum_{k=0}^{r}\sum_{j=0}^{k} C_p b_j \gamma^{\mu}_{r+j+1,k+j}(\phi)\|f_k\|_q.
\end{aligned}
$$

9.4 Inversion Formula of the Continuous Bessel Wavelet Transform of the Distributions

In this section, using structure formula and the theory of Hankel transformation, inversion formula of the continuous Bessel wavelet transform of distributions and its properties in $H'_\mu(I)$ are obtained.

Lemma 9.4 *Let $\psi \in H_\mu(I)$ be a Bessel wavelet and $\phi \in H_\mu(I)$, then*

$$
\frac{1}{C_{\mu,\psi}}\int_0^\infty\int_0^\infty\int_0^\infty S^k_{\mu,t}\phi(t)\psi\left(\frac{t}{a},\frac{b}{a}\right)\psi\left(\frac{x_0}{a},\frac{b}{a}\right)\frac{dt\,db\,da}{a^3} = S^k_{\mu,x}\phi(x)\Big|_{x=x_0},
$$

in the pointwise sense.

Proof Since $\phi \in H_\mu(I)$, from Theorem 9.6, we have

$$\frac{1}{C_{\mu,\psi}}\int_0^\infty\int_0^\infty\int_0^\infty S^k_{\mu,t}\phi(t)\psi\left(\frac{t}{a},\frac{b}{a}\right)\psi\left(\frac{x_0}{a},\frac{b}{a}\right)\frac{dtdbda}{a^3} = S^k_{\mu,x}\phi(x)\Big|_{x=x_0},$$

where $S^k_{\mu,x}$ is Bessel operator of order $k \in \mathbb{N}_0$. □

Lemma 9.5 *Let $\psi \in H_\mu(I)$ be a Bessel wavelet and $\phi \in H_\mu(I)$, then*

$$\frac{1}{C_{\mu,\psi}}\int_0^\infty\int_0^\infty\int_0^\infty S^k_{\mu,t}\phi(t)\psi\left(\frac{t}{a},\frac{b}{a}\right)\psi\left(\frac{x}{a},\frac{b}{a}\right)\frac{dtdbda}{a^3},$$

converges uniformly to $S^k_{\mu,x}\phi(x)$ for every $x \in I$.

Proof From Theorem 9.5, convergence in $L^2(I)$ sense, we have

$$\frac{1}{C_{\mu,\psi}}\int_0^\infty\int_0^\infty\int_0^\infty S^k_{\mu,t}\phi(t)\psi\left(\frac{t}{a},\frac{b}{a}\right)\psi\left(\frac{x}{a},\frac{b}{a}\right)\frac{dtdbda}{a^3}$$
$$= \int_0^\infty (yx)^{\frac{1}{2}} J_\mu(yx)\left(h_\mu S^k_{\mu,x}\phi(x)\right)(y)dy = S^k_{\mu,x}\phi(x).$$

By Weierstrass $M-$test, we have

$$\left|\int_0^\infty (yx)^{\frac{1}{2}} J_\mu(yx)\Big(h_\mu S^k_{\mu,x}\phi(x)\Big)(y)dy\right| \le \int_0^\infty \left|\Big(h_\mu S^k_{\mu,x}\phi(x)\Big)(y)\right|dy < \infty,$$

and $S^k_{\mu,x}\phi(x) \in H_\mu(I)$. Therefore,

$$\frac{1}{C_{\mu,\psi}}\int_0^\infty\int_0^\infty\int_0^\infty S^k_{\mu,t}\phi(t)\psi\left(\frac{t}{a},\frac{b}{a}\right)\psi\left(\frac{x}{a},\frac{b}{a}\right)\frac{dtdbda}{a^3}, \tag{9.31}$$

converges uniformly to $S^k_{\mu,x}\phi(x)$. □

Lemma 9.6 *Let $\mu \ge -\frac{1}{2}$ and $\psi\left(\frac{x}{a},\frac{b}{a}\right)$ be Hankel translation and dilation of $\psi \in H_\mu(I)$ then*

$$S_{\mu,x}\psi\left(\frac{x}{a},\frac{b}{a}\right) = S_{\mu,b}\psi\left(\frac{x}{a},\frac{b}{a}\right).$$

Proof From (1.80), we have

$$S_{\mu,x}\psi\Big(\frac{x}{a},\frac{b}{a}\Big) = S_{\mu,x}\int_0^\infty \psi(z)D_\mu\Big(\frac{x}{a},\frac{b}{a},z\Big)dz$$

$$\begin{aligned}
&= S_{\mu,x}\int_0^\infty \phi(z)\int_0^\infty t^{-\mu-\frac{1}{2}}\Big(\frac{xt}{a}\Big)^{\frac{1}{2}}J_\mu\Big(\frac{xt}{a}\Big)\Big(\frac{bt}{a}\Big)^{\frac{1}{2}}J_\mu\Big(\frac{bt}{a}\Big)(zt)^{\frac{1}{2}}J_\mu(zt)dtdz\\
&= \int_0^\infty \phi(z)\int_0^\infty t^{-\mu-\frac{1}{2}}S_{\mu,x}\Big\{\Big(\frac{xt}{a}\Big)^{\frac{1}{2}}J_\mu\Big(\frac{xt}{a}\Big)\Big\}\Big(\frac{bt}{a}\Big)^{\frac{1}{2}}J_\mu\Big(\frac{bt}{a}\Big)(zt)^{\frac{1}{2}}J_\mu(zt)dtdz.
\end{aligned}$$

On using differential operators from (1.117) and (1.120), we find that

$$\begin{aligned}
S_{\mu,x}x^{\frac{1}{2}}J_\mu\Big(\frac{xt}{a}\Big) &= x^{-\mu-\frac{1}{2}}D_x x^{2\mu+1}D_x x^{-\mu}J_\mu\Big(\frac{xt}{a}\Big)\\
&= x^{-\mu-\frac{1}{2}}D_x x^{2\mu+1}\Big(-\frac{t}{a}\Big)x^{-\mu}J_{\mu+1}\Big(\frac{xt}{a}\Big)\\
&= \Big(-\frac{t}{a}\Big)x^{-\mu-\frac{1}{2}}D_x x^{\mu+1}J_{\mu+1}\Big(\frac{xt}{a}\Big)\\
&= -\Big(\frac{t}{a}\Big)^2 x^{-\mu-\frac{1}{2}}x^{\mu+1}J_\mu\Big(\frac{xt}{a}\Big)\\
&= -\Big(\frac{t}{a}\Big)^2 x^{\frac{1}{2}}J_\mu\Big(\frac{xt}{a}\Big).
\end{aligned}$$

Similarly,

$$S_{\mu,b}b^{\frac{1}{2}}J_\mu\Big(\frac{bt}{a}\Big) = -\Big(\frac{t}{a}\Big)^2 b^{\frac{1}{2}}J_\mu\Big(\frac{bt}{a}\Big).$$

So,

$$\begin{aligned}
&S_{\mu,x}\psi\Big(\frac{x}{a},\frac{b}{a}\Big)\\
&= \int_0^\infty \phi(z)\int_0^\infty t^{-\mu-\frac{1}{2}}(-1)\Big(\frac{t}{a}\Big)^2\Big(\frac{xt}{a}\Big)^{\frac{1}{2}}J_\mu\Big(\frac{xt}{a}\Big)\Big(\frac{bt}{a}\Big)^{\frac{1}{2}}J_\mu\Big(\frac{bt}{a}\Big)(zt)^{\frac{1}{2}}J_\mu(zt)dtdz\\
&= \int_0^\infty \phi(z)\int_0^\infty t^{-\mu-\frac{1}{2}}\Big(\frac{xt}{a}\Big)^{\frac{1}{2}}J_\mu\Big(\frac{xt}{a}\Big)S_{\mu,b}\Big\{\Big(\frac{bt}{a}\Big)^{\frac{1}{2}}J_\mu\Big(\frac{bt}{a}\Big)\Big\}(zt)^{\frac{1}{2}}J_\mu(zt)dtdz\\
&= S_{\mu,b}\int_0^\infty \psi(z)D_\mu\Big(\frac{x}{a},\frac{b}{a},z\Big)dz\\
&= S_{\mu,b}\psi\Big(\frac{x}{a},\frac{b}{a}\Big).
\end{aligned}$$

□

Theorem 9.8 *Let $f \in H'_{\mu,F}(I)$ and $\psi \in H_\mu(I)$ be a Bessel wavelet. Define the continuous Bessel wavelet transform of f with respect to Bessel wavelet ψ by*

$$(B_\psi f)(a,b) = \left\langle f(t), a^{\mu-\frac{1}{2}}\psi\left(\frac{t}{a},\frac{b}{a}\right)\right\rangle, \tag{9.32}$$

where $\langle , \rangle$ is functional notation.

Then the inversion formula of the continuous Bessel wavelet transform is given by

$$\lim_{\substack{A,B\to\infty\\ \epsilon\to 0+}} \left\langle \frac{1}{C_{\mu,\psi}} \int_\epsilon^A \int_0^B (B_\psi f)(a,b) a^{\mu-\frac{1}{2}} \psi\left(\frac{x}{a},\frac{b}{a}\right)\frac{dbda}{a^{2\mu+2}}, \phi\right\rangle = \langle f, \phi\rangle, \tag{9.33}$$

for all $\phi \in H_\mu(I)$.

Proof From Definition 9.1, for $\psi \in H_\mu(I)$, the Bessel wavelet and $f \in H'_{\mu,F}(I)$

$$(B_\psi f)(a,b) = \left\langle f(t), a^{\mu-\frac{1}{2}}\psi\left(\frac{t}{a},\frac{b}{a}\right)\right\rangle.$$

From Theorem 9.7, the above expression can be written as

$$\begin{aligned}(B_\psi f)(a,b) &= \left\langle \sum_{k=0}^{r} S^k_{\mu,t}(1+t^2)^r t^{-\mu-\frac{1}{2}} f_k(t), a^{\mu-\frac{1}{2}}\psi\left(\frac{t}{a},\frac{b}{a}\right)\right\rangle \\ &= \sum_{k=0}^{r} \left\langle S^k_{\mu,t}(1+t^2)^r t^{-\mu-\frac{1}{2}} f_k(t), a^{\mu-\frac{1}{2}}\psi\left(\frac{t}{a},\frac{b}{a}\right)\right\rangle.\end{aligned}$$

Applying distributional differentiation, we find

$$\begin{aligned}(B_\psi f)(a,b) &= \sum_{k=0}^{r} \left\langle f_k(t), (1+t^2)^r t^{-\mu-\frac{1}{2}} S^k_{\mu,t} a^{\mu-\frac{1}{2}}\psi\left(\frac{t}{a},\frac{b}{a}\right)\right\rangle \\ &= \sum_{k=0}^{r} \left\langle f_k(t), (1+t^2)^r t^{-\mu-\frac{1}{2}} a^{\mu-\frac{1}{2}} S^k_{\mu,t}\psi\left(\frac{t}{a},\frac{b}{a}\right)\right\rangle.\end{aligned} \tag{9.34}$$

Let us consider

$$F(x) = \frac{1}{C_{\mu,\psi}} \int_\epsilon^A \int_0^B (B_\psi f)(a,b) a^{\mu-\frac{1}{2}}\psi\left(\frac{x}{a},\frac{b}{a}\right)\frac{dbda}{a^{2\mu+2}}. \tag{9.35}$$

Therefore,

$$\lim_{\substack{A,B\to\infty\\ \epsilon\to 0+}}\Big\langle F(x),\phi(x)\Big\rangle$$
$$=\lim_{\substack{A,B\to\infty\\ \epsilon\to 0+}}\Big\langle\frac{1}{C_{\mu,\psi}}\int_\epsilon^A\int_0^B (B_\psi f)(a,b)a^{\mu-\frac{1}{2}}\psi\Big(\frac{x}{a},\frac{b}{a}\Big)\frac{dbda}{a^{2\mu+2}},\phi(x)\Big\rangle. \tag{9.36}$$

Using structure formula (9.29) for f, the distributional problem (9.36) is converted into a classical one. If we take lower limit $\epsilon\to 0+$ and upper limits $A, B\to\infty$, then from (9.34), we obtain

$$\lim_{\substack{A,B\to\infty\\ \epsilon\to 0+}}\Big\langle F(x),\phi(x)\Big\rangle$$
$$=\Big\langle\frac{1}{C_{\mu,\psi}}\int_0^\infty\int_0^\infty\Big\{\sum_{k=0}^r\int_0^\infty f_k(t)(1+t^2)^r t^{-\mu-\frac{1}{2}}a^{\mu-\frac{1}{2}}S^k_{\mu,t}\psi\Big(\frac{t}{a},\frac{b}{a}\Big)dt\Big\}$$
$$\times a^{\mu-\frac{1}{2}}\psi\Big(\frac{x}{a},\frac{b}{a}\Big)\frac{dbda}{a^{2\mu+2}},\phi(x)\Big\rangle$$
$$=\sum_{k=0}^r\Big\langle\frac{1}{C_{\mu,\psi}}\int_0^\infty\int_0^\infty\Big\{\int_0^\infty f_k(t)(1+t^2)^r t^{-\mu-\frac{1}{2}}a^{\mu-\frac{1}{2}}S^k_{\mu,t}\psi\Big(\frac{t}{a},\frac{b}{a}\Big)dt\Big\}$$
$$\times a^{\mu-\frac{1}{2}}\psi\Big(\frac{x}{a},\frac{b}{a}\Big)\frac{dbda}{a^{2\mu+2}},\phi(x)\Big\rangle$$
$$=\sum_{k=0}^r\Big\langle\frac{1}{C_{\mu,\psi}}\int_0^\infty\Big[\int_0^\infty\Big\{\int_0^\infty f_k(t)(1+t^2)^r t^{-\mu-\frac{1}{2}}a^{\mu-\frac{1}{2}}S^k_{\mu,b}\psi\Big(\frac{t}{a},\frac{b}{a}\Big)dt\Big\}$$
$$\times a^{\mu-\frac{1}{2}}\psi\Big(\frac{x}{a},\frac{b}{a}\Big)db\Big]\frac{da}{a^{2\mu+2}},\phi(x)\Big\rangle.$$

From Lemma 9.6, $S^k_{\mu,t}\psi\Big(\frac{t}{a},\frac{b}{a}\Big)=S^k_{\mu,b}\psi\Big(\frac{t}{a},\frac{b}{a}\Big)$ and using integration by parts, we get

$$\lim_{\substack{A,B\to\infty\\ \epsilon\to 0+}}\Big\langle F(x),\phi(x)\Big\rangle$$
$$=\sum_{k=0}^r\Big\langle\frac{1}{C_{\mu,\psi}}\int_0^\infty\Big[\int_0^\infty\Big\{\int_0^\infty f_k(t)(1+t^2)^r t^{-\mu-\frac{1}{2}}a^{\mu-\frac{1}{2}}\psi\Big(\frac{t}{a},\frac{b}{a}\Big)dt\Big\}$$
$$\times a^{\mu-\frac{1}{2}}S^k_{\mu,b}\psi\Big(\frac{x}{a},\frac{b}{a}\Big)db\Big]\frac{da}{a^{2\mu+2}},\phi(x)\Big\rangle$$
$$=\sum_{k=0}^r\Big\langle\frac{1}{C_{\mu,\psi}}\int_0^\infty\Big[\int_0^\infty\Big\{\int_0^\infty f_k(t)(1+t^2)^r t^{-\mu-\frac{1}{2}}a^{\mu-\frac{1}{2}}\psi\Big(\frac{t}{a},\frac{b}{a}\Big)dt\Big\}$$
$$\times a^{\mu-\frac{1}{2}}S^k_{\mu,x}\psi\Big(\frac{x}{a},\frac{b}{a}\Big)db\Big]\frac{da}{a^{2\mu+2}},\phi(x)\Big\rangle$$

as $S^k_{\mu,b}\psi\Big(\frac{t}{a},\frac{b}{a}\Big)=S^k_{\mu,x}\psi\Big(\frac{t}{a},\frac{b}{a}\Big)$.

Now using distributional derivative and Fubini's theorem, we get

$$\begin{aligned}
&\lim_{\substack{A,B\to\infty\\ \epsilon\to 0+}} \Big\langle F(x), \phi(x) \Big\rangle \\
&= \sum_{k=0}^{r} \Big\langle \frac{1}{C_{\mu,\psi}} \int_0^\infty \Big[\int_0^\infty \Big\{ \int_0^\infty f_k(t)(1+t^2)^r t^{-\mu-\frac{1}{2}} a^{\mu-\frac{1}{2}} \psi\Big(\frac{t}{a}, \frac{b}{a}\Big) dt \Big\} \\
&\qquad\qquad \times a^{\mu-\frac{1}{2}} \psi\Big(\frac{x}{a}, \frac{b}{a}\Big) db \Big] \frac{da}{a^{2\mu+2}}, S_{\mu,x}^k \phi(x) \Big\rangle \\
&= \sum_{k=0}^{r} \frac{1}{C_{\mu,\psi}} \int_0^\infty \int_0^\infty \Big[\int_0^\infty \Big\{ \int_0^\infty f_k(t)(1+t^2)^r t^{-\mu-\frac{1}{2}} a^{\mu-\frac{1}{2}} \psi\Big(\frac{t}{a}, \frac{b}{a}\Big) dt \Big\} \\
&\qquad\qquad \times a^{\mu-\frac{1}{2}} \psi\Big(\frac{x}{a}, \frac{b}{a}\Big) db \Big] \frac{da}{a^{2\mu+2}} S_{\mu,x}^k \phi(x) dx \\
&= \sum_{k=0}^{r} \frac{1}{C_{\mu,\psi}} \int_0^\infty \Big[\int_0^\infty \int_0^\infty \int_0^\infty \Big\{ S_{\mu,x}^k \phi(x) \Big\} \psi\Big(\frac{t}{a}, \frac{b}{a}\Big) \psi\Big(\frac{x}{a}, \frac{b}{a}\Big) \frac{dx\,db\,da}{a^3} \Big] \\
&\qquad\qquad \times f_k(t)(1+t^2)^r t^{-\mu-\frac{1}{2}} dt.
\end{aligned}$$

Now, using the continuous Bessel wavelet transform inversion formula, Lemmas 9.4 and 9.5, the expression in the bracket

$$\int_0^\infty \int_0^\infty \int_0^\infty \Big\{ S_{\mu,x}^k \phi(x) \Big\} \psi\Big(\frac{t}{a}, \frac{b}{a}\Big) \psi\Big(\frac{x}{a}, \frac{b}{a}\Big) \frac{dx\,db\,da}{a^3},$$

converges to $S_{\mu,t}^k \phi(t)$

(i) in $L^2(I)$
(ii) pointwise $\forall\, t \in I$
(iii) uniformly $\forall\, t \in I$

Therefore,

$$\begin{aligned}
\lim_{\substack{A,B\to\infty\\ \epsilon\to 0+}} \Big\langle F(x), \phi(x) \Big\rangle &= \sum_{k=0}^{r} \int_0^\infty \Big\{ S_{\mu,t}^k \phi(t) \Big\} f_k(t) \Big(1+t^2\Big)^r t^{-\mu-\frac{1}{2}} dt \\
&= \sum_{k=0}^{r} \Big\langle f_k(t), (1+t^2)^r t^{-\mu-\frac{1}{2}} S_{\mu,t}^k \phi(t) \Big\rangle \\
&= \Big\langle f(x), \phi(x) \Big\rangle, \quad \forall\, \phi(x) \in H_\mu(I) \text{ and } f \in H'_{\mu,F}(I)
\end{aligned}$$

using Theorem 9.7.

Thus,

$$\lim_{\substack{A,B\to\infty \\ \epsilon\to 0+}} \left\langle \frac{1}{C_{\mu,\psi}} \int_{\epsilon}^{A} \int_{0}^{B} (B_{\psi} f)(a,b) a^{\mu-\frac{1}{2}} \psi\left(\frac{x}{a}, \frac{b}{a}\right) \frac{dbda}{a^{2\mu+2}}, \phi \right\rangle = \langle f, \phi \rangle, \tag{9.37}$$

for all $\phi \in H_{\mu}(I)$, and $f \in H'_{\mu,F}(I)$. This inversion formula is valid uniquely if $f \in H'_{\mu,F}(I)$. If $f \in H'_{\mu}(I)$, then $f = h + Cx^{\mu+\frac{1}{2}}$, where $h \in H'_{\mu,F}(I)$ and C is constant. Therefore, the Bessel wavelet transform of f is

$$\begin{aligned}\left\langle f(x), a^{\mu-\frac{1}{2}} \psi\left(\frac{x}{a}, \frac{b}{a}\right) \right\rangle &= \left\langle h(x), a^{\mu-\frac{1}{2}} \psi\left(\frac{x}{a}, \frac{b}{a}\right) \right\rangle + \int_{0}^{\infty} C\, x^{\mu+\frac{1}{2}} a^{\mu-\frac{1}{2}} \psi\left(\frac{x}{a}, \frac{b}{a}\right) dx \\ &= \left\langle h(x), a^{\mu-\frac{1}{2}} \psi\left(\frac{x}{a}, \frac{b}{a}\right) \right\rangle, \end{aligned} \tag{9.38}$$

as the second term will be zero.
Hence,

$$(B_{\psi} f)(a,b) = (B_{\psi} h)(a,b),$$

and so, using (9.37), we find

$$\begin{aligned} &\lim_{\substack{A,B\to\infty \\ \epsilon\to 0+}} \left\langle \frac{1}{C_{\mu,\psi}} \int_{\epsilon}^{A} \int_{0}^{B} (B_{\psi} f)(a,b) a^{\mu-\frac{1}{2}} \psi\left(\frac{x}{a}, \frac{b}{a}\right) \frac{dbda}{a^{2\mu+2}}, \phi \right\rangle \\ &\quad = \lim_{\substack{A,B\to\infty \\ \epsilon\to 0+}} \left\langle \frac{1}{C_{\mu,\psi}} \int_{\epsilon}^{A} \int_{0}^{B} (B_{\psi} h)(a,b) a^{\mu-\frac{1}{2}} \psi\left(\frac{x}{a}, \frac{b}{a}\right) \frac{dbda}{a^{2\mu+2}}, \phi \right\rangle \\ &\quad = \left\langle h, \phi \right\rangle \\ &\quad = \left\langle f - C\, x^{\mu+\frac{1}{2}}, \phi \right\rangle \\ &\quad = \left\langle f, \phi \right\rangle + \left\langle -C\, x^{\mu+\frac{1}{2}}, \phi \right\rangle. \end{aligned}$$

Thus, for the validity of the uniqueness in our inversion formula 9.37, f must belong to $H'_{\mu,F}(I)$. □

9.5 Calderón Reproducing Formula and the Applications of the Continuous Bessel Wavelet Transform of Distributions

In the present section, the Calderón reproducing formula associated with inversion formula of the continuous Bessel wavelet transform of distributions is given. The application of the continuous Bessel wavelet transform of distributions through heat equation is given and the solution of heat equation is expressed in form of the continuous Bessel wavelet transform of distributions in $H'_{\mu}(I)$ space.

Theorem 9.9 *If $f \in H'_{\mu,F}(I)$ and $\psi \in H_{\mu}(I)$, then the Calderón reproducing formula associated with the inversion formula of the continuous Bessel wavelet transform can be expressed in the following form:*

$$\lim_{\substack{A\to\infty \\ \epsilon\to 0+}} \Big\langle \frac{1}{C_{\mu,\psi}} \int_{\epsilon}^{A} (f\#\overline{\psi_a}\#\psi_a)(x)\frac{da}{a^{2\mu+2}}, \phi\Big\rangle = \langle f, \phi\rangle, \quad \forall\, \phi \in H_{\mu}(I). \tag{9.39}$$

Proof From [32, p. 318] and Definition 9.1, for $f \in H'_{\mu}(I)$ and $\psi \in H_{\mu}(I)$, we have

$$\begin{aligned}(B_{\psi} f)(a,b) &= \Big\langle f(x), a^{\mu-\frac{1}{2}}\psi\Big(\frac{x}{a},\frac{b}{a}\Big)\Big\rangle \\ &= \Big\langle f(x), h_{\mu}\Big\{(b\omega)^{\frac{1}{2}} J_{\mu}(b\omega)\omega^{-\mu-\frac{1}{2}}(h_{\mu}\psi)(a\omega)\Big\}\Big\rangle. \end{aligned}\tag{9.40}$$

From [4, p. 142] and [34, p. 364], the above expression will be

$$\begin{aligned}(B_{\psi} f)(a,b) &= \Big\langle h'_{\mu} f, (b\omega)^{\frac{1}{2}} J_{\mu}(b\omega)\omega^{-\mu-\frac{1}{2}}(h_{\mu}\psi)(a\omega)\Big\rangle \\ &= \int_0^{\infty} (b\omega)^{\frac{1}{2}} J_{\mu}(b\omega)\omega^{-\mu-\frac{1}{2}}(h'_{\mu} f)(\omega)\overline{(h_{\mu}\psi)}(a\omega)d\omega \\ &= \int_0^{\infty} (b\omega)^{\frac{1}{2}} J_{\mu}(b\omega) h'_{\mu}\{f\#\overline{\psi_a}\}(\omega)d\omega. \end{aligned}\tag{9.41}$$

From Theorem 9.8, we have

$$\langle f, \phi\rangle = \lim_{\substack{A,B\to\infty \\ \epsilon\to 0+}} \Big\langle \frac{1}{C_{\mu,\psi}} \int_{\epsilon}^{A}\int_0^{B} (B_{\psi} f)(a,b) a^{\mu-\frac{1}{2}}\psi\Big(\frac{x}{a},\frac{b}{a}\Big)\frac{dbda}{a^{2\mu+2}}, \phi\Big\rangle.$$

Using the same technique as in the proof of Theorem 9.8 and from (9.41), we get

$$\begin{aligned}\langle f, \phi\rangle &= \Big\langle \frac{1}{C_{\mu,\psi}} \int_0^{\infty}\int_0^{\infty} \Big(\int_0^{\infty} (b\omega)^{\frac{1}{2}} J_{\mu}(b\omega) h'_{\mu}\{f\#\overline{\psi_a}\}(\omega)d\omega\Big) a^{\mu-\frac{1}{2}}\psi\Big(\frac{x}{a},\frac{b}{a}\Big)\frac{dbda}{a^{2\mu+2}}, \phi\Big\rangle \\ &= \Big\langle \frac{1}{C_{\mu,\psi}} \int_0^{\infty}\int_0^{\infty} h'_{\mu}\{f\#\overline{\psi_a}\}(\omega)(x\omega)^{\frac{1}{2}} J_{\mu}(x\omega)\omega^{-\mu-\frac{1}{2}}(h_{\mu}\psi_a)(\omega)\frac{d\omega da}{a^{2\mu+2}}, \phi\Big\rangle \\ &= \Big\langle \frac{1}{C_{\mu,\psi}} \int_0^{\infty}\int_0^{\infty} (x\omega)^{\frac{1}{2}} J_{\mu}(x\omega)\omega^{-\mu-\frac{1}{2}} h'_{\mu}\{f\#\overline{\psi_a}\}(\omega)(h_{\mu}\psi_a)(\omega)d\omega\frac{da}{a^{2\mu+2}}, \phi\Big\rangle \\ &= \Big\langle \frac{1}{C_{\mu,\psi}} \int_0^{\infty}\int_0^{\infty} (x\omega)^{\frac{1}{2}} J_{\mu}(x\omega) h'_{\mu}\{f\#\overline{\psi_a}\#\psi_a\}(\omega)d\omega\frac{da}{a^{2\mu+2}}, \phi\Big\rangle \\ &= \Big\langle \frac{1}{C_{\mu,\psi}} \int_0^{\infty} (f\#\overline{\psi_a}\#\psi_a)(x)\frac{da}{a^{2\mu+2}}, \phi\Big\rangle. \end{aligned}$$

If ψ satisfies orthonormal condition

$$C_{\mu,\psi} := \int_0^\infty \frac{|(h_\mu \psi)(\omega)|^2}{\omega^{2\mu+2}} d\omega = 1. \tag{9.42}$$

Then

$$\langle f, \phi \rangle = \left\langle \int_0^\infty (f \# \overline{\psi_a} \# \psi_a)(x) \frac{da}{a^{2\mu+2}}, \phi \right\rangle. \tag{9.43}$$

□

Theorem 9.10 *Consider heat equation*

$$\frac{\partial u(x,t)}{\partial t} = S_{\mu,x} u(x,t), \quad 0 < x < \infty, \; t > 0 \tag{9.44}$$

with initial condition

$$u(x, 0) = S_{\mu,x} f(x), \tag{9.45}$$

where $S_{\mu,x} = x^{-\mu-\frac{1}{2}} D_x x^{2\mu+1} D_x x^{-\mu-\frac{1}{2}}$ *is the Bessel operator. Then the solution of (9.44) and (9.45) in* $H'_\mu(I)$ *space can be obtained in the following form:*

$$u(x,t) = \frac{1}{2^{\frac{3}{2}} t^{\frac{1}{2}(\mu+\frac{5}{2})}} (B_\psi f)(2\sqrt{t}, x). \tag{9.46}$$

Proof Exploiting (1.114) and using Hankel transformation on (9.44) and (9.45), we get

$$\begin{aligned} \frac{\partial U(\omega,t)}{\partial t} &= h_\mu (S_{\mu,x} u)(\omega, t) \\ &= -\omega^2 U(\omega, t), \end{aligned} \tag{9.47}$$

and

$$\begin{aligned} U(\omega, 0) &= h_\mu (S_{\mu,x} f)(\omega) \\ &= -\omega^2 (h_\mu f)(\omega), \end{aligned} \tag{9.48}$$

where $U(\omega, t) = (h_\mu u)(\omega, t)$.

Now, from (9.47), the solution will be

$$U(\omega, t) = C e^{-\omega^2 t}. \tag{9.49}$$

Taking $t = 0$ in (9.49), we get

$$U(\omega, 0) = C. \tag{9.50}$$

So that,

$$U(\omega, t) = -\omega^2 (h_\mu f)(\omega) e^{-\omega^2 t}. \tag{9.51}$$

Taking the inversion formula of Hankel transformation (1.76), we get

$$\begin{aligned} u(x,t) &= \int_0^\infty (x\omega)^{\frac{1}{2}} J_\mu(x\omega)(-\omega^2)(h_\mu f)(\omega) e^{-\omega^2 t} d\omega \\ &= \int_0^\infty (x\omega)^{\frac{1}{2}} J_\mu(x\omega)\omega^{-\mu-\frac{1}{2}}\omega^{\mu+\frac{1}{2}}(-\omega^2)(h_\mu f)(\omega) e^{-\omega^2 t} d\omega \\ &= \int_0^\infty (x\omega)^{\frac{1}{2}} J_\mu(x\omega)\omega^{-\mu-\frac{1}{2}}(h_\mu f)(\omega)(-\omega^2)\omega^{\mu+\frac{1}{2}} e^{-\omega^2 t} d\omega \\ &= \int_0^\infty (x\omega)^{\frac{1}{2}} J_\mu(x\omega)\omega^{-\mu-\frac{1}{2}}(h_\mu f)(\omega) \frac{1}{2^{\frac{3}{2}} t^{\frac{1}{2}(\mu+\frac{5}{2})}} h_\mu \left\{ S_{\mu,s} s^{\mu+\frac{1}{2}} e^{-s^2} \right\}(2\sqrt{t}\omega) d\omega, \end{aligned}$$

since $h_\mu \left\{ S_{\mu,s} s^{\mu+\frac{1}{2}} e^{-s^2} \right\}(2\sqrt{t}\omega) = 2^{\frac{3}{2}} t^{\frac{1}{2}(\mu+\frac{5}{2})}(-\omega^2)\omega^{\mu+\frac{1}{2}} e^{-\omega^2 t}$.

Let $\psi(s) = S_{\mu,s} s^{\mu+\frac{1}{2}} e^{-s^2}$. Since $(h_\mu \psi)(a\omega) = (h_\mu \psi_a)(\omega)$, $\psi_a(s) = \frac{1}{a}\psi\left(\frac{s}{a}\right)$; taking $a = 2\sqrt{t}$ we get

$$\begin{aligned} u(x,t) &= \int_0^\infty (x\omega)^{\frac{1}{2}} J_\mu(x\omega)\omega^{-\mu-\frac{1}{2}}(h_\mu f)(\omega) \frac{1}{2^{\frac{3}{2}} t^{\frac{1}{2}(\mu+\frac{5}{2})}} (h_\mu \psi)(2\sqrt{t}\omega) d\omega \\ &= \frac{1}{2^{\frac{3}{2}} t^{\frac{1}{2}(\mu+\frac{5}{2})}} \int_0^\infty (x\omega)^{\frac{1}{2}} J_\mu(x\omega)\omega^{-\mu-\frac{1}{2}}(h_\mu f)(\omega)(h_\mu \psi)(2\sqrt{t}\omega) d\omega \\ &= \frac{1}{2^{\frac{3}{2}} t^{\frac{1}{2}(\mu+\frac{5}{2})}} \int_0^\infty (x\omega)^{\frac{1}{2}} J_\mu(x\omega) h_\mu \{ f \# \psi_{2\sqrt{t}} \}(\omega) d\omega \\ &= \frac{1}{2^{\frac{3}{2}} t^{\frac{1}{2}(\mu+\frac{5}{2})}} (f \# \psi_{2\sqrt{t}})(x). \end{aligned}$$

Using (1.79) and (1.80), we get

$$\begin{aligned} u(x,t) &= \frac{1}{2^{\frac{3}{2}} t^{\frac{1}{2}(\mu+\frac{5}{2})}} \int_0^\infty f(s)\psi_{2\sqrt{t}}(s,x) ds \\ &= \frac{1}{2^{\frac{3}{2}} t^{\frac{1}{2}(\mu+\frac{5}{2})}} \int_0^\infty f(s)(2\sqrt{t})^{\mu-\frac{1}{2}} \psi\left(\frac{s}{2\sqrt{t}}, \frac{x}{2\sqrt{t}}\right) ds \\ &= \frac{1}{2^{\frac{3}{2}} t^{\frac{1}{2}(\mu+\frac{5}{2})}} \left\langle f(s), (2\sqrt{t})^{\mu-\frac{1}{2}} \psi\left(\frac{s}{2\sqrt{t}}, \frac{x}{2\sqrt{t}}\right) \right\rangle. \end{aligned} \tag{9.52}$$

From [34], $\psi\left(\frac{s}{2\sqrt{t}}, \frac{x}{2\sqrt{t}}\right)$ will be an element of $H_\mu(I)$ and from [4, p. 130, p. 137], it can be easily seen that $\psi(s) = S_{\mu,s} s^{\mu+\frac{1}{2}} e^{-s^2} \in H_\mu(I)$.

In view of Definition 9.1, we have

$$f \in H'_\mu(I).$$

Therefore (9.52) yields

$$u(x,t) = \frac{1}{2^{\frac{3}{2}} t^{\frac{1}{2}(\mu+\frac{1}{2})}} (B_\psi f)(2\sqrt{t}, x). \tag{9.53}$$

□

Theorem 9.11 *If*

$$(B_\psi f)(2\sqrt{t}, x) = \Big\langle f(s), (2\sqrt{t})^{\mu-\frac{1}{2}} \psi\Big(\frac{s}{2\sqrt{t}}, \frac{x}{2\sqrt{t}}\Big)\Big\rangle.$$

Then

$$\lim_{\substack{A,B\to\infty \\ \epsilon\to 0+}} \Big\langle \frac{2}{C_{\mu,\psi}} \int_\epsilon^A \int_0^B (B_\psi f)(2\sqrt{t}, x)(2\sqrt{t})^{\mu-\frac{1}{2}} \psi\Big(\frac{y}{2\sqrt{t}}, \frac{x}{2\sqrt{t}}\Big) \frac{dxdt}{(2\sqrt{t})^{2\mu+3}}, \phi(y)\Big\rangle = \langle f, \phi\rangle,$$

for all $\phi \in H_\mu(I)$.

Proof From Definition 9.1, for $\psi \in H_\mu(I)$, the Bessel wavelet and $f \in H'_{\mu,F}(I)$

$$(B_\psi f)(2\sqrt{t}, x) = \Big\langle f(s), (2\sqrt{t})^{\mu-\frac{1}{2}} \psi\Big(\frac{s}{2\sqrt{t}}, \frac{x}{2\sqrt{t}}\Big)\Big\rangle.$$

From Theorem 9.7, the above expression can be written as

$$\begin{aligned}(B_\psi f)(2\sqrt{t}, x) &= \Big\langle \sum_{k=0}^{r} S^k_{\mu,s}(1+s^2)^r s^{-\mu-\frac{1}{2}} f_k(s), (2\sqrt{t})^{\mu-\frac{1}{2}} \psi\Big(\frac{s}{2\sqrt{t}}, \frac{x}{2\sqrt{t}}\Big)\Big\rangle \\ &= \sum_{k=0}^{r} \Big\langle S^k_{\mu,s}(1+s^2)^r s^{-\mu-\frac{1}{2}} f_k(s), (2\sqrt{t})^{\mu-\frac{1}{2}} \psi\Big(\frac{s}{2\sqrt{t}}, \frac{x}{2\sqrt{t}}\Big)\Big\rangle.\end{aligned}$$

Applying distributional differentiation, we find

$$\begin{aligned}(B_\psi f)(2\sqrt{t}, x) &= \sum_{k=0}^{r} \Big\langle f_k(s), (1+s^2)^r s^{-\mu-\frac{1}{2}} S^k_{\mu,s} (2\sqrt{t})^{\mu-\frac{1}{2}} \psi\Big(\frac{s}{2\sqrt{t}}, \frac{x}{2\sqrt{t}}\Big)\Big\rangle \\ &= \sum_{k=0}^{r} \Big\langle f_k(s), (1+s^2)^r s^{-\mu-\frac{1}{2}} (2\sqrt{t})^{\mu-\frac{1}{2}} S^k_{\mu,s} \psi\Big(\frac{s}{2\sqrt{t}}, \frac{x}{2\sqrt{t}}\Big)\Big\rangle.\end{aligned}$$

Let us consider

$$\begin{aligned}F(y) &= \frac{1}{C_{\mu,\psi}}\int_{\epsilon}^{A}\int_{0}^{B}(B_{\psi}f)(2\sqrt{t},x)(2\sqrt{t})^{\mu-\frac{1}{2}}\psi\Big(\frac{y}{2\sqrt{t}},\frac{x}{2\sqrt{t}}\Big)\frac{dx d(2\sqrt{t})}{(2\sqrt{t})^{2\mu+2}}\\ &= \frac{2}{C_{\mu,\psi}}\int_{\epsilon}^{A}\int_{0}^{B}(B_{\psi}f)(2\sqrt{t},x)(2\sqrt{t})^{\mu-\frac{1}{2}}\psi\Big(\frac{y}{2\sqrt{t}},\frac{x}{2\sqrt{t}}\Big)\frac{dx dt}{(2\sqrt{t})^{2\mu+3}}.\end{aligned}$$

Using the proof of Theorem 9.8, we can conclude that

$$\begin{aligned}&\lim_{\substack{A,B\to\infty\\ \epsilon\to 0+}}\Big\langle F(y),\phi(y)\Big\rangle\\ &= \lim_{\substack{A,B\to\infty\\ \epsilon\to 0+}}\Big\langle\frac{2}{C_{\mu,\psi}}\int_{\epsilon}^{A}\int_{0}^{B}(B_{\psi}f)(2\sqrt{t},x)(2\sqrt{t})^{\mu-\frac{1}{2}}\psi\Big(\frac{y}{2\sqrt{t}},\frac{x}{2\sqrt{t}}\Big)\frac{dx dt}{(2\sqrt{t})^{2\mu+3}},\phi(y)\Big\rangle\\ &= \langle f,\phi\rangle.\end{aligned}$$

□

Example 9.5
For $f(x) = x^{\mu+\frac{1}{2}}e^{-x^2}$, the solution of the heat Eqs. (9.44) and (9.45) is given by

$$u(x,t) = \int_0^{\infty}(x\omega)^{\frac{1}{2}}J_{\mu}(x\omega)(-\omega)^2(h_{\mu}x^{\mu+\frac{1}{2}}e^{-x^2})(\omega)e^{-\omega^2 t}d\omega.$$

Using (1.114) and Erdélyi et al. [33, p. 30], the above expression yields

$$\begin{aligned}u(x,t) &= S_{\mu,x}\Big\{\int_0^{\infty}(x\omega)^{\frac{1}{2}}J_{\mu}(x\omega)(h_{\mu}x^{\mu+\frac{1}{2}}e^{-x^2})(\omega)e^{-\omega^2 t}d\omega\Big\}\\ &= S_{\mu,x}\Big\{\int_0^{\infty}(x\omega)^{\frac{1}{2}}J_{\mu}(x\omega)\frac{\omega^{\mu+\frac{1}{2}}}{2^{\mu+1}}e^{-\frac{\omega^2}{4}}e^{-\omega^2 t}d\omega\Big\}\\ &= S_{\mu,x}\Big\{\int_0^{\infty}(x\omega)^{\frac{1}{2}}J_{\mu}(x\omega)\frac{\omega^{\mu+\frac{1}{2}}}{2^{\mu+1}}e^{-\frac{\omega^2}{4}}e^{-\omega^2 t}d\omega\Big\}.\end{aligned}$$

Again, using [33, p. 30], we get

$$u(x,t) = S_{\mu,x}\Big\{\frac{x^{\mu+\frac{1}{2}}}{(1+4t)^{\mu+1}}e^{-\frac{x^2}{1+4t}}\Big\},$$

so that

$$u(x,t) = \frac{4x^{\mu+\frac{1}{2}}}{(1+4t)^{\mu+3}}\{x^2-(\mu+1)(1+4t)\}e^{-\frac{x^2}{1+4t}}. \tag{9.54}$$

With the help of MATLAB, the graphical representations of the solution (9.54) of the heat equation at $\mu = 0$ and $\mu = 1$ are given in Figs. 9.1 and 9.2, respectively.

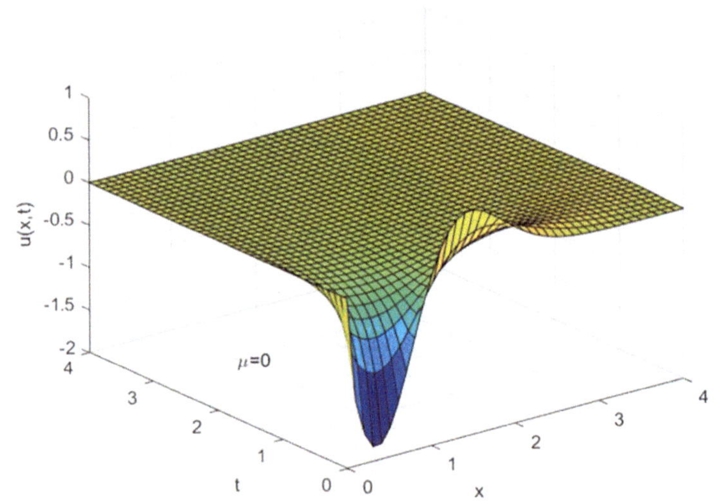

Fig. 9.1 $u(x, t)$ at $\mu = 0$

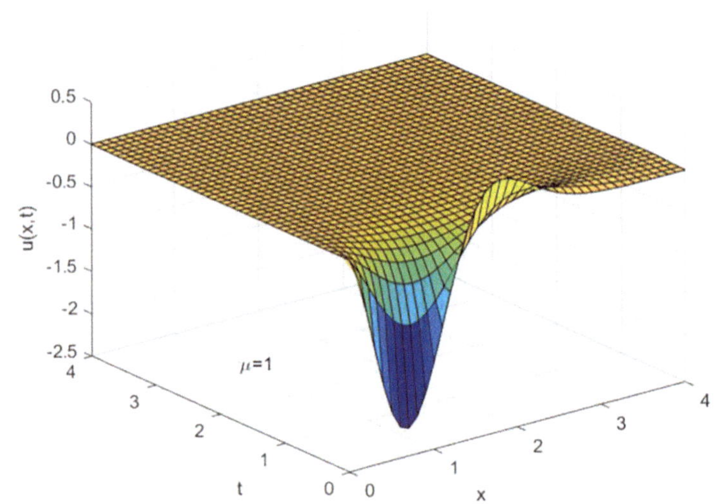

Fig. 9.2 $u(x, t)$ at $\mu = 1$

References

1. A.H. Zemanian, "A distributional Hankel transformation," *SIAM J. Appl. Math.*, (3),**14**(1966)561-576
2. A.H. Zemanian, "The Hankel transformation of certain distributions of rapid growth," *SIAM J. Appl. Math.*, (4),**14**(1966)678-690
3. A.H. Zemanian, "Hankel transforms of arbitrary order," *Duke Math. J.*, (4),**34**(1967)761-769
4. Zemanian, A.H.: Generalized integral transformations. Interscience Publishers, New York, Pure and Applied Mathematics XVIII (1968)
5. E.L. Koh, "The Hankel transformation of negative order for distributions of rapid growth," *SIAM J. Math. Anal.*, (3),**1**(1970)322-327
6. E.L. Koh, "The n-dimensional distributional Hankel transformation," *Canad. J. Math.*, (2),**27**(1975)423-433
7. W.Y.K. Lee, "On spaces of type H_μ and their Hankel transformations," *SIAM J. Math. Anal.*, (2),**5**(1974)336-348
8. L.S. Dube and J.N. Pandey, "On the Hankel transform of distributions," *Tohoku Math. J.*, (3),**27**(1975)337-354
9. C. Arteaga and I. Marrero, "Structure, boundedness, and convergence in the dual of a Hankel-$K\{M_p\}$ space," *Integral Transforms Spec. Funct.*, (2020)1-17
10. J.J. Betancor, "A new characterization of the bounded operators commuting with Hankel translation," *Arch. Math.*, (5),**69**(1997)403-408
11. J.J. Betancor, "On Hankel transformable distribution spaces," *Publ. Inst. Math. (Beograd)(N.S.)*, (79),**65**(1999)123-141
12. J.J. Betancor, "A generalized Hankel convolution on Zemanian spaces," *Int. J. Math. Math. Sci.*, (2),**23**(2000)131-140
13. J.J. Betancor and B.J. González, "A convolution operation for a distributional Hankel transformation," *Studia Math.*, (1),**117**(1995)57-72
14. J.J. Betancor and C. Jerez, "Convolution Hankel transforms on the Zemanian spaces," *Acta Math. Hungar.*, (3),**80**(1998)225-235
15. J.J. Betancor and I. Marrero, "Some properties of Hankel convolution operators," *Canad. Math. Bull.*, (4),**36**(1993)398-406
16. J.J. Betancor and I. Marrero, "Structure and convergence in certain spaces of distributions and the generalized Hankel convolution," *Math. Japon.*, (6),**38**(1993)1141-1155
17. Betancor, J.J., Marrero, I.: The Hankel convolution and the Zemanian spaces β_μ and β'_μ. Math. Nachr. **160**, 277–298 (1993)
18. J.J. Betancor and I. Marrero, "Algebraic characterization of convolution and multiplication operators on Hankel-transformable function and distribution spaces," *Rocky Mountain J. Math.*, (4),**25**(1995)1189-1204
19. J.J. Betancor and L. Rodríguez-Mesa, "Hankel convolution on distribution spaces with exponential growth," *Studia Math.*, (1),**121**(1996)35-52
20. J.J. Betancor and L. Rodríguez-Mesa, "On Hankel convolution equations in distribution spaces," *Rocky Mountain J. Math.*, (1),**29**(1999)93-114
21. R.S. Pathak, "On Hankel transformable spaces and a Cauchy problem," *Canad. J. Math.*, (1),**37**(1985)84-106
22. Pathak, R.S.: Integral transforms of generalized functions and their applications. Gordon and Breach Science Publishers, Amsterdam (1997)
23. R.S. Pathak and M.M. Dixit, "Continuous and discrete Bessel wavelet transforms," *J. Comput. Appl. Math.*, (1-2),**160**(2003)241-250
24. R.S. Pathak and A.B. Pandey, "On Hankel transforms of ultradistributions," *Applicable Anal.*, (3-4),**20**(1985)245-268
25. R.S. Pathak and P.K. Pandey, "Sobolev type spaces associated with Bessel operators," *J. Math. Anal. Appl.*, (1),**215**(1997)95-111
26. R.S. Pathak, S.K. Upadhyay, and R.S. Pandey, "The Bessel wavelet convolution product," *Rend. Semin. Mat. Univ. Politec. Torino*, (3),**69**(2011)267-279

27. S.K. Upadhyay and R. Singh, "Integrability of the continuum Bessel wavelet kernel," *Int. J. Wavelets Multiresolut. Inf. Process.*, (5),**13**(2015),article id. 1550032
28. S.K. Upadhyay and R. Singh, "Bessel wavelet transform on the spaces with exponential growth," *Filomat*, (8),**31**(2017)2459-2466
29. S.K. Upadhyay and R. Singh, "Linear time invariant filter associated with Bessel wavelet transform," *J. Anal.*, (2),**26**(2018)323-332
30. S.K. Upadhyay and R. Singh, "Abelian theorems for the Bessel wavelet transform," *J. Anal.*, (1),**28**(2020)179-190
31. S.K. Upadhyay, R. Singh, and A. Tripathi, "The relation between Bessel wavelet convolution product and Hankel convolution product involving Hankel transform," *Int. J. Wavelets Multiresolut. Inf. Process.*, (4),**15**(2017),article id. 1750030
32. S.K. Upadhyay, R.N. Yadav, and L. Debnath, "On continuous Bessel wavelet transformation associated with the Hankel-Hausdorff operator,"*Integral transforms Spec. Funct.*, (5),**23**(2012)315-323
33. A. Erdélyi, W. Magnus, F. Oberhettinger, F.G. Tricomi (eds.), Tables of Integral Transforms, Vol.:2, McGraw-Hill, New York 19542, 1954
34. I. Marrero and J.J. Betancor, "Hankel convolution of generalized functions," *Rend. Mat. Appl.*, (3),**15**(1995)351-380

Chapter 10
The Continuous Bessel Wavelet Transform of Distributions in β'_μ-Space

10.1 Introduction

In the previous chapter, characterizations of the inversion formula of the continuous Bessel wavelet transform in $H'_\mu(I)$ were discussed and found applications in the Heat equation and the Calderón reproducing formula in $H'_\mu(I)$. In this chapter, the inversion formula and its properties are discussed exploiting the theory of the continuous Bessel wavelet transform of distributions on β'_μ-space.

From Zemanian [1, 2] and Betancor et al. [3], the definitions of various test function spaces are given below.

For $\mu \in \mathbb{R}$ and $c > 0$, the space $\beta_{\mu,c}$ consists of all complex-valued function $\phi \in C^\infty(I)$ such that $\phi(x) = 0$, for $x \geq c$ and

$$\gamma_k^\mu(\phi) = \sup_{x\in I} \left| \left(x^{-1}D_x\right)^k x^{-\mu-\frac{1}{2}}\phi(x)\right| < \infty, \quad k \in \mathbb{N}_0, \tag{10.1}$$

when endowed with the topology generated by the family of seminorms $\{\gamma_k^\mu\}_{k\in\mathbb{N}_0}$, $\beta_{\mu,c}$ becomes a Fréchet space. It is clear that $\beta_{\mu,c} \subset \beta_{\mu,d}$ provided that $c \leq d$. The above fact allows to define $\beta_\mu = \bigcup_{c>0} \beta_{\mu,c}$ as the inductive limit of $\{\beta_{\mu,c}\}_{c>0}$. $\beta'_{\mu,c}$ and β'_μ denote duals of $\beta_{\mu,c}$ and β_μ, respectively.

Let $\eta = y + i\omega,\ y, \omega \in \mathbb{R}$ and $\mu, c \in \mathbb{R}$ with $c > 0$. Then Φ is an element of $\mathscr{Y}_{\mu,c}$ if and only if $\eta^{-\mu-\frac{1}{2}}\Phi$ is an even entire function of η such that

$$\alpha_{c,k}^\mu(\Phi) = \sup_\eta |e^{-c|\omega|}\eta^{2k-\mu-\frac{1}{2}}\Phi(\eta)| < \infty, \quad k \in \mathbb{N}_0. \tag{10.2}$$

The topology of $\mathscr{Y}_{\mu,c}$ is the one generated by using the seminorms $\alpha_{c,k}^\mu$, $k = 0, 1, 2, 3, \cdots$. From Zemanian [1, p. 682, p. 685], it is clear that $\mathscr{Y}_{\mu,c}$ is a Fréchet space and $\mathscr{Y}_{\mu,c} \subset \mathscr{Y}_{\mu,d}$ for $c < d$. In view of the above fact, $\mathscr{Y}_\mu = \bigcup_{c>0} \mathscr{Y}_{\mu,c}$ is the

S. K. Upadhyay and J. S. Maurya, *The Bessel Wavelet Transform*, Industrial and Applied Mathematics,
https://doi.org/10.1007/978-981-96-9938-4_10

inductive limit of $\mathscr{Y}_{\mu,c},\ c > 0$. The dual space of $\mathscr{Y}_\mu$ is $\mathscr{Y}'_\mu$ which is the space of all continuous linear functional on $\mathscr{Y}_\mu$-space.

Contents of this chapter are organized in the following way:

Section 10.1 is introductory. It gives basic information about the continuous Bessel wavelet transform and its inversion formula. In Sect. 10.2, various definitions and useful results related to the present chapter are provided. Properties of the continuous Bessel wavelet transform in β'_μ-space are discussed. In Sect. 10.3, useful lemmas and theorems related to the inversion formula of the continuous Bessel wavelet transform of distributions are given, the main theorem of inversion formula of the continuous Bessel wavelet transform of distributions in $\beta'_{\mu,F}$-space is established.

10.2 The Continuous Bessel Wavelet Transform and Its Properties

In this section, the various properties of the continuous Bessel wavelet transform on the Zemanian spaces β_μ and β'_μ are obtained by exploiting the theory of the Hankel transform.

Lemma 10.1 *Let $\psi \in \beta_\mu$ with $\psi(x) = 0$ for $x \geq c,\ c > 0$ and $\mu > -\frac{1}{2}$. Then, ψ is a basic Bessel wavelet if and only if $\int_0^\infty x^{\mu+\frac{1}{2}}\psi(x)dx = 0$.*

Proof Let $\psi \in \beta_\mu$ be the basic Bessel wavelet which satisfies (2.9). Since $\omega^{-\mu-\frac{1}{2}}(h_\mu\psi)(\omega)$ is continuous on I, therefore

$$\omega^{-\mu-\frac{1}{2}}(h_\mu\psi)(\omega) = \omega^{-\mu-\frac{1}{2}}\int_0^\infty (x\omega)^{\frac{1}{2}}J_\mu(x\omega)\psi(x)dx$$
$$= \int_0^\infty (x\omega)^{-\mu}J_\mu(x\omega)x^{\mu+\frac{1}{2}}\psi(x)dx.$$

In the last integral, $(x\omega)^{-\mu}J_\mu(x\omega) \to \frac{1}{2^\mu\Gamma(\mu+1)}$ as $\omega \to 0$ and from (2.9) it is clear that $\omega^{-\mu-\frac{1}{2}}(h_\mu\psi)(\omega)$ must go to zero. Then, we have

$$\frac{1}{2^\mu\Gamma(\mu+1)}\int_0^\infty x^{\mu+\frac{1}{2}}\psi(x)dx = 0.$$

Hence

$$\int_0^\infty x^{\mu+\frac{1}{2}}\psi(x)dx = 0. \tag{10.3}$$

Conversely, for $\psi \in \beta_{\mu,c} \subset L^2(I)$, we can write

$$\int_0^\infty \frac{|(h_\mu\psi)(\omega)|^2}{\omega^{2\mu+2}}d\omega = \int_0^1 \frac{|(h_\mu\psi)(\omega)|^2}{\omega^{2\mu+2}}d\omega + \int_1^\infty \frac{|(h_\mu\psi)(\omega)|^2}{\omega^{2\mu+2}}d\omega. \tag{10.4}$$

The second integral of the R.H.S. of (10.4) is estimated as by following the technique of (9.2) and (9.3).

Therefore,

$$\int_1^\infty \frac{|(h_\mu \psi)(\omega)|^2}{\omega^{2\mu+2}} d\omega \leq \|\psi(x)\|_2^2. \tag{10.5}$$

Since $\omega^{-\mu-\frac{1}{2}}(h_\mu \psi)(\omega) \to 0$ as $\omega \to 0$, then for the boundedness of the first integral of the R.H.S of (10.4), we have

$$\begin{aligned}
4\left|\omega^{-\mu-\frac{1}{2}}(h_\mu \psi)(\omega)\right| &= \left|\lim_{\epsilon\to 0}\int_\epsilon^\omega \frac{\partial}{\partial y} y^{-\mu-\frac{1}{2}}(h_\mu \psi)(y)dy\right| \\
&\leq \lim_{\epsilon\to 0}\int_\epsilon^\omega \left|y^{-\mu-\frac{1}{2}} y^{\mu+\frac{1}{2}} \frac{\partial}{\partial y} y^{-\mu-\frac{1}{2}}(h_\mu \psi)(y)\right| dy \\
&\leq \lim_{\epsilon\to 0}\int_\epsilon^\omega \left|y y^{-\mu-1-\frac{1}{2}} N_\mu(h_\mu \psi)(y)\right| dy \\
&\leq \sup_{y\in I}\left|y^{-\mu-1-\frac{1}{2}} N_\mu(h_\mu \psi)(y)\right| \lim_{\epsilon\to 0}\int_\epsilon^\omega y dy \\
&\leq \frac{\omega^2}{2}\sup_{\eta\in\mathbb{C}}\left|e^{-c|\mathrm{Im}\eta|}\eta^{-\mu-1-\frac{1}{2}} N_\mu(h_\mu \psi)(\eta)\right| \\
&\leq \frac{\omega^2}{2}\alpha_{c,0}^{\mu+1}(N_\mu(h_\mu \psi)).
\end{aligned}$$

Hence

$$\left|\omega^{-\mu-1}(h_\mu \psi)(\omega)\right| \leq \frac{\omega^{\frac{3}{2}}}{2}\alpha_{c,0}^{\mu+1}(N_\mu(h_\mu \psi)).$$

Therefore,

$$\int_0^1 \left|\omega^{-\mu-1}(h_\mu \psi)(\omega)\right|^2 d\omega \leq \frac{1}{4}\left\{\alpha_{c,0}^{\mu+1}(N_\mu(h_\mu \psi))\right\}^2 \int_0^1 \omega^3\, d\omega.$$

This implies that

$$\int_0^1 \frac{|(h_\mu \psi)(\omega)|^2}{\omega^{2\mu+2}} d\omega \leq \frac{1}{16}\left\{\alpha_{c,0}^{\mu+1}(N_\mu(h_\mu \psi))\right\}^2, \tag{10.6}$$

for $\psi \in \beta_{\mu,c}$ and $N_\mu(h_\mu \psi) \in \mathscr{Y}_{\mu+1,c}$.

From (10.5) and (10.6), we get

$$\int_0^\infty \frac{|(h_\mu \psi)(\omega)|^2}{\omega^{2\mu+2}} d\omega < \infty.$$

Definition 10.1 Let $\psi \in \beta_\mu$ be the Bessel wavelet and $f \in \beta'_\mu$, then the Bessel wavelet transform of f is defined by

$$\left(B_\psi f\right)(b,a) = (f\#\psi_a)(b) = \left\langle f(t), a^{\mu-\frac{1}{2}}\psi\left(\frac{t}{a},\frac{b}{a}\right)\right\rangle, \qquad (10.7)$$

where $a > 0, b > 0$ and $\mu > -\frac{1}{2}$.

Remark 10.1 From [1, p. 681], β_μ is a subspace of H_μ and the topology of β_μ is stronger than the topology induced on it by H_μ. Therefore, the restrictions of the elements of H'_μ to β_μ comprise a subspace of β'_μ. So we observed that $x^{\mu+\frac{1}{2}}$ belongs to H'_μ, then this implies that $x^{\mu+\frac{1}{2}} \in \beta'_\mu$.

Theorem 10.1 *Let $\psi \in \beta_\mu$ be the Bessel wavelet, then the continuous Bessel wavelet transform of distributions $Cx^{\mu+\frac{1}{2}}$ is zero for $C > 0$ which is a constant.*

Proof In view of the Theorem 9.1, we obtain

$$\left(B_\psi C x^{\mu+\frac{1}{2}}\right)(b,a) = 0.$$

Lemma 10.2 *Let $\mu > -\frac{1}{2}$, $a > 0$, $b > 0$ and $c > 0$. Let $\psi \in \beta_{\mu,\frac{c}{a}}$, then $\psi(\frac{x}{a},\frac{b}{a})$ belongs to $\beta_{\mu,c+b}$.*

Proof From [3, 4], for $\psi \in \beta_\mu \subset L^2(I)$ and $a > 0$, $b > 0$, the following relations hold

$$h_\mu\{\psi(\frac{x}{a},\frac{b}{a})\}(t) = a^{-\mu+\frac{1}{2}} t^{-\mu-\frac{1}{2}} (bt)^{\frac{1}{2}} J_\mu(bt)(h_\mu\psi)(at), \quad t \in I. \qquad (10.8)$$

$$h_\mu\{\psi(\frac{x}{a},\frac{b}{a})\}(\eta) = a^{-\mu+\frac{1}{2}} \eta^{-\mu-\frac{1}{2}} (b\eta)^{\frac{1}{2}} J_\mu(b\eta)(h_\mu\psi)(a\eta), \quad \eta \in \mathbb{C}. \qquad (10.9)$$

Since $z^{-\mu} J_\mu(z)$ is an even entire function therefore there exists $M(\mu) > 0$ such that

$$|e^{-b|\text{Im}\eta|}(b\eta)^{-\mu} J_\mu(b\eta)| \le M(\mu), \quad \eta \in \mathbb{C}. \qquad (10.10)$$

For proving Lemma 10.2, we take $h_\mu\psi \in \mathscr{Y}_{\mu,\frac{c}{a}}$, using from [3, p. 285] $\eta^{-\mu-\frac{1}{2}} h_\mu \{\psi(\frac{x}{a},\frac{b}{a})\}(\eta)$ is even entire function, then we have

$$\alpha^\mu_{c+b,k}(h_\mu\{\psi(\frac{x}{a},\frac{b}{a})\}(\eta)) = \sup_\eta |e^{-(c+b)|\text{Im}\eta|} \eta^{2k-\mu-\frac{1}{2}} h_\mu\{\psi(\frac{x}{a},\frac{b}{a})\}(\eta)|.$$

In view of (10.9), we get

$$\begin{aligned}
\alpha^{\mu}_{c+b,k}&(h_{\mu}\{\psi(\frac{x}{a},\frac{b}{a})\}(\eta)) \\
&= \sup_{\eta} |e^{-(c+b)|\mathrm{Im}\eta|}\eta^{2k-\mu-\frac{1}{2}}a^{-\mu+\frac{1}{2}}\eta^{-\mu-\frac{1}{2}}(b\eta)^{\frac{1}{2}}J_{\mu}(b\eta)(h_{\mu}\psi)(a\eta)| \\
&= \sup_{\eta} |e^{-(c+b)|\mathrm{Im}\eta|}\eta^{2k-\mu-\frac{1}{2}}a^{-\mu+\frac{1}{2}}b^{\mu+\frac{1}{2}}(b\eta)^{-\mu}J_{\mu}(b\eta)(h_{\mu}\psi)(a\eta)| \\
&= b^{\mu+\frac{1}{2}}\sup_{\eta} |e^{-b|\mathrm{Im}\eta|}(b\eta)^{-\mu}J_{\mu}(b\eta)e^{-c|\mathrm{Im}\eta|}\eta^{2k-\mu-\frac{1}{2}}a^{-\mu+\frac{1}{2}}(h_{\mu}\psi)(a\eta)|.
\end{aligned}$$

Using (10.10), the last expression yields

$$\alpha^{\mu}_{c+b,k}(h_{\mu}\{\psi(\frac{x}{a},\frac{b}{a})\}(\eta)) \le b^{\mu+\frac{1}{2}}M(\mu)\sup_{\eta}|e^{-c|\mathrm{Im}\eta|}\eta^{2k-\mu-\frac{1}{2}}a^{-\mu+\frac{1}{2}}(h_{\mu}\psi)(a\eta)|.$$

Now, substituting $a\eta = z$, we get

$$\begin{aligned}
\alpha^{\mu}_{c+b,k}(h_{\mu}\{\psi(\frac{x}{a},\frac{b}{a})\}(\eta)) &\le b^{\mu+\frac{1}{2}}M(\mu)\sup_{z}|e^{-\frac{c}{a}|\mathrm{Im}z|}(\frac{z}{a})^{2k-\mu-\frac{1}{2}}a^{-\mu+\frac{1}{2}}(h_{\mu}\psi)(z)| \\
&\le b^{\mu+\frac{1}{2}}a^{-2k+1}M(\mu)\sup_{z}|e^{-\frac{c}{a}|\mathrm{Im}z|}z^{2k-\mu-\frac{1}{2}}(h_{\mu}\psi)(z)| \\
&\le b^{\mu+\frac{1}{2}}a^{-2k+1}M(\mu)\alpha^{\mu}_{\frac{c}{a},k}(h_{\mu}\psi).
\end{aligned}$$

Thus $h_{\mu}\{\psi(\frac{x}{a},\frac{b}{a})\} \in \mathscr{Y}_{\mu,c+b}$. Then by [1, Theorem 1, p. 683], it follows that $\psi(\frac{x}{a},\frac{b}{a}) \in \beta_{\mu,c+b}$. □

Theorem 10.2 *Let $\mu > -\frac{1}{2}$, $a > 0$ and $c > 0$. Let $\psi \in \beta_{\mu,\frac{c}{a}}$ be a Bessel wavelet and $f \in \beta_{\mu,d}$, then the function*

$$(B_{\psi}f)(b,a) = (f\#\psi_a)(b), \quad b > 0 \tag{10.11}$$

belongs to $\beta_{\mu,d+c}$.

Proof By Betancor et al. [3, Proposition 3.4, p. 286],

$$\begin{aligned}
h_{\mu}\{(B_{\psi}f)(b,a)\}(\eta) = h_{\mu}(f\#\psi_a)(\eta) &= \eta^{-\mu-\frac{1}{2}}(h_{\mu}f)(\eta)(h_{\mu}\psi_a)(\eta) \\
&= \eta^{-\mu-\frac{1}{2}}(h_{\mu}f)(\eta)(h_{\mu}\psi)(a\eta).
\end{aligned} \tag{10.12}$$

Now, for $k \in \mathbb{N}_0$

$$\alpha^{\mu}_{d+c,k}\{h_{\mu}((B_{\psi}f)(b,a))(\eta)\} = \sup_{\eta}|e^{-(d+c)|\mathrm{Im}\eta|}\eta^{2k-\mu-\frac{1}{2}}h_{\mu}((B_{\psi}f)(b,a))(\eta)|.$$

Using (10.12), we find

$$\begin{aligned}
&\alpha^{\mu}_{d+c,k}\{h_\mu((B_\psi f)(b,a))(\eta)\}\\
&= \sup_\eta |e^{-(d+c)|\mathrm{Im}\eta|}\eta^{2k-\mu-\frac{1}{2}}\eta^{-\mu-\frac{1}{2}}(h_\mu f)(\eta)(h_\mu\psi)(a\eta)|\\
&\le \sup_\eta |e^{-d|\mathrm{Im}\eta|}\eta^{2k-\mu-\frac{1}{2}}(h_\mu f)(\eta)| \sup_\eta |e^{-c|\mathrm{Im}\eta|}\eta^{-\mu-\frac{1}{2}}(h_\mu\psi)(a\eta)|\\
&\le \alpha^{\mu}_{d,k}(h_\mu f) \sup_\eta |e^{-c|\mathrm{Im}\eta|}\eta^{-\mu-\frac{1}{2}}(h_\mu\psi)(a\eta)|.
\end{aligned}$$

Taking $a\eta = z$, we get

$$\begin{aligned}
\alpha^{\mu}_{d+c,k}\{h_\mu((B_\psi f)(b,a))(\eta)\} &\le \alpha^{\mu}_{d,k}(h_\mu f) \sup_z |e^{-\frac{c}{a}|\mathrm{Im}z|}\left(\frac{z}{a}\right)^{-\mu-\frac{1}{2}}(h_\mu\psi)(z)|\\
&\le a^{\mu+\frac{1}{2}}\alpha^{\mu}_{d,k}(h_\mu f) \sup_z |e^{-\frac{c}{a}|\mathrm{Im}z|}z^{-\mu-\frac{1}{2}}(h_\mu\psi)(z)|\\
&\le a^{\mu+\frac{1}{2}}\alpha^{\mu}_{d,k}(h_\mu f)\alpha^{\mu}_{\frac{c}{a},0}(h_\mu\psi),
\end{aligned}$$

for every $k \in \mathbb{N}_0$.

Since $f \in \beta_{\mu,d}$ and $\psi \in \beta_{\mu,\frac{c}{a}}$, then by Zemanian [1, Theorem1, p. 683], $(h_\mu f) \in \mathscr{Y}_{\mu,d}$ and $(h_\mu\psi) \in \mathscr{Y}_{\mu,\frac{c}{a}}$, then we obtain $h_\mu((B_\psi f)(b,a)) \in \mathscr{Y}_{\mu,d+c}$. Thus by Zemanian [1, Theorem1, p. 683] $(B_\psi f)(b,a) = (f\#\psi_a)(b) \in \beta_{\mu,d+c}$. □

Theorem 10.3 *Let $f \in \mathscr{E}'_\mu(I)$, $\mu > -\frac{1}{2}$ and $a > 0$, $c > 0$. Let $\psi \in \beta_{\mu,\frac{c}{a}}$ be a Bessel wavelet, then*

$$(B_\psi f)(b,a) = (f\#\psi_a)(b), \quad b > 0$$

belongs to $\beta_{\mu,n+c}$ for suitable $n \in \mathbb{N}_0$.

Proof From Betancor et al. [3, Proposition 4.7, p. 293],

$$\begin{aligned}
h_\mu((B_\psi f)(b,a))(\eta) = h_\mu(f\#\psi_a)(\eta) &= \eta^{-\mu-\frac{1}{2}}(h'_\mu f)(\eta)(h_\mu\psi_a)(\eta)\\
&= \eta^{-\mu-\frac{1}{2}}(h'_\mu f)(\eta)(h_\mu\psi)(a\eta).
\end{aligned}$$

The above expression becomes

$$\begin{aligned}
&|e^{-(n+c)|\mathrm{Im}\eta|}\eta^{2k-\mu-\frac{1}{2}}h_\mu((B_\psi f)(b,a))(\eta)|\\
&= |e^{-(n+c)|\mathrm{Im}\eta|}\eta^{2k-\mu-\frac{1}{2}}\eta^{-\mu-\frac{1}{2}}(h'_\mu f)(\eta)(h_\mu\psi)(a\eta)|\\
&\le |e^{-n|\mathrm{Im}\eta|}\eta^{-\mu-\frac{1}{2}}(h'_\mu f)(\eta)||e^{-c|\mathrm{Im}\eta|}\eta^{2k-\mu-\frac{1}{2}}(h_\mu\psi)(a\eta)|.
\end{aligned}$$

From Betancor et al. [3, Proposition 4.5], for some $n, r \in \mathbb{N}_0$ and all $\eta \in \mathbb{C}$, using the result $|\eta^{-\mu-\frac{1}{2}} h'_\mu(f)(\eta)| \leq B(1+|\eta|^{2r})e^{n|\mathrm{Im}\eta|}$ where B is constant then, we obtain

$$\begin{aligned}
&|e^{-(n+c)|\mathrm{Im}\eta|}\eta^{2k-\mu-\frac{1}{2}} h_\mu((B_\psi f)(b,a))(\eta)| \\
&\leq B|e^{-n|\mathrm{Im}\eta|}(1+|\eta|^{2r})e^{n|\,\mathrm{Im}\eta|}||e^{-c|\,\mathrm{Im}\eta|}\eta^{2k-\mu-\frac{1}{2}}(h_\mu\psi)(a\eta)| \\
&\leq B\{|e^{-c|\,\mathrm{Im}\eta|}\eta^{2k-\mu-\frac{1}{2}}(h_\mu\psi)(a\eta)| + |e^{-c|\,\mathrm{Im}\eta|}\eta^{2(k+r)-\mu-\frac{1}{2}}(h_\mu\psi)(a\eta)|\}.
\end{aligned}$$

So that

$$\begin{aligned}
\sup_{\eta\in\mathbb{C}} |e^{-(n+c)|\,\mathrm{Im}\eta|}\eta^{2k-\mu-\frac{1}{2}} h_\mu((B_\psi f)(b,a))(\eta)| &\leq B\{\sup_{\eta\in\mathbb{C}} |e^{-c|\,\mathrm{Im}\eta|}\eta^{2k-\mu-\frac{1}{2}}(h_\mu\psi)(a\eta)| \\
&\quad + \sup_{\eta\in\mathbb{C}} |e^{-c|\,\mathrm{Im}\eta|}\eta^{2(k+r)-\mu-\frac{1}{2}}(h_\mu\psi)(a\eta)|\}.
\end{aligned}$$

Next, substituting $a\eta = z$, we get

$$\begin{aligned}
\alpha^\mu_{n+c,k}\{h_\mu((B_\psi f)(b,a))(\eta)\} &\leq B\{\sup_z |e^{-\frac{c}{a}|\,\mathrm{Im}z|}\left(\frac{z}{a}\right)^{2k-\mu-\frac{1}{2}}(h_\mu\psi)(z)| \\
&\quad + \sup_z |e^{-\frac{c}{a}|\,\mathrm{Im}z|}\left(\frac{z}{a}\right)^{2(k+r)-\mu-\frac{1}{2}}(h_\mu\psi)(z)|\} \\
&\leq Ba^{-2k+\mu+\frac{1}{2}}\{\sup_z |e^{-\frac{c}{a}|\,\mathrm{Im}z|}z^{2k-\mu-\frac{1}{2}}(h_\mu\psi)(z)| \\
&\quad + a^{-2r}\sup_z |e^{-\frac{c}{a}|\,\mathrm{Im}z|}z^{2(k+r)-\mu-\frac{1}{2}}(h_\mu\psi)(z)|\} \\
&\leq Ba^{-2k+\mu+\frac{1}{2}}\{\alpha^\mu_{\frac{c}{a},k}(h_\mu\psi)| + a^{-2r}\alpha^\mu_{\frac{c}{a},k+r}(h_\mu\psi)\},
\end{aligned}$$

for every $k \in \mathbb{N}_0$. Since $\psi \in \beta_{\mu,\frac{c}{a}}$ by Zemanian [1, Theorem1, p. 683], $(h_\mu\psi) \in \mathcal{Y}_{\mu,\frac{c}{a}}$, therefore $h_\mu((B_\psi f)(b,a)) \in \mathcal{Y}_{\mu,n+c}$. Thus by Zemanian [1, Theorem1, p. 683], $(B_\psi f)(b,a) = (f\#\psi_a)(b) \in \beta_{\mu,n+c}$. □

10.3 Inversion Formula of the Continuous Bessel Wavelet Transform of the Distributions

In this section, the inversion formula of the Bessel wavelet transform of distributions in β'_μ and associated results are discussed by exploiting the theory of Hankel transform.

From Theorem 10.1, we find that the continuous Bessel wavelet transform of the distribution of type $Cx^{\mu+\frac{1}{2}}$ will be zero. Therefore, the inversion formula of the Bessel wavelet transform in β'_μ cannot be defined. Therefore, the inversion formula of the continuous Bessel wavelet transform will be valid for modulo a $Cx^{\mu+\frac{1}{2}}$ distributions.

For investigating the inversion formula of the continuous Bessel wavelet transform of distributions, our result will be based on the following considerations:

(I) Inversion formula of the continuous Bessel wavelet transform of distributions will be found on $\beta'_{\mu,F}$, which can be obtained by filtering of β'_μ. Filtering can be done by the following way:

   (i) Removing all the non-zero $Cx^{\mu+\frac{1}{2}}$ distributions from β'_μ.

   (ii) Removing all non-zero $Cx^{\mu+\frac{1}{2}}$ that appear with a distribution as a union. For example in the distribution $\frac{x^{\mu+\frac{5}{2}}}{1+x^2} = x^{\mu+\frac{1}{2}} - \frac{x^{\mu+\frac{1}{2}}}{1+x^2}$, we would omit $x^{\mu+\frac{1}{2}}$ and retain only $-\frac{x^{\mu+\frac{1}{2}}}{1+x^2}$.

(II) The Bessel wavelet kernels under consideration for determining the Bessel wavelet transform are those Bessel wavelets whose all the moments weighted by $x^{\mu+\frac{1}{2}}$ are non-zero. Let β_μ^{2m} be a collection of such Bessel wavelet kernel.

Lemma 10.3 *Let $\mu > -\frac{1}{2}$ and $\psi\left(\frac{x}{a}, \frac{b}{a}\right)$ be Hankel translation and dilation of $\psi \in \beta_\mu(I)$, then*

$$S_{\mu,x}\psi\left(\frac{x}{a}, \frac{b}{a}\right) = S_{\mu,b}\psi\left(\frac{x}{a}, \frac{b}{a}\right).$$

Proof Using the techniques of Lemma 9.6, it can be proved that

$$S_{\mu,x}\psi\left(\frac{x}{a}, \frac{b}{a}\right) = S_{\mu,b}\psi\left(\frac{x}{a}, \frac{b}{a}\right).$$

Theorem 10.4 *Let $\psi \in \beta_\mu$ be a Bessel wavelet with $\psi(x) = 0,\ x \geq c,\ c > 0$. Then for $f \in \beta'_\mu$, the continuous Bessel wavelet transform $(B_\psi f)(b, a)$ is a continuous function of a, b in a compact neighborhood of the point (b, a), $a > 0, b > 0$.*

Proof For $\psi \in \beta_\mu$ is a Bessel wavelet and $f \in \beta'_\mu$, then

$$(B_\psi f)(b, a) = \left\langle f(t), a^{\mu-\frac{1}{2}}\psi\left(\frac{t}{a}, \frac{b}{a}\right)\right\rangle, \quad a > 0,\ b > 0.$$

To check the continuity of $(B_\psi f)(b, a)$, we have

$$\begin{aligned}
&(B_\psi f)(b + \Delta b, a + \Delta a) - (B_\psi f)(b, a) \\
&= \left\langle f(t), (a + \Delta a)^{\mu-\frac{1}{2}}\psi\left(\frac{t}{a + \Delta a}, \frac{b + \Delta b}{a + \Delta a}\right)\right\rangle - \left\langle f(t), a^{\mu-\frac{1}{2}}\psi\left(\frac{t}{a}, \frac{b}{a}\right)\right\rangle \\
&= \left\langle f(t), (a + \Delta a)^{\mu-\frac{1}{2}}\psi\left(\frac{t}{a + \Delta a}, \frac{b + \Delta b}{a + \Delta a}\right) - a^{\mu-\frac{1}{2}}\psi\left(\frac{t}{a}, \frac{b}{a}\right)\right\rangle.
\end{aligned}$$

Therefore, we have to show the expression

$$(a+\Delta a)^{\mu-\frac{1}{2}}\psi\Big(\frac{t}{a+\Delta a},\frac{b+\Delta b}{a+\Delta a}\Big)-a^{\mu-\frac{1}{2}}\psi\Big(\frac{t}{a},\frac{b}{a}\Big)\to 0,$$

in the topology of β_μ as $\Delta a, \Delta b \to 0$.

Using (1.80) and [4, p. 318], we obtain

$$\begin{aligned}
&(t^{-1}D_t)^k t^{-\mu-\frac{1}{2}}\Big\{(a+\Delta a)^{\mu-\frac{1}{2}}\psi\Big(\frac{t}{a+\Delta a},\frac{b+\Delta b}{a+\Delta a}\Big)-a^{\mu-\frac{1}{2}}\psi\Big(\frac{t}{a},\frac{b}{a}\Big)\Big\}\\
&=(t^{-1}D_t)^k t^{-\mu-\frac{1}{2}}\Big[(a+\Delta a)^{\mu-\frac{1}{2}}.(a+\Delta a)^{-\mu+\frac{1}{2}}\\
&\quad\times h_\mu\Big\{y^{-\mu-\frac{1}{2}}(ty)^{\frac{1}{2}}J_\mu(ty)(h_\mu\psi)((a+\delta a)y)\Big\}(b+\delta b)\\
&\quad-a^{\mu-\frac{1}{2}}.a^{-\mu+\frac{1}{2}}h_\mu\Big\{y^{-\mu-\frac{1}{2}}(ty)^{\frac{1}{2}}J_\mu(ty)(h_\mu\psi)(ay)\Big\}(b)\Big]\\
&=h_\mu\Big\{y^{-\mu}(t^{-1}D_t)^k t^{-\mu}J_\mu(ty)(h_\mu\psi)((a+\delta a)y)\Big\}(b+\delta b)\\
&\quad-h_\mu\Big\{y^{-\mu}(t^{-1}D_t)^k t^{-\mu}J_\mu(ty)(h_\mu\psi)(ay)\Big\}(b)\\
&=h_\mu\Big\{y^{-\mu}(-y)^k t^{-\mu-k}J_{\mu+k}(ty)(h_\mu\psi)((a+\delta a)y)\Big\}(b+\delta b)\\
&\quad-h_\mu\Big\{y^{-\mu}(-y)^k t^{-\mu-k}J_{\mu+k}(ty)(h_\mu\psi)(ay)\Big\}(b)\\
&=h_\mu\Big\{(-y^2)^k(yt)^{-\mu-k}J_{\mu+k}(ty)(h_\mu\psi)((a+\delta a)y)\Big\}(b+\delta b)\\
&\quad-h_\mu\Big\{(-y^2)^k(yt)^{-\mu-k}J_{\mu+k}(ty)(h_\mu\psi)(ay)\Big\}(b)\\
&=h_\mu\Big\{(yt)^{-\mu-k}J_{\mu+k}(ty)(h_\mu(S_\mu^k\psi))((a+\delta a)y).(a+\delta a)^{2k}(-1))^k\Big\}(b+\delta b)\\
&\quad-h_\mu\Big\{(yt)^{-\mu-k}J_{\mu+k}(ty)(h_\mu(S_\mu^k\psi))(ay).(-a^2)^k\Big\}(b).
\end{aligned}$$

Since

$$\begin{aligned}
\Big|h_\mu\Big\{(yt)^{-\mu-k}J_{\mu+k}(ty)(h_\mu(S_\mu^k\psi))((a+\delta a)y).(a+\delta a)^{2k}(-1))^k\Big\}(b+\delta b)&\\
-h_\mu\Big\{(yt)^{-\mu-k}J_{\mu+k}(ty)(h_\mu(S_\mu^k\psi))(ay).(-a^2)^k\Big\}(b)\Big|&
\end{aligned}$$

converges to zero as $\Delta a, \Delta b \to 0$, therefore,

$$\sup_{t\in I}\Big|(t^{-1}D_t)^k t^{-\mu-\frac{1}{2}}\Big\{(a+\Delta a)^{\mu-\frac{1}{2}}\psi\Big(\frac{t}{a+\Delta a},\frac{b+\Delta b}{a+\Delta a}\Big)-a^{\mu-\frac{1}{2}}\psi\Big(\frac{t}{a},\frac{b}{a}\Big)\Big\}\Big|\to 0,$$

as $\Delta a, \Delta b \to 0$.

This implies,

$$(a+\Delta a)^{\mu-\frac{1}{2}}\psi\Big(\frac{t}{a+\Delta a},\frac{b+\Delta b}{a+\Delta a}\Big)-a^{\mu-\frac{1}{2}}\psi\Big(\frac{t}{a},\frac{b}{a}\Big)\to 0,$$

in the topology of β_μ as $\Delta a, \Delta b \to 0$. □

Theorem 10.5 *Let $f \in \beta'_{\mu,F}$, $\phi \in \beta_\mu$ and ψ be a basic Bessel wavelet belongs to β_μ for $\mu > -\frac{1}{2}$. Then*

$$\begin{aligned}&\Big\langle\frac{1}{C_{\mu,\psi}}\int_\nu^A\int_0^B\Big\langle f(t),a^{\mu-\frac{1}{2}}\psi\Big(\frac{t}{a},\frac{b}{a}\Big)\Big\rangle a^{\mu-\frac{1}{2}}\psi\Big(\frac{x}{a},\frac{b}{a}\Big)\frac{dbda}{a^{2\mu+2}},\phi(x)\Big\rangle\\&\quad=\Big\langle f(t),\frac{1}{C_{\mu,\psi}}\int_0^C\int_\nu^A\int_0^B\psi\Big(\frac{t}{a},\frac{b}{a}\Big)\psi\Big(\frac{x}{a},\frac{b}{a}\Big)\phi(x)\frac{dbda}{a^3}dx\Big\rangle.\end{aligned}\tag{10.13}$$

To prove the Theorem 10.5, we require the following lemmas:

Lemma 10.4 *Let $F_{A,B,C,\nu}(t)$ be the function which is defined by*

$$F_{A,B,C,\nu}(t)=\frac{1}{C_{\mu,\psi}}\int_0^C\int_\nu^A\int_0^B\psi\Big(\frac{t}{a},\frac{b}{a}\Big)\psi\Big(\frac{x}{a},\frac{b}{a}\Big)\phi(x)\frac{dbdadx}{a^3},\quad a,b,x,t>0\tag{10.14}$$

then $F_{A,B,C,\nu}(t)\neq 0$ for $t\in(0,C+2C_1)$, where $\phi,\psi\in\beta_\mu$ with $\phi(x)=0$, for $x\geq C$ and $\psi(x)=0$, for $x\geq C_1$.

Proof For showing $F_{A,B,C,\nu}(t)\neq 0$ for $t\in(0,C+2C_1)$, we need the following steps:

Step 1: For showing the support of $\psi\left(\frac{t}{a},\frac{b}{a}\right)$ in terms of t, we have to prove that $\psi\left(\frac{t}{a},\frac{b}{a}\right)\neq 0$.

In view of Betancor [5, p. 58], we take

$$\psi\Big(\frac{t}{a},\frac{b}{a}\Big)=\int_0^\infty\psi(z)D_\mu\Big(\frac{t}{a},\frac{b}{a},z\Big)dz,\tag{10.15}$$

where

$$D_\mu\Big(\frac{t}{a},\frac{b}{a},z\Big)=\begin{cases}\frac{1}{2^{3\mu-1}\sqrt{\pi}\Gamma(\mu+\frac{1}{2})}\left(\frac{tbz}{a^2}\right)^{\frac{1}{2}-\mu}\left[z^2-\left(\frac{t-b}{a}\right)^2\right]^{\mu-\frac{1}{2}}\left[\left(\frac{t+b}{a}\right)^2-z^2\right]^{\mu-\frac{1}{2}}, & |\frac{t-b}{a}|<z<\frac{t+b}{a}\\ 0, & z<|\frac{t-b}{a}| \text{ or } z>\frac{t+b}{a}.\end{cases}\tag{10.16}$$

Then $\psi(z),\ D_\mu\left(\frac{t}{a}, \frac{b}{a}, z\right)$ can be non-zero under the following conditions:

(i) $0 < z < C_1$; as $\psi \in \beta_\mu$, so $\psi \in \beta_{\mu,C_1}$ for $C_1 > 0$,
(ii) $\left|\frac{t-b}{a}\right| < z < \frac{t+b}{a}$; as $D_\mu\left(\frac{t}{a}, \frac{b}{a}, z\right) \neq 0$ from(10.16).

From (i), we get

(iii) $-C_1 < -z < 0.$

Now, adding (ii) and (iii), we find

$$\left|\frac{t-b}{a}\right| - C_1 < z - z < \frac{t+b}{a},$$

so that

$$\left|\frac{t-b}{a}\right| < C_1 \quad \text{and} \quad \frac{t+b}{a} > 0,$$

Hence $\psi\left(\frac{t}{a}, \frac{b}{a}\right)$ is non-zero for $-C_1 < \frac{t-b}{a} < C_1,\ t > 0$.

Step 2. Like step 1, we can prove $\psi\left(\frac{x}{a}, \frac{b}{a}\right) \neq 0$ for $-C_1 < \frac{x-b}{a} < C_1$ or $-C_1 < \frac{x-b}{a} < C_1$.

Step 3. As $\phi \in \beta_\mu$, so $\phi(x) \neq 0$ for $0 < x < C,\ C > 0$.

Now, from step 1, step 2, and step 3, we conclude that $F_{A,B,C,\nu}(t)$ is non-zero for

(1) $-C_1 < \frac{t-b}{a} < C_1$.
(2) $-C_1 < \frac{b-x}{a} < C_1$.
(3) $0 < x < C$.

In view of (1) and (2), we get

$$\left|\frac{t-x}{a}\right| < 2C_1.$$

For dilation parameter a, we found the following cases:
Case I: If $a \leq 1$, $|t-x| < 2C_1$.
This shows that $F_{A,B,C,\nu}(t) \neq 0$ if $|t-x| < 2C_1$.
Case II: If $a \geq 1$, then $|t-x| \geq 2C_1$.
Hence, we find that $F_{A,B,C,\nu}(t) = 0$ for $|t-x| \geq 2C_1$.

From the aforesaid steps and cases, we find the support of $F_{A,B,C,\nu}(t)$ is $t = t - x + x$.
The above implies that

$$t \leq |t-x| + |x| < 2C_1 + C.$$

Then, the support of $F_{A,B,C,\nu}(t)$ is contained in $(0, C + 2C_1)$. □

After showing the support of $F_{A,B,C,\nu}(t)$, with help of following Lemma we shall prove that $F_{A,B,C,\nu}(t) \in \beta_\mu$.

Lemma 10.5 *Let $F_{A,B,C,\nu}(t)$ be the function which is defined by*

$$F_{A,B,C,\nu}(t) = \frac{1}{C_{\mu,\psi}} \int_0^C \int_\nu^A \int_0^B \psi\Big(\frac{t}{a}, \frac{b}{a}\Big)\psi\Big(\frac{x}{a}, \frac{b}{a}\Big)\phi(x)\frac{dbdadx}{a^3}, \quad a, b, x, t > 0 \tag{10.17}$$

then $F_{A,B,C,\nu}(t)$ belongs to β_μ.

Proof From Lemma 10.2, we have $\psi\Big(\frac{t}{a}, \frac{b}{a}\Big)$ is an element of β_μ, so $\psi\Big(\frac{t}{a}, \frac{b}{a}\Big)$ be a smooth function of variable t. Hence $F_{A,B,C,\nu}(t)$ be smooth. From (10.17) and [4, p. 318], we find

$$\begin{aligned}
&\Big|(t^{-1}D_t)^k t^{-\mu-\frac{1}{2}} F_{A,B,C,\nu}(t)\Big| \\
&= \Big|(t^{-1}D_t)^k t^{-\mu-\frac{1}{2}} \frac{1}{C_{\mu,\psi}} \int_0^C \int_\nu^A \int_0^B \psi\Big(\frac{t}{a}, \frac{b}{a}\Big)\psi\Big(\frac{x}{a}, \frac{b}{a}\Big)\phi(x)\frac{dbdadx}{a^3}\Big| \\
&= \Big|\frac{1}{C_{\mu,\psi}} \int_0^C \int_\nu^A \int_0^B (t^{-1}D_t)^k t^{-\mu-\frac{1}{2}} h_\mu\Big(y^{-\mu-\frac{1}{2}}(ty)^{\frac{1}{2}} J_\mu(ty)(h_\mu\psi)(ay)\Big)(b) \\
&\quad \times h_\mu\Big(\xi^{-\mu-\frac{1}{2}}(x\xi)^{\frac{1}{2}} J_\mu(x\xi)(h_\mu\psi)(a\xi)\Big)(b)\phi(x)\frac{dbdadx}{a^{2\mu+2}}\Big| \\
&= \Big|\frac{1}{C_{\mu,\psi}} \int_0^C \int_\nu^A \int_0^B h_\mu\Big(y^{-\mu-\frac{1}{2}} y^{\frac{1}{2}} (t^{-1}D_t)^k t^{-\mu} J_\mu(ty)(h_\mu\psi)(ay)\Big)(b) \\
&\quad \times h_\mu\Big(\xi^{-\mu-\frac{1}{2}}(x\xi)^{\frac{1}{2}} J_\mu(x\xi)(h_\mu\psi)(a\xi)\Big)(b)\phi(x)\frac{dbdadx}{a^{2\mu+2}}\Big|.
\end{aligned}$$

Applying $(t^{-1}D_t)^k t^{-\mu} J_\mu(yt) = (-y)^k t^{-\mu-k} J_{\mu+k}(yt)$, we get

$$\begin{aligned}
&\Big|(t^{-1}D_t)^k t^{-\mu-\frac{1}{2}} F_{A,B,C,\nu}(t)\Big| \\
&= \Big|\frac{1}{C_{\mu,\psi}} \int_0^C \int_\nu^A \int_0^B h_\mu\Big(y^{-\mu}(-y)^k t^{-\mu-k} J_{\mu+k}(ty)(h_\mu\psi)(ay)\Big)(b) \\
&\quad \times h_\mu\Big(\xi^{-\mu-\frac{1}{2}}(x\xi)^{\frac{1}{2}} J_\mu(x\xi)(h_\mu\psi)(a\xi)\Big)(b)\phi(x)\frac{dbdadx}{a^{2\mu+2}}\Big| \\
&= \Big|\frac{1}{C_{\mu,\psi}} \int_0^C \int_\nu^A \int_0^B h_\mu\Big((-y^2)^k (ty)^{-\mu-k} J_{\mu+k}(ty)(h_\mu\psi)(ay)\Big)(b) \\
&\quad \times x^{\mu+\frac{1}{2}} h_\mu\Big((x\xi)^{-\mu} J_\mu(x\xi)(h_\mu\psi)(a\xi)\Big)(b)\phi(x)\frac{dbdadx}{a^{2\mu+2}}\Big|.
\end{aligned}$$

Taking the formula $h_\mu(S_{\mu,x}\phi(x))(y) = -y^2(h_\mu\phi)(y)$ from (1.114), we have

$$\begin{aligned}
&\left|(t^{-1}D_t)^k t^{-\mu-\frac{1}{2}} F_{A,B,C,\nu}(t)\right| \\
&\leq \frac{1}{C_{\mu,\psi}} \int_0^C \int_\nu^A \int_0^B \left| h_\mu\Big((ty)^{-\mu-k} J_{\mu+k}(ty)(h_\mu(S^k_{\mu,x}\psi))(ay)a^{-2k}\Big)(b) \right. \\
&\quad \left. \times\, h_\mu\Big((x\xi)^{-\mu} J_\mu(x\xi)(h_\mu\psi)(a\xi)\Big)(b)x^{\mu+\frac{1}{2}}\phi(x) \right| \frac{dbdadx}{a^{2\mu+2}} \\
&\leq \frac{1}{C_{\mu,\psi}} \int_0^C \int_\nu^A \int_0^B \left| h_\mu\Big((ty)^{-\mu-k} J_{\mu+k}(ty)(h_\mu(S^k_{\mu,x}\psi))(ay)\Big)(b) \right. \\
&\quad \left. \times\, h_\mu\Big((x\xi)^{-\mu} J_\mu(x\xi)(h_\mu\psi)(a\xi)\Big)(b)x^{\mu+\frac{1}{2}} \frac{\phi(x)}{a^{2k+2\mu+2}} \right| dbdadx.
\end{aligned}$$

Since the integrand in the above integral

$$h_\mu\Big((ty)^{-\mu-k} J_{\mu+k}(ty)(h_\mu(S^k_{\mu,x}\psi))(ay)\Big)(b) h_\mu\Big((x\xi)^{-\mu} J_\mu(x\xi)(h_\mu\psi)(a\xi)\Big)(b) \frac{x^{\mu+\frac{1}{2}}\phi(x)}{a^{2k+2\mu+2}}$$

is uniformly continuous in the compact set

$$\Lambda = \{(a,b,x,t) : \nu \leq a \leq A, 0 \leq b \leq B, 0 \leq x \leq C, s_1 \leq t \leq s_2\},$$

and bounded over Λ,

$$\sup_{t\in I} \left|(t^{-1}D_t)^k t^{-\mu-\frac{1}{2}} F_{A,B,C,\nu}(t)\right| < \infty. \tag{10.18}$$

From aforesaid facts and Lemma 10.4, (10.18) shows that $F_{A,B,C,\nu}(t)$ is smooth function with $F_{A,B,C,\nu}(t) = 0$ for $t \geq C + 2C_1$ such that

$$\gamma_k^\mu(F_{A,B,C,\nu}) = \sup_{t\in I} \left|(t^{-1}D_t)^k t^{-\mu-\frac{1}{2}} F_{A,B,C,\nu}(t)\right| < \infty, \forall\, k \in \mathbb{N}_0.$$

This implies that $F_{A,B,C,\nu}(t) \in \beta_{\mu,C+2C_1} \subset \beta_\mu$. □

Lemma 10.6 *Let $\psi \in \beta_\mu$ be a Bessel wavelet, $\phi \in \beta_\mu$ for $\mu > -\frac{1}{2}$,and*

$$F(t) = \int_0^C \int_\nu^A \int_0^B \psi\Big(\frac{t}{a}, \frac{b}{a}\Big)\psi\Big(\frac{x}{a}, \frac{b}{a}\Big)\phi(x)\frac{dbda}{a^3}dx, \qquad a,b,x,t > 0 \tag{10.19}$$

then

$$t^{-\mu-\frac{1}{2}} S^k_{\mu,t} F(t) = \int_0^C \int_\nu^A \int_0^B h_\mu\Big((yt)^{-\mu} J_\mu(yt)(h_\mu\psi)(ay)\Big)(b) \\ \times h_\mu\Big((\xi x)^{-\mu} J_\mu(\xi x)(h_\mu\psi)(a\xi)\Big)(b) x^{\mu+\frac{1}{2}} S^k_{\mu,x}\phi(x)\frac{dbdadx}{a^{2\mu+2}}.$$

Proof From (10.19), we have

$$t^{-\mu-\frac{1}{2}} S^k_{\mu,t} F(t) = t^{-\mu-\frac{1}{2}} S^k_{\mu,t} \int_0^C \int_\nu^A \int_0^B \psi\left(\frac{t}{a}, \frac{b}{a}\right)\psi\left(\frac{x}{a}, \frac{b}{a}\right)\phi(x)\frac{dbda}{a^3}dx \\ = t^{-\mu-\frac{1}{2}} \int_0^C \int_\nu^A \int_0^B S^k_{\mu,t}\psi\left(\frac{t}{a}, \frac{b}{a}\right)\psi\left(\frac{x}{a}, \frac{b}{a}\right)\phi(x)\frac{dbda}{a^3}dx.$$

Using the Lemma 10.3, we get

$$t^{-\mu-\frac{1}{2}} S^k_{\mu,t} F(t) = t^{-\mu-\frac{1}{2}} \int_0^C \int_\nu^A \int_0^B \left\{S^k_{\mu,b}\psi\left(\frac{t}{a}, \frac{b}{a}\right)\right\}\psi\left(\frac{x}{a}, \frac{b}{a}\right)\phi(x)\frac{dbdadx}{a^3}.$$

Therefore, by integration by parts,

$$t^{-\mu-\frac{1}{2}} S^k_{\mu,t} F(t) = t^{-\mu-\frac{1}{2}} \int_0^C \int_\nu^A \int_0^B \psi\left(\frac{t}{a}, \frac{b}{a}\right)\left\{S^k_{\mu,b}\psi\left(\frac{x}{a}, \frac{b}{a}\right)\right\}\phi(x)\frac{dbdadx}{a^3}.$$

Note that in the integration by parts with respect to b the boundary terms when evaluated at 0 and B will vanish in the limiting process as $B \to \infty$. So, we omit the remainder terms when evaluated at points 0 and B.

So that

$$t^{-\mu-\frac{1}{2}} S^k_{\mu,t} F(t) = t^{-\mu-\frac{1}{2}} \int_0^C \int_\nu^A \int_0^B \psi\left(\frac{t}{a}, \frac{b}{a}\right)\left\{S^k_{\mu,x}\psi\left(\frac{x}{a}, \frac{b}{a}\right)\right\}\phi(x)\frac{dbdadx}{a^3} \\ = \left\langle S^k_{\mu,x} \int_\nu^A \int_0^B t^{-\mu-\frac{1}{2}}\psi\left(\frac{t}{a}, \frac{b}{a}\right)\psi\left(\frac{x}{a}, \frac{b}{a}\right)\frac{dbda}{a^3}, \phi(x)\right\rangle.$$

By exploiting the distributional derivative, we get

$$t^{-\mu-\frac{1}{2}} S^k_{\mu,t} F(t) = \left\langle \int_\nu^A \int_0^B t^{-\mu-\frac{1}{2}}\psi\left(\frac{t}{a}, \frac{b}{a}\right)\psi\left(\frac{x}{a}, \frac{b}{a}\right)\frac{dbda}{a^3}, S^k_{\mu,x}\phi(x)\right\rangle \\ = \int_0^C \int_\nu^A \int_0^B t^{-\mu-\frac{1}{2}}\psi\left(\frac{t}{a}, \frac{b}{a}\right)\psi\left(\frac{x}{a}, \frac{b}{a}\right)S^k_{\mu,x}\phi(x)\frac{dbdadx}{a^3}. \tag{10.20}$$

In view of [4, p. 318], we find

$$t^{-\mu-\frac{1}{2}}S^k_{\mu,t}F(t)=\int_0^C\int_\nu^A\int_0^B t^{-\mu-\frac{1}{2}}h_\mu\Big(y^{-\mu-\frac{1}{2}}(yt)^{\frac{1}{2}}J_\mu(yt)(h_\mu\psi)(ay)\Big)(b)$$
$$\times\, h_\mu\Big(\xi^{-\mu-\frac{1}{2}}(\xi x)^{\frac{1}{2}}J_\mu(\xi x)(h_\mu\psi)(a\xi)\Big)(b)S^k_{\mu,x}\phi(x)\frac{dbdadx}{a^{2\mu+2}}$$
$$=\int_0^C\int_\nu^A\int_0^B h_\mu\Big((yt)^{-\mu}J_\mu(yt)(h_\mu\psi)(ay)\Big)(b)$$
$$\times\, h_\mu\Big((\xi x)^{-\mu}J_\mu(\xi x)(h_\mu\psi)(a\xi)\Big)(b)x^{\mu+\frac{1}{2}}S^k_{\mu,x}\phi(x)\frac{dbdadx}{a^{2\mu+2}}.$$

Lemma 10.7 *Let $F_{A,B,C,\nu}(t)$ be a function which is defined in Lemma 10.4, then*

$$\int_0^C\int_\nu^A\int_0^B\psi\Big(\frac{t}{a},\frac{b}{a}\Big)\psi\Big(\frac{x}{a},\frac{b}{a}\Big)\phi(x)\frac{dbda}{a^3}dx$$
$$=\lim_{m\to\infty}\Big[\sum_{i=1}^{m+1}\sum_{j=1}^{m}\sum_{l=1}^{m}\psi\Big(\frac{t}{a_i},\frac{b_j}{a_i}\Big)\psi\Big(\frac{x_l}{a_i},\frac{b_j}{a_i}\Big)\phi(x_l)\frac{1}{a_i^3}\Box_{i,j,l}\Big],$$

in the topology of β_μ, where

$$\Box_{i,j,l}=(a_i-a_{i-1})(b_j-b_{j-1})(x_l-x_{l-1})=\triangle a\triangle b\triangle x,$$

is volume of the elementary cuboid of the partition of the region $\{(a,b,x):\nu\le a\le A, 0\le b\le B, 0\le x\le C\}$.

Proof From (10.14), we have

$$F_{A,B,C,\nu}(t)=\frac{1}{C_{\mu,\psi}}\int_0^C\int_\nu^A\int_0^B\psi\Big(\frac{t}{a},\frac{b}{a}\Big)\psi\Big(\frac{x}{a},\frac{b}{a}\Big)\phi(x)\frac{dbda}{a^3}dx.$$

From the R.H.S. of the above integral, we denote

$$F(a,b,x,t)=\psi\Big(\frac{t}{a},\frac{b}{a}\Big)\psi\Big(\frac{x}{a},\frac{b}{a}\Big)\phi(x)\frac{1}{a^3}.$$

From [4, p. 318], we have

$$F(a,b,x,t)=a^{-\mu+\frac{1}{2}}h_\mu\Big(y^{-\mu-\frac{1}{2}}(yt)^{\frac{1}{2}}J_\mu(yt)(h_\mu\psi)(ay)\Big)(b)$$
$$\times\, a^{-\mu+\frac{1}{2}}h_\mu\Big(\xi^{-\mu-\frac{1}{2}}(\xi x)^{\frac{1}{2}}J_\mu(\xi x)(h_\mu\psi)(a\xi)\Big)(b)\phi(x)\frac{1}{a^3}$$
$$=h_\mu\Big((yt)^{-\mu}J_\mu(yt)(h_\mu\psi)(ay)\Big)(b)h_\mu\Big((\xi x)^{-\mu}J_\mu(\xi x)(h_\mu\psi)(a\xi)\Big)(b)$$
$$\times\,(xt)^{\mu+\frac{1}{2}}\phi(x)\frac{1}{a^{2\mu+2}}.$$

Since from Lemma 10.5, we get $F_{A,B,C,\nu}(t) \in \beta_{\mu,C+2C_1} \subset \beta_\mu$. Then it clearly shows that $F(a,b,x,t)$ is a continuous function of a, b, x and t over a compact set in $I^4(= I \times I \times I \times I)$ which is not intersecting the axis $a = 0$.

Let $\Lambda = \{(a,b,x,t) : \nu \le a \le A, 0 \le b \le B, 0 \le x \le C, s_1 \le t \le s_2\}$. Then $F(a,b,x,t)$ is uniformly continuous over the compact set Λ as a function of a, b, x and t. Hence for a given $\epsilon > 0$, there exists $\delta_0 > 0$ (independent of a, b, x and t) such that

$$\left| F(a+ \triangle a, b+ \triangle b, x+ \triangle x, t+ \triangle t) - F(a,b,x,t) \right| < \epsilon, \tag{10.21}$$

whenever $\|(\triangle a, \triangle b, \triangle x, \triangle t)\|_1 < \delta_0$. Using the technique of [6, Lemma 4.3, p. 2018], the topology generated by $\|(a,b,x,t)\|_1 = max\{|a|, |b|, |x|, |t|\}$ and $\|(a,b,x,t)\| = \sqrt{a^2+b^2+x^2+t^2}$ is the same over $I^4(= I \times I \times I \times I)$ as

$$\|(a,b,x,t)\|_1 \le \|(a,b,x,t)\| \le 2\|(a,b,x,t)\|_1.$$

To avoid the singularity at $a = 0$, we shall consider $m-$partitions on each of the axes B, X and $m+1$-partitions are taken on A axis equal in length, that is

$$\begin{aligned} a_{i+1} - a_i &= a_{i+2} - a_{i+1} = \dots \\ b_{j+1} - b_j &= b_{j+2} - b_{j+1} = \dots \\ x_{l+1} - x_l &= x_{l+2} - x_{l+1} = \dots \end{aligned}$$

such that

$$\begin{aligned} &\nu = a_0 < a_1 < \cdots < a_{m+1} = A, \quad 0 = b_0 < b_1 < \cdots < b_m = B \\ &\text{and} \quad 0 = x_0 < x_1 < \cdots < x_m = C. \end{aligned}$$

Taking m is sufficiently large partitions, the length of each of the sides of the sub-rectangles of the partitioning is less than δ_0. We shall use Lemma 10.6, we get

$$\begin{aligned} &t^{-\mu-\frac{1}{2}} S^k_{\mu,t} \int_0^C \int_\nu^A \int_0^B \psi\left(\frac{t}{a}, \frac{b}{a}\right) \psi\left(\frac{x}{a}, \frac{b}{a}\right) \phi(x) \frac{dbdadx}{a^3} \\ &= \int_0^C \int_\nu^A \int_0^B t^{-\mu-\frac{1}{2}} \psi\left(\frac{t}{a}, \frac{b}{a}\right) \psi\left(\frac{x}{a}, \frac{b}{a}\right) S^k_{\mu,x} \phi(x) \frac{dbdadx}{a^3}. \end{aligned} \tag{10.22}$$

From [4, p. 318], we find

$$t^{-\mu-\frac{1}{2}} S^k_{\mu,t} \int_0^C \int_\nu^A \int_0^B \psi\Big(\frac{t}{a}, \frac{b}{a}\Big)\psi\Big(\frac{x}{a}, \frac{b}{a}\Big)\phi(x)\frac{dbdadx}{a^3}$$
$$= \int_0^C \int_\nu^A \int_0^B h_\mu\Big((yt)^{-\mu} J_\mu(yt)(h_\mu\psi)(ay)\Big)(b)$$
$$\times h_\mu\Big((\xi x)^{-\mu} J_\mu(\xi x)(h_\mu\psi)(a\xi)\Big)(b)x^{\mu+\frac{1}{2}} S^k_{\mu,x}\phi(x)\frac{dbdadx}{a^{2\mu+2}}. \tag{10.23}$$

Now, the integrand of the above integral becomes

$$t^{-\mu-\frac{1}{2}} S^k_{\mu,t} F(a, b, x, t)$$
$$= h_\mu\Big((yt)^{-\mu} J_\mu(yt)(h_\mu\psi)(ay)\Big)(b)x^{\mu+\frac{1}{2}} h_\mu\Big((\xi x)^{-\mu} J_\mu(\xi x)(h_\mu\psi)(a\xi)\Big)(b)\frac{S^k_{\mu,x}\phi(x)}{a^{2\mu+2}}.$$

The above expression is uniformly continuous over any compact subset Λ as mentioned earlier (10.21). If we put $\triangle\, t = 0$ in (10.21), then after using (1.124), we get

$$\Big|t^{-\mu-\frac{1}{2}} S^k_{\mu,t} F(a+\triangle\, a, b+\triangle\, b, x+\triangle\, x, t) - t^{-\mu-\frac{1}{2}} S^k_{\mu,t} F(a, b, x, t)\Big|$$
$$= \Big|\sum_{j=0}^k A_j t^{2j}\Big(t^{-1}\frac{\partial}{\partial t}\Big)^{k+j} t^{-\mu-\frac{1}{2}} F(a+\triangle\, a, b+\triangle\, b, x+\triangle\, x, t)$$
$$- \sum_{j=0}^k A_j t^{2j}\Big(t^{-1}\frac{\partial}{\partial t}\Big)^{k+j} t^{-\mu-\frac{1}{2}} F(a, b, x, t)\Big| < \epsilon, \tag{10.24}$$

whenever $\|(\triangle\, a, \triangle\, b, \triangle\, x, 0)\|_1 < \delta_k,\ s_1 \le t \le s_2,\ k = 0, 1, 2, \ldots$.

The volume of the elementary cuboid of the partition for the Riemann sum is

$$\square_{i,j,l} = (a_i - a_{i-1})(b_j - b_{j-1})(x_l - x_{l-1}) = \triangle\, a \triangle\, b \triangle\, x,$$

where $i = 0, 1, \ldots, m + 1$, $j = 0, 1, \ldots, m$ and $l = 0, 1, 2, \ldots, m$. Therefore, the volume of the region $\{(a, b, x) : \nu \le a \le A, 0 \le b \le B, 0 \le x \le C\}$ can be written as $\cup_{i,j,l}\square_{i,j,l} = (A - \nu)BC$.

Now, we have to show that

$$\Big|t^{-\mu-\frac{1}{2}} \int_0^C \int_\nu^A \int_0^B \psi\Big(\frac{t}{a}, \frac{b}{a}\Big)\psi\Big(\frac{x}{a}, \frac{b}{a}\Big)\Big\{S^k_{\mu,x}\phi(x)\Big\}\frac{dbdadx}{a^3}$$
$$- \sum_{i=1}^{m+1}\sum_{j=1}^{m}\sum_{l=1}^{m} t^{-\mu-\frac{1}{2}}\psi\Big(\frac{t}{a_i}, \frac{b_j}{a_i}\Big)\psi\Big(\frac{x_l}{a_i}, \frac{b_j}{a_i}\Big)\Big\{S^k_{\mu,x}\phi(x)\Big\}\Big|_{x=x_l}\frac{1}{a_i^3}\square_{i,j,l}\Big| \to 0,$$

as $m \to \infty$.

Using the concept of (10.22), (10.23) and [4, p. 318], the last expression yields

$$\Big| t^{-\mu-\frac{1}{2}} \int_0^C \int_\nu^A \int_0^B \psi\Big(\frac{t}{a},\frac{b}{a}\Big)\psi\Big(\frac{x}{a},\frac{b}{a}\Big)\Big\{S^k_{\mu,x}\phi(x)\Big\}\frac{dbdadx}{a^3}$$

$$-\sum_{i=1}^{m+1}\sum_{j=1}^{m}\sum_{l=1}^{m} t^{-\mu-\frac{1}{2}}\psi\Big(\frac{t}{a_i},\frac{b_j}{a_i}\Big)\psi\Big(\frac{x_l}{a_i},\frac{b_j}{a_i}\Big)\Big\{S^k_{\mu,x}\phi(x)\Big\}\Big|_{x=x_l}\frac{1}{a_i^3}\Box_{i,j,l}\Big|$$

$$=\Big|\int_{\cup_{i,j,l}\Box_{i,j,l}} h_\mu\Big((yt)^{-\mu}J_\mu(yt)(h_\mu\psi)(ay)\Big)(b)h_\mu\Big((\xi x)^{-\mu}J_\mu(\xi x)(h_\mu\psi)(a\xi)\Big)(b)$$

$$\times x^{\mu+\frac{1}{2}}S^k_{\mu,x}\phi(x)\frac{dbdadx}{a^{2\mu+2}}$$

$$-\sum_{i=1}^{m+1}\sum_{j=1}^{m}\sum_{l=1}^{m} h_\mu\Big((yt)^{-\mu}J_\mu(yt)(h_\mu\psi)(a_iy)\Big)(b_j)$$

$$\times h_\mu\Big((\xi x_l)^{-\mu}J_\mu(\xi x_l)(h_\mu\psi)(a_i\xi)\Big)(b_j)x_l^{\mu+\frac{1}{2}}\Big\{S^k_{\mu,x}\phi(x)\Big\}\Big|_{x=x_l}\frac{1}{a_i^{2\mu+2}}\Box_{i,j,l}\Big|.$$

From (10.24), we get

$$\Big| t^{-\mu-\frac{1}{2}} \int_0^C \int_\nu^A \int_0^B \psi\Big(\frac{t}{a},\frac{b}{a}\Big)\psi\Big(\frac{x}{a},\frac{b}{a}\Big)\Big\{S^k_{\mu,x}\phi(x)\Big\}\frac{dbdadx}{a^3}$$

$$-\sum_{i=1}^{m+1}\sum_{j=1}^{m}\sum_{l=1}^{m} t^{-\mu-\frac{1}{2}}\psi\Big(\frac{t}{a_i},\frac{b_j}{a_i}\Big)\psi\Big(\frac{x_l}{a_i},\frac{b_j}{a_i}\Big)\Big\{S^k_{\mu,x}\phi(x)\Big\}\Big|_{x=x_l}\frac{1}{a_i^3}\Box_{i,j,l}\Big| \le \epsilon BC(A-\nu), \tag{10.25}$$

whenever $\|(a_i-a_{i-1}, b_j-b_{j-1}, x_l-x_{l-1}, 0)\|_1 < \delta_k$, $\forall i=1,2,\ldots,m+1,\ j=1,2,\ldots,m, l=1,2,\ldots,m$ and $k=0,1,2,\ldots$ and as $\epsilon>0$ is an arbitrarily small number. It follows that the last expression (10.25) converges to zero uniformly for all $t\in I$ as $m\to\infty$, for each $k=0,1,2,\ldots$.

Then we get

$$\int_0^C \int_\nu^A \int_0^B \psi\Big(\frac{t}{a},\frac{b}{a}\Big)\psi\Big(\frac{x}{a},\frac{b}{a}\Big)\phi(x)\frac{dbda}{a^3}dx$$

$$=\lim_{m\to\infty}\Big[\sum_{i=1}^{m+1}\sum_{j=1}^{m}\sum_{l=1}^{m}\psi\Big(\frac{t}{a_i},\frac{b_j}{a_i}\Big)\psi\Big(\frac{x_l}{a_i},\frac{b_j}{a_i}\Big)\phi(x_l)\frac{1}{a_i^3}\Box_{i,j,l}\Big],$$

in the topology of β_μ. □

Proof of the main Theorem 10.5**:**

Proof By definition of the distributions, we again write

$$\Big\langle\frac{1}{C_{\mu,\psi}}\int_{\nu}^{A}\int_{0}^{B}\Big\langle f(t),a^{\mu-\frac{1}{2}}\psi\Big(\frac{t}{a},\frac{b}{a}\Big)\Big\rangle a^{\mu-\frac{1}{2}}\psi\Big(\frac{x}{a},\frac{b}{a}\Big)\frac{dbda}{a^{2\mu+2}},\phi(x)\Big\rangle$$
$$=\int_{0}^{C}\int_{\nu}^{A}\int_{0}^{B}\frac{1}{C_{\mu,\psi}}\Big\langle f(t),a^{\mu-\frac{1}{2}}\psi\Big(\frac{t}{a},\frac{b}{a}\Big)\Big\rangle a^{\mu-\frac{1}{2}}\psi\Big(\frac{x}{a},\frac{b}{a}\Big)\frac{dbda}{a^{2\mu+2}}\phi(x)dx, \tag{10.26}$$

where $\phi\in\beta_{\mu,C}\subset\beta_{\mu}$ for $C>0$.

Taking the partition of the region $\{(a,b,x):\nu\le a\le A,0\le b\le B,0\le x\le C\}$, we denote as

$$\Box_{i,j,l}=(a_i-a_{i-1})(b_j-b_{j-1})(x_l-x_{l-1})=\triangle a\triangle b\triangle x,$$

where $i=0,1,\ldots,m+1$, $j=0,l,\ldots,m$ and $l=0,1,2,\ldots,m$.

Therefore, using the concept of Riemann integral as a sum we find

$$\int_{0}^{C}\int_{\nu}^{A}\int_{0}^{B}\frac{1}{C_{\mu,\psi}}\Big\langle f(t),a^{\mu-\frac{1}{2}}\psi\Big(\frac{t}{a},\frac{b}{a}\Big)\Big\rangle a^{\mu-\frac{1}{2}}\psi\Big(\frac{x}{a},\frac{b}{a}\Big)\frac{dbda}{a^{2\mu+2}}\phi(x)dx$$
$$=\frac{1}{C_{\mu,\psi}}\lim_{m\to\infty}\Big[\sum_{i=1}^{m+1}\sum_{j=1}^{m}\sum_{l=1}^{m}\Big\langle f(t),a_i^{\mu-\frac{1}{2}}\psi\Big(\frac{t}{a_i},\frac{b_j}{a_i}\Big)\Big\rangle a_i^{\mu-\frac{1}{2}}\psi\Big(\frac{x_l}{a_i},\frac{b_j}{a_i}\Big)\frac{\phi(x_l)}{a_i^{2\mu+2}}\Box_{i,j,l}\Big]$$
$$=\lim_{m\to\infty}\Big\langle f(t),\frac{1}{C_{\mu,\psi}}\sum_{i=1}^{m+1}\sum_{j=1}^{m}\sum_{l=1}^{m}\psi\Big(\frac{t}{a_i},\frac{b_j}{a_i}\Big)\psi\Big(\frac{x_l}{a_i},\frac{b_j}{a_i}\Big)\frac{\phi(x_l)}{a_i^{3}}\Box_{i,j,l}\Big\rangle$$
$$=\Big\langle f(t),\frac{1}{C_{\mu,\psi}}\lim_{m\to\infty}\sum_{i=1}^{m+1}\sum_{j=1}^{m}\sum_{l=1}^{m}\psi\Big(\frac{t}{a_i},\frac{b_j}{a_i}\Big)\psi\Big(\frac{x_l}{a_i},\frac{b_j}{a_i}\Big)\frac{\phi(x_l)}{a_i^{3}}\Box_{i,j,l}\Big\rangle.$$

In view of Lemma 10.7, we observe

$$\int_{0}^{C}\int_{\nu}^{A}\int_{0}^{B}\frac{1}{C_{\mu,\psi}}\Big\langle f(t),a^{\mu-\frac{1}{2}}\psi\Big(\frac{t}{a},\frac{b}{a}\Big)\Big\rangle a^{\mu-\frac{1}{2}}\psi\Big(\frac{x}{a},\frac{b}{a}\Big)\frac{dbda}{a^{2\mu+2}}\phi(x)dx$$
$$=\Big\langle f(t),\frac{1}{C_{\mu,\psi}}\int_{0}^{C}\int_{\nu}^{A}\int_{0}^{B}\psi\Big(\frac{t}{a},\frac{b}{a}\Big)\psi\Big(\frac{x}{a},\frac{b}{a}\Big)\phi(x)\frac{dbda}{a^{3}}dx\Big\rangle.$$

Employing the definition of distributions, we find

$$\Big\langle \frac{1}{C_{\mu,\psi}} \int_\nu^A \int_0^B \Big\langle f(t), a^{\mu-\frac{1}{2}} \psi\Big(\frac{t}{a}, \frac{b}{a}\Big)\Big\rangle a^{\mu-\frac{1}{2}} \psi\Big(\frac{x}{a}, \frac{b}{a}\Big) \frac{dbda}{a^{2\mu+2}}, \phi(x)\Big\rangle$$
$$= \Big\langle f(t), \frac{1}{C_{\mu,\psi}} \int_0^C \int_\nu^A \int_0^B \psi\Big(\frac{t}{a}, \frac{b}{a}\Big)\psi\Big(\frac{x}{a}, \frac{b}{a}\Big)\phi(x)\frac{dbda}{a^3} dx\Big\rangle.$$

Lemma 10.8 *Let $\psi \in \beta_\mu$ be a Bessel wavelet with $\psi(x) = 0$ for $x \geq C_1 > 0$ and $\phi \in \beta_\mu$ with $\phi(x) = 0$ for $x \geq C > 0$. Then*

$$t^{-\mu-\frac{1}{2}} S^k_{\mu,t} F_{A,B,C,\nu}(t) = \frac{1}{C_{\mu,\psi}} \int_0^C \int_\nu^A \int_0^B t^{-\mu-\frac{1}{2}} \psi\Big(\frac{t}{a}, \frac{b}{a}\Big)\psi\Big(\frac{x}{a}, \frac{b}{a}\Big) S^k_{\mu,x}\phi(x) \frac{dbdadx}{a^3}$$

converges uniformly to $t^{-\mu-\frac{1}{2}} S^k_{\mu,t}\phi(t)$ for all $t \in I$ as $A, B, C \to \infty$ and $\nu \to 0$.

Proof Invoking Lemma 10.6, we have

$$t^{-\mu-\frac{1}{2}} S^k_{\mu,t} F_{A,B,C,\nu}(t) = \frac{1}{C_{\mu,\psi}} \int_0^C \int_\nu^A \int_0^B t^{-\mu-\frac{1}{2}} \psi\Big(\frac{t}{a}, \frac{b}{a}\Big)\psi\Big(\frac{x}{a}, \frac{b}{a}\Big) S^k_{\mu,x}\phi(x) \frac{dbdadx}{a^3}. \tag{10.27}$$

Now, we have to prove that the expression in (10.27) converges to $t^{-\mu-\frac{1}{2}} S^k_{\mu,t}\phi(t)$ uniformly for all $t \in I$ as $A, B, C \to \infty$ and $\nu \to 0$ for each $k = 0, 1, 2, \ldots$.

If we take $B \to \infty$,

$$\int_0^B \psi\Big(\frac{t}{a}, \frac{b}{a}\Big)\psi\Big(\frac{x}{a}, \frac{b}{a}\Big) db \to \Big\langle \psi\Big(\frac{t}{a}, \frac{b}{a}\Big), \psi\Big(\frac{x}{a}, \frac{b}{a}\Big)\Big\rangle.$$

Using the Parseval relation of the Hankel transform (1.77), we get

$$\begin{aligned}\int_0^B \psi\Big(\frac{t}{a}, \frac{b}{a}\Big)\psi\Big(\frac{x}{a}, \frac{b}{a}\Big) db \to &\Big\langle h^b_\mu \psi\Big(\frac{t}{a}, \frac{b}{a}\Big), h^b_\mu \psi\Big(\frac{x}{a}, \frac{b}{a}\Big)\Big\rangle \\ &= \int_0^\infty a^{-\mu+\frac{1}{2}} y^{-\mu-\frac{1}{2}} (ty)^{\frac{1}{2}} J_\mu(ty)(h_\mu\psi)(ay) \\ &\quad \times a^{-\mu+\frac{1}{2}} y^{-\mu-\frac{1}{2}} (xy)^{\frac{1}{2}} J_\mu(xy)(h_\mu\psi)(ay)dy \\ &= a \int_0^\infty a a^{-2\mu-1} y^{-2\mu-1} (ty)^{\frac{1}{2}} J_\mu(ty)(xy)^{\frac{1}{2}} J_\mu(xy) \\ &\quad \times |(h_\mu\psi)(ay)|^2 dy.\end{aligned} \tag{10.28}$$

Using (10.28), then we have

$$\begin{aligned}
&\left|\int_0^\infty aa^{-2\mu-1}y^{-2\mu-1}(ty)^{\frac{1}{2}}J_\mu(ty)(xy)^{\frac{1}{2}}J_\mu(xy)|(h_\mu\psi)(ay)|^2dy\right| \\
&\le \int_0^\infty aa^{-2\mu-1}y^{-2\mu-1}\left|(ty)^{\frac{1}{2}}J_\mu(ty)\right|\left|(xy)^{\frac{1}{2}}J_\mu(xy)\right||(h_\mu\psi)(ay)|^2dy \\
&\le A_\mu B_\mu\int_0^\infty aa^{-2\mu-1}y^{-2\mu-1}|(h_\mu\psi)(ay)|^2dy.
\end{aligned}$$

Putting $ay = u$, we find

$$\begin{aligned}
&\left|\int_0^\infty aa^{-2\mu-1}y^{-2\mu-1}(ty)^{\frac{1}{2}}J_\mu(ty)(xy)^{\frac{1}{2}}J_\mu(xy)|(h_\mu\psi)(ay)|^2dy\right| \\
&\le A_\mu B_\mu\int_0^\infty \left|u^{-\mu-\frac{1}{2}}(h_\mu\psi)(u)\right|^2du \\
&\le A_\mu B_\mu\int_0^\infty \left|(1+u^2)u^{-\mu-\frac{1}{2}}(h_\mu\psi)(u)\right|^2\frac{1}{(1+u^2)^2}du \\
&\le A_\mu B_\mu\left\{\sup_{u\in I}\left|(1+u^2)u^{-\mu-\frac{1}{2}}(h_\mu\psi)(u)\right|\right\}^2\int_0^\infty\frac{1}{(1+u^2)^2}du.
\end{aligned}$$

From [1, p. 684], the last expression yields

$$\begin{aligned}
&\left|\int_0^\infty aa^{-2\mu-1}y^{-2\mu-1}(ty)^{\frac{1}{2}}J_\mu(ty)(xy)^{\frac{1}{2}}J_\mu(xy)|(h_\mu\psi)(ay)|^2dy\right| \\
&\le A_\mu B_\mu\left\{\sup_{z\in\mathbb{C}}\left|e^{-C_1|\,\mathrm{Im}z|}(1+z^2)z^{-\mu-\frac{1}{2}}(h_\mu\psi)(z)\right|\right\}^2\frac{\pi}{4}
\end{aligned}$$

$$\begin{aligned}
&\le \frac{\pi}{4}A_\mu B_\mu\left\{\sup_{z\in\mathbb{C}}\left|e^{-C_1|\,\mathrm{Im}z|}z^{-\mu-\frac{1}{2}}(h_\mu\psi)(z)\right|\right. \\
&\qquad\left.+\sup_{z\in\mathbb{C}}\left|e^{-C_1|\,\mathrm{Im}z|}z^2z^{-\mu-\frac{1}{2}}(h_\mu\psi)(z)\right|\right\}^2 \\
&\le \frac{\pi}{4}A_\mu B_\mu\left\{\alpha^\mu_{C_1,0}(\psi)+\alpha^\mu_{C_1,1}(\psi)\right\}^2<\infty.
\end{aligned}$$

Hence the R.H.S of (10.28)

$$\int_0^\infty a^{-2\mu+1}y^{-2\mu-1}(ty)^{\frac{1}{2}}J_\mu(ty)\Big(h_\mu\psi\Big)(ay)(xy)^{\frac{1}{2}}J_\mu(xy)\Big(h_\mu\psi\Big)(ay)dy<\infty.$$

From the above, we find (10.28), i.e.,

$$\int_0^B \psi\left(\frac{t}{a},\frac{b}{a}\right)\psi\left(\frac{x}{a},\frac{b}{a}\right)db \to \int_0^\infty \Big\{aa^{-2\mu-1}y^{-2\mu-1}(ty)^{\frac{1}{2}}J_\mu(ty) \times (xy)^{\frac{1}{2}}J_\mu(xy)\left|\left(h_\mu\psi\right)(ay)\right|^2\Big\}dy,$$

uniformly for all $x, t \in I$ when $B \to \infty$.

In view of (10.27) and the above expression, we find that

$$\begin{aligned}&\lim_{\substack{A,B,C\to\infty\\ \nu\to 0+}} t^{-\mu-\frac{1}{2}}S^k_{\mu,t}F_{A,B,C,\nu}(t)\\ &= \frac{1}{C_{\mu,\psi}}\lim_{\substack{A,C\to\infty\\ \nu\to 0+}}\int_0^C\int_\nu^A t^{-\mu-\frac{1}{2}}\Big(\int_0^\infty a^{-2\mu+1}y^{-2\mu-1}(ty)^{\frac{1}{2}}J_\mu(ty)(xy)^{\frac{1}{2}}J_\mu(xy)\\ &\quad\times|(h_\mu\psi)(ay)|^2dy\Big)S^k_{\mu,x}\phi(x)\frac{dadx}{a^3}.\end{aligned}$$

Using Fubini's theorem, in the R.H.S of the aforesaid integral we can write

$$\lim_{\substack{A,B,C\to\infty\\ \nu\to 0+}} t^{-\mu-\frac{1}{2}}S^k_{\mu,t}F_{A,B,C,\nu}(t) = \frac{1}{C_{\mu,\psi}}\lim_{\substack{A,C\to\infty\\ \nu\to 0+}}\int_0^C\int_0^\infty t^{-\mu-\frac{1}{2}}(ty)^{\frac{1}{2}}J_\mu(ty)(xy)^{\frac{1}{2}}J_\mu(xy) \times\Big(\int_\nu^A\frac{|(h_\mu\psi)(ay)|^2}{a^{2\mu+2}y^{2\mu+1}}da\Big)S^k_{\mu,x}\phi(x)dydx.$$

Using the concept of convergence, the last expression becomes

$$\begin{aligned}\lim_{\substack{A,B,C\to\infty\\ \nu\to 0+}} t^{-\mu-\frac{1}{2}}S^k_{\mu,t}F_{A,B,C,\nu}(t) &= \frac{1}{C_{\mu,\psi}}\lim_{C\to\infty}\int_0^C\int_0^\infty t^{-\mu-\frac{1}{2}}(ty)^{\frac{1}{2}}J_\mu(ty)(xy)^{\frac{1}{2}}J_\mu(xy)\\ &\quad\times\Big(\lim_{\substack{A\to\infty\\ \nu\to 0+}}\int_\nu^A\frac{\left|\left(h_\mu\psi\right)(ay)\right|^2}{a^{2\mu+2}y^{2\mu+1}}da\Big)S^k_{\mu,x}\phi(x)dydx.\\ &= \frac{1}{C_{\mu,\psi}}\lim_{C\to\infty}\int_0^C\int_0^\infty t^{-\mu-\frac{1}{2}}(ty)^{\frac{1}{2}}J_\mu(ty)(xy)^{\frac{1}{2}}J_\mu(xy)\\ &\quad\times\Big(\int_0^\infty\frac{\left|\left(h_\mu\psi\right)(ay)\right|^2}{a^{2\mu+2}y^{2\mu+1}}da\Big)S^k_{\mu,x}\phi(x)dydx.\end{aligned}$$

Using the admissibility condition (2.9), $\int_0^\infty\frac{|(h_\mu\psi)(ay)|^2}{a^{2\mu+2}y^{2\mu+1}}da = \int_0^\infty\frac{|(h_\mu\psi)(u)|^2}{u^{2\mu+2}}du = C_{\mu,\psi}$, we get

$$\begin{aligned}
&\lim_{\substack{A,B,C\to\infty\\ \nu\to 0+}} t^{-\mu-\frac{1}{2}} S^k_{\mu,t} F_{A,B,C,\nu}(t)\\
&= \frac{t^{-\mu-\frac{1}{2}}}{C_{\mu,\psi}} C_{\mu,\psi} \lim_{C\to\infty} \int_0^\infty \int_0^\infty (ty)^{\frac{1}{2}} J_\mu(ty)(xy)^{\frac{1}{2}} J_\mu(xy) S^k_{\mu,x}\phi(x)dxdy\\
&= t^{-\mu-\frac{1}{2}} \int_0^\infty \int_0^\infty (ty)^{\frac{1}{2}} J_\mu(ty)(xy)^{\frac{1}{2}} J_\mu(xy) S^k_{\mu,x}\phi(x)dxdy\\
&= t^{-\mu-\frac{1}{2}} S^k_{\mu,t}\phi(t).
\end{aligned}$$

By Weierstrass M-test, the above implies that $t^{-\mu-\frac{1}{2}} S^k_{\mu,t} F_{A,B,C,\nu}(t)$ converges to $t^{-\mu-\frac{1}{2}} S^k_{\mu,t}\phi(t)$ uniformly for all $t \in I$ as $A, B, C \to \infty$ and $\nu \to 0+$ for each $k = 0, 1, 2, \ldots$. □

Lemma 10.9 *Let $\phi \in \beta_\mu$ with $\phi(x) = 0,\ x \geq C > 0$ and $\psi \in \beta_\mu$ be a Bessel wavelet with $\psi(x) = 0$ for $x \geq C_1 > 0$. Then the sequence $\{\phi_n(t)\}_{n=1}^\infty$ defined by*

$$\phi_n(t) = \frac{1}{C_{\mu,\psi}} \int_0^n \int_{1/n}^n \int_0^n \phi(x)\psi\Big(\frac{t}{a}, \frac{b}{a}\Big)\psi\Big(\frac{x}{a}, \frac{b}{a}\Big)\frac{dbdadx}{a^3}, \tag{10.29}$$

is in β_μ and $\phi_n(t) \to \phi(t)$ as $n \to \infty$ in the topology of β_μ.

Proof By the Lemma 10.5, $\phi_n(t) \in \beta_\mu$ for each $n = 1, 2, 3, \ldots$. Therefore, the sequence $\{\phi_n(t)\}_{n=1}^\infty$ is in β_μ.
Applying (10.20) in (10.29), we obtain

$$t^{-\mu-\frac{1}{2}} S^k_{\mu,t}\phi_n(t) = \frac{1}{C_{\mu,\psi}} \int_0^n \int_{1/n}^n \int_0^n t^{-\mu-\frac{1}{2}} \{S^k_{\mu,x}\phi(x)\}\psi\Big(\frac{t}{a}, \frac{b}{a}\Big)\psi\Big(\frac{x}{a}, \frac{b}{a}\Big)\frac{dbdadx}{a^3}.$$

With help of the Lemma 10.8, we observe that $t^{-\mu-\frac{1}{2}} S^k_{\mu,t}\phi_n(t)$ converges uniformly to $t^{-\mu-\frac{1}{2}} S^k_{\mu,t}\phi(t)$ for all $t \in I$ and for each $k = 0, 1, 2, \ldots$ as $n \to \infty$.

Therefore, the sequence $\phi_n(t) \to \phi(t)$ in the topology of β_μ as $n \to \infty$. □

Remark 10.2 In view of Theorem 10.4, the Bessel wavelet transform $B_\psi f(b, a)$ is a continuous function of $a, b > 0$. Therefore the integral

$$\int_{1/n}^n \int_0^n (B_\psi f)(b, a)a^{\mu-\frac{1}{2}}\psi\Big(\frac{x}{a}, \frac{b}{a}\Big)\frac{dbda}{a^{2\mu+2}}$$

is meaningful. Our main aim is to prove that

$$\frac{1}{C_{\mu,\psi}} \int_{1/n}^n \int_0^n (B_\psi f)(b, a)a^{\mu-\frac{1}{2}}\psi\Big(\frac{x}{a}, \frac{b}{a}\Big)\frac{dbda}{a^{2\mu+2}} \to f \text{ as } n \to \infty$$

in the weak topology of β'_μ.

Or in other words

$$\left\langle \frac{1}{C_{\mu,\psi}} \int_{1/n}^{n} \int_{0}^{n} (B_\psi f)(b,a) a^{\mu-\frac{1}{2}} \psi\left(\frac{x}{a}, \frac{b}{a}\right) \frac{dbda}{a^{2\mu+2}}, \phi(x) \right\rangle \to \langle f, \phi \rangle \text{ as } n \to \infty.$$

Main result of the inversion formula of the continuous Bessel wavelet transform of distributions is

Theorem 10.6 *Let $f \in \beta'_{\mu,F}$ and ψ be a Bessel wavelet in $\beta^{2m}_\mu \subset \beta_\mu$. Then the following inversion formula of the Bessel wavelet transform holds*

$$\left\langle \frac{1}{C_{\mu,\psi}} \int_{1/n}^{n} \int_{0}^{n} \left\langle f(t), a^{\mu-\frac{1}{2}} \psi\left(\frac{t}{a}, \frac{b}{a}\right) \right\rangle a^{\mu-\frac{1}{2}} \psi\left(\frac{x}{a}, \frac{b}{a}\right) \frac{dbda}{a^{2\mu+2}}, \phi(x) \right\rangle \to \langle f, \phi \rangle, \tag{10.30}$$

as $n \to \infty$, for all $\phi \in \beta_\mu$.

Proof Taking n sufficiently large, the support of $\phi(x)$ is contained in $[0, n]$. Therefore, from (10.30),

$$\begin{aligned} &\left\langle \frac{1}{C_{\mu,\psi}} \int_{1/n}^{n} \int_{0}^{n} \left\langle f(t), a^{\mu-\frac{1}{2}} \psi\left(\frac{t}{a}, \frac{b}{a}\right) \right\rangle a^{\mu-\frac{1}{2}} \psi\left(\frac{x}{a}, \frac{b}{a}\right) \frac{dbda}{a^{2\mu+2}}, \phi(x) \right\rangle \\ &= \frac{1}{C_{\mu,\psi}} \int_{0}^{n} \int_{1/n}^{n} \int_{0}^{n} \left\langle f(t), a^{\mu-\frac{1}{2}} \psi\left(\frac{t}{a}, \frac{b}{a}\right) \right\rangle a^{\mu-\frac{1}{2}} \psi\left(\frac{x}{a}, \frac{b}{a}\right) \phi(x) \frac{dbdadx}{a^{2\mu+2}} \\ &= \frac{1}{C_{\mu,\psi}} \int_{0}^{n} \int_{1/n}^{n} \int_{0}^{n} \left\langle f(t), \psi\left(\frac{t}{a}, \frac{b}{a}\right) \right\rangle \psi\left(\frac{x}{a}, \frac{b}{a}\right) \phi(x) \frac{dbdadx}{a^{3}}. \end{aligned} \tag{10.31}$$

By Theorem 10.5, the above yields

$$\begin{aligned} &\frac{1}{C_{\mu,\psi}} \int_{0}^{n} \int_{1/n}^{n} \int_{0}^{n} \left\langle f(t), \psi\left(\frac{t}{a}, \frac{b}{a}\right) \right\rangle \psi\left(\frac{x}{a}, \frac{b}{a}\right) \phi(x) \frac{dbdadx}{a^{3}} \\ &= \left\langle f(t), \frac{1}{C_{\mu,\psi}} \int_{0}^{n} \int_{1/n}^{n} \int_{0}^{n} \psi\left(\frac{t}{a}, \frac{b}{a}\right) \psi\left(\frac{x}{a}, \frac{b}{a}\right) \phi(x) \frac{dbda}{a^{3}} dx \right\rangle \\ &= \langle f(t), \phi_n(t) \rangle, \end{aligned} \tag{10.32}$$

where

$$\phi_n(t) = \frac{1}{C_{\mu,\psi}} \int_{0}^{n} \int_{1/n}^{n} \int_{0}^{n} \psi\left(\frac{t}{a}, \frac{b}{a}\right) \psi\left(\frac{x}{a}, \frac{b}{a}\right) \phi(x) \frac{dbda}{a^{3}} dx.$$

Exploiting the Lemma 10.5, the sequence $\{\phi_n(t)\}_{n=1}^{\infty}$ belongs in β_μ and its each term becomes zero outside the interval $(0, C + 2C_1)$. Hence

$$\phi_n(t) \to \phi(t) \text{ in } \beta_\mu \text{ as } n \to \infty.$$

In view of (10.31) and (10.32), we find that

$$\lim_{n\to\infty}\Big\langle\frac{1}{C_{\mu,\psi}}\int_{1/n}^{n}\int_{0}^{n}\Big\langle f(t),a^{\mu-\frac{1}{2}}\psi\Big(\frac{t}{a},\frac{b}{a}\Big)\Big\rangle a^{\mu-\frac{1}{2}}\psi\Big(\frac{x}{a},\frac{b}{a}\Big)\frac{dbda}{a^{2\mu+2}},\phi(x)\Big\rangle$$
$$=\lim_{n\to\infty}\langle f(t),\phi_n(t)\rangle=\langle f(t),\phi(t)\rangle.$$

This implies that

$$\Big\langle\frac{1}{C_{\mu,\psi}}\int_{1/n}^{n}\int_{0}^{n}\Big\langle f(t),a^{\mu-\frac{1}{2}}\psi\Big(\frac{t}{a},\frac{b}{a}\Big)\Big\rangle a^{\mu-\frac{1}{2}}\psi\Big(\frac{x}{a},\frac{b}{a}\Big)\frac{dbda}{a^{2\mu+2}},\phi(x)\Big\rangle\to\langle f,\phi\rangle,$$

as $n\to\infty$. □

Theorem 10.7 *Let $f\in\beta'_\mu$ and ψ be a Bessel wavelet belonging to $\beta_\mu^{2m}\subset\beta_\mu$. Then*

$$\Big\langle\frac{1}{C_{\mu,\psi}}\int_{1/n}^{n}\int_{0}^{n}\Big\langle f(t),\psi\Big(\frac{t}{a},\frac{b}{a}\Big)\Big\rangle\psi\Big(\frac{x}{a},\frac{b}{a}\Big)\frac{dbda}{a^{3}},\phi(x)\Big\rangle\to\langle f-Kx^{\mu+\frac{1}{2}},\phi\rangle,\tag{10.33}$$

as $n\to\infty$, where K is non-zero constant.

Proof As $f\in\beta'_\mu$,

$$f(x)=g(x)+K.x^{\mu+\frac{1}{2}},\quad\text{where}\quad g\in\beta'_{\mu,F}.\tag{10.34}$$

Using Theorem 10.1, we have found that

$$\Big\langle K.t^{\mu+\frac{1}{2}},\psi\Big(\frac{t}{a},\frac{b}{a}\Big)\Big\rangle=\int_0^\infty K.t^{\mu+\frac{1}{2}}\psi\Big(\frac{t}{a},\frac{b}{a}\Big)dt=0.\tag{10.35}$$

In view of (10.34) and (10.35), we get

$$\begin{aligned}\Big\langle f(t),\psi\Big(\frac{t}{a},\frac{b}{a}\Big)\Big\rangle&=\Big\langle g(t)+K.t^{\mu+\frac{1}{2}},\psi\Big(\frac{t}{a},\frac{b}{a}\Big)\Big\rangle\\&=\Big\langle g(t),\psi\Big(\frac{t}{a},\frac{b}{a}\Big)\Big\rangle+\Big\langle K.t^{\mu+\frac{1}{2}},\psi\Big(\frac{t}{a},\frac{b}{a}\Big)\Big\rangle\\&=\Big\langle g(t),\psi\Big(\frac{t}{a},\frac{b}{a}\Big)\Big\rangle.\end{aligned}$$

Therefore, from Theorem 10.6, we find that

$$\Big\langle\frac{1}{C_{\mu,\psi}}\int_{1/n}^{n}\int_{0}^{n}\Big\langle f(t),\psi\Big(\frac{t}{a},\frac{b}{a}\Big)\Big\rangle\psi\Big(\frac{x}{a},\frac{b}{a}\Big)\frac{dbda}{a^{3}},\phi(x)\Big\rangle$$
$$=\langle g(x),\phi\rangle=\langle f-Kx^{\mu+\frac{1}{2}},\phi\rangle,\ \text{as } n\to\infty.$$

From above argument, the inversion formula is true for modulo $K.\, x^{\mu+\frac{1}{2}}$ distributions. But if $f \in \beta'_{\mu,F}$ and $\psi \in \beta_\mu^{2m} \subset \beta_\mu$, the uniqueness theorem holds. □

Example 10.3
For validation of the inversion formula of continuous Bessel wavelet transform in β'_μ-space, consider

$$\phi(x) = \begin{cases} e^{-\frac{1}{x(1-x)}}, \text{ for } 0 < x < 1 \\ 0, \text{ for } x \le 0,\ x \ge 1 \end{cases}$$

$\phi \in D(I) \subset \beta_\mu$ for every μ. We take $\psi(x) = M_\mu \phi(x)$, represents a Bessel wavelet in β_μ and containing non-vanishing moments of all even orders weighted by $x^{\mu+\frac{1}{2}}$.

Proof For $\psi(x) = M_\mu \phi(x)$,

$$\begin{aligned}\int_0^\infty x^{\mu+\frac{1}{2}} \psi(x)dx &= \int_0^1 x^{\mu+\frac{1}{2}} M_\mu \phi(x)dx \\ &= \int_0^1 x^{\mu+\frac{1}{2}} x^{-\mu-\frac{1}{2}} D_x x^{\mu+\frac{1}{2}} e^{-\frac{1}{x(1-x)}} dx \\ &= \int_0^1 D_x x^{\mu+\frac{1}{2}} e^{-\frac{1}{x(1-x)}} dx = \left\{ x^{\mu+\frac{1}{2}} e^{-\frac{1}{x(1-x)}} \right\}\Big|_{x=0}^1 \\ &= 0.\end{aligned}$$

By Lemma 10.1, we conclude that $\psi(x) \in \beta_\mu$ is a Bessel wavelet.

Now, the moment of $\psi(x)$ of even order weighted by $x^{\mu+\frac{1}{2}}$ be

$$\begin{aligned}\int_0^\infty x^{2m} x^{\mu+\frac{1}{2}} \psi(x)dx &= \int_0^1 x^{2m} x^{\mu+\frac{1}{2}} x^{-\mu-\frac{1}{2}} D_x x^{\mu+\frac{1}{2}} e^{-\frac{1}{x(1-x)}} dx \\ &= \int_0^1 x^{2m} D_x x^{\mu+\frac{1}{2}} e^{-\frac{1}{x(1-x)}} dx \\ &= \left\{ x^{2m} x^{\mu+\frac{1}{2}} e^{-\frac{1}{x(1-x)}} \right\}\Big|_{x=0}^1 - \int_0^1 2m x^{2m-1} x^{\mu+\frac{1}{2}} e^{-\frac{1}{x(1-x)}} dx \\ &= -2m \int_0^1 x^{2m-1} x^{\mu+\frac{1}{2}} e^{-\frac{1}{x(1-x)}} dx \neq 0.\end{aligned}$$

This implies that moments of even orders weighted by $x^{\mu+\frac{1}{2}}$ of $\psi(x)$ are non-zero. □

References

1. Zemanian, A.H.: The hankel transformation of certain distributions of rapid growth. SIAM J. Appl. Math. **4**(14), 678–690 (1966)
2. Zemanian, A.H.: Generalized integral transformations. Pure and applied mathematics XVIII. Interscience Publishers, New York (1968)
3. Betancor, J.J., Marrero, I.: The Hankel convolution and the Zemanian spaces β_μ and β'_μ. Math. Nachr. **160**, 277–298 (1993)
4. Upadhyay, S.K., Yadav, R.N., Debnath, L.: On continuous Bessel wavelet transformation associated with the Hankel-Hausdorff operator. Integral Transforms Spec. Funct. **5**(23), 315–323 (2012)
5. Betancor, J.J., González, B.J.: A convolution operation for a distributional Hankel transformation. Studia Math. **1**(117), 57–72 (1995)
6. Pandey, J.N.: Continuous wavelet transform of Schwartz distributions. Rocky Mountain J. Math. **6**(49), 2005–2028 (2019)

Chapter 11
The Bessel Wavelet Transform of Distributions in $H'_{\mu,2}$ Space

11.1 Introduction

In the previous chapters, using the theory of the conventional Hankel transform and the Hankel convolution, inversion formulae of the Bessel wavelet transform of distributions in H'_μ and β'_μ spaces have been established and found various results from the concept of Pandey [1–4]. In this chapter, inversion formula of the Bessel wavelet transform of distributions in and its associated results are discussed using the transformation as mentioned before.

In this regard, there are some useful definitions, properties of the Hankel transformation, the Bessel wavelet transform, $H'_{\mu,p}$ space and differential operators from Betancor and González [5] which are useful in other subsequent sections.

Let $\mu \geq -\frac{1}{2}$, then we take following arguments from [6, 7]

$$\sigma(x) = \frac{x^{2\mu+2}}{2^{\mu+1}\Gamma(\mu+2)} \tag{11.1}$$

and

$$j_\mu(x) = c_\mu x^{-\mu} J_\mu(x), \;\; c_\mu = 2^\mu \Gamma(\mu+1) \tag{11.2}$$

where J_μ denotes the Bessel function of first kind and of order μ.

For every $1 \leq p \leq \infty$, the space $L_{\mu,p}$ consists of all those measurable functions ϕ on $(0, \infty)$ such that

$$\|\phi\|_{\mu,p} = \Big(\int_0^\infty |\phi(x)|^p x^{2\mu+1} dx\Big)^{\frac{1}{p}} < \infty, \;\; 1 \leq p < \infty, \tag{11.3}$$

$$\|\phi\|_{\mu,\infty} = \operatorname*{ess\,sup}_{0<x<\infty} |\phi(x)| < \infty. \tag{11.4}$$

S. K. Upadhyay and J. S. Maurya, *The Bessel Wavelet Transform*,
Industrial and Applied Mathematics,
https://doi.org/10.1007/978-981-96-9938-4_11

From [5, 8], the Hankel transformation of a function $f \in L_{\mu,1}$ is defined by

$$\left(h_\mu f\right)(y) = \int_0^\infty (xy)^{-\mu} J_\mu(xy) f(x) x^{2\mu+1} dx, \tag{11.5}$$

where J_μ denotes the Bessel function of first kind of order μ.

If $f \in L_{\mu,1}$ and $h_\mu f \in L_{\mu,1}$, then the inverse Hankel transform is

$$f(x) = \int_0^\infty (xy)^{-\mu} J_\mu(xy) h_\mu f(y) y^{2\mu+1} dy. \tag{11.6}$$

Using (11.1) and (11.2), the Hankel transform and its inversion given by (11.5) and (11.6) can be expressed respectively as

$$\left(h_\mu f\right)(y) = \int_0^\infty j_\mu(xy) f(x) d\sigma(x), \tag{11.7}$$

$$f(x) = \int_0^\infty j_\mu(xy)(h_\mu f)(y) d\sigma(y). \tag{11.8}$$

If $f(x), g(x) \in L_{\mu,1}$, then from [5, 8], the Hankel convolution is given by

$$(f\#g)(x) = \int_0^\infty f(y) \left(\tau_x g\right)(y) \frac{y^{2\mu+1}}{2^\mu \Gamma(\mu+1)} dy, \tag{11.9}$$

where the Hankel translation operator $\tau_x,\ x \in [0, \infty)$ is defined by

$$\left(\tau_x g\right)(y) = g(x, y) = \int_0^\infty g(z) D(x, y, z) \frac{z^{2\mu+1}}{2^\mu \Gamma(\mu+1)} dz \tag{11.10}$$

and $\tau_0 g = g$, and being, for each $x, y, z \in (0, \infty)$,

$$D(x, y, z) = \int_0^\infty j_\mu(xt) j_\mu(yt) j_\mu(zt) \frac{t^{2\mu+1}}{2^\mu \Gamma(\mu+1)} dt \tag{11.11}$$

with

(i) $D(x, y, z) \geq 0$,

(ii) $\displaystyle\int_0^\infty D(x, y, z) j_\mu(tz) d\sigma(z) = j_\mu(tx) j_\mu(ty)$,

(iii) $\displaystyle\int_0^\infty D(x, y, z) d\sigma(z) = 1$.

The Hankel tranformation of the Hankel convolution is given by the following formula

$$h_\mu\left(f\#g\right)(x) = h_\mu f(x) h_\mu g(x). \tag{11.12}$$

In view of Pathak et al. [6], let $\psi \in L_{\mu,p}(0,\infty)$, $1 \le p < \infty$, then for $b \ge 0$ and $a > 0$, the Bessel wavelet is defined by

$$\begin{aligned}\psi_{b,a}(x) &:= D_a \tau_b \psi(x) = D_a \psi(b,x) = a^{-2\mu-2}\psi\Big(\frac{b}{a},\frac{x}{a}\Big)\\ &:= a^{-2\mu-2}\int_0^\infty D\Big(\frac{b}{a},\frac{x}{a},z\Big)\psi(z)d\sigma(z).\end{aligned} \tag{11.13}$$

and it satisfies the admissibility condition

$$A_\psi := \int_0^\infty \frac{|(h_\mu\psi)(\omega)|^2}{\omega^{2\mu+2}}d\sigma(\omega) < \infty. \tag{11.14}$$

The Bessel wavelet transform of f with respect to kernel $\psi_{b,a}$ is defined by

$$(B_\psi f)(b,a) = \int_0^\infty f(t)\overline{\psi_{b,a}(t)}d\sigma(t). \tag{11.15}$$

From [5, 9], the space H constituted by all those complex valued and smooth functions ϕ on $(0,\infty)$ such that

$$\gamma_{m,n}(\phi) = \sup_{x\in(0,\infty)} (1+x^2)^m|(x^{-1}D_x)^n\phi(x)| < \infty,\ m,n\in\mathbb{N}. \tag{11.16}$$

Let $1 \le p \le \infty$, then a measurable function f on $(0,\infty)$ is in $H_{\mu,p}$ if for every $k\in\mathbb{N}$, $\Delta_\mu^k f \in L_{\mu,p}$, that is, there exists $h_k \in L_{\mu,p}$ such that

$$\begin{aligned}\langle \Delta_\mu^k f,\phi\rangle &= \int_0^\infty (\Delta_\mu^k\phi)(x)f(x)x^{2\mu+1}dx\\ &= \int_0^\infty \phi(x)h_k(x)x^{2\mu+1}dx,\ \phi\in H.\end{aligned} \tag{11.17}$$

The space $H_{\mu,p}$ is endowed with the topology generated by the system $\{\gamma_{\mu,p}^k\}_{k\in\mathbb{N}}$ of seminorms, where

$$\gamma_{\mu,p}^k(f) = \|\Delta_\mu^k f\|_{\mu,p},\ f\in H_{\mu,p} \text{ and } k\in\mathbb{N}. \tag{11.18}$$

$H'_{\mu,p}$-space denotes the dual of $H_{\mu,p}$. H is continuously contained in $H_{\mu,p}$.

From Zemanian [10], Koh [11], and others the following results are considered:

$$D_x x^\mu J_\mu(xy) = yx^\mu J_{\mu-1}(xy), \tag{11.19}$$

$$D_x x^{-\mu} J_\mu(xy) = -yx^{-\mu} J_{\mu+1}(xy). \tag{11.20}$$

For the operator $\triangle_{\mu,x} \equiv x^{-2\mu-1} D_x x^{2\mu+1} D_x$,

$$h_\mu \left(\triangle_{\mu,x}\phi\right) = -y^2 h_\mu \phi, \quad \phi \in H_{\mu,2}, \tag{11.21}$$

$$\triangle_{\mu,y} \left(h_\mu \phi\right) = h_\mu(-x^2\phi), \quad \phi \in H_{\mu,2}. \tag{11.22}$$

Contents of this chapter are organized as follows:

Section 11.1 is introductory, which provides a brief descriptions for the continuous Bessel wavelet transform of distributions and its inversion formula. The continuous Bessel wavelet transform in $H'_{\mu,2}$-space and its properties are discussed in Sect. 11.2. In Sect. 11.3, the inversion formula of the continuous Bessel wavelet transform of distributions in $H'_{\mu,2}$-type space and its associated results are investigated.

11.2 The Bessel Wavelet Transform in $H'_{\mu,2}$ Space

In this section, the inversion formula and its properties of the continuous Bessel wavelet transform and its properties in $H_{\mu,2}$ and $H'_{\mu,2}$ are obtained by exploiting Hankel transform theory.

Definition 11.1 Let $\psi \in H_{\mu,2}$ be the Bessel wavelet and $f \in H'_{\mu,2}$, then the Bessel wavelet transform of f is defined by

$$\begin{aligned}(B_\psi f)(b,a) &= c_\mu^{-1} \left\langle f(t), \psi_{b,a}(t)\right\rangle \\ &= c_\mu^{-1} \left\langle f(t), a^{-2\mu-2}\psi\left(\frac{b}{a}, \frac{t}{a}\right)\right\rangle,\end{aligned} \tag{11.23}$$

where $a > 0$, $b \geq 0$ and $\mu > -\frac{1}{2}$ and $c_\mu = 2^\mu \Gamma(\mu+1)$.

Now, we show that $(B_\psi f)(b,a)$ is continuous function of a, b.

Lemma 11.1 *Let $\psi \in H_{\mu,2}$ be a Bessel wavelet. Let $f \in L_{\mu,2}$ and $(B_\psi f)(b,a)$, the continuous Bessel wavelet transform of f with respect to kernel $\psi_{b,a}$, then*

$$\psi_{b,a}(x) = a^{-2\mu-2}\psi\left(\frac{b}{a}, \frac{x}{a}\right) = h_\mu\{j_\mu(xy)(h_\mu\psi)(ay)\}(b), \tag{11.24}$$

and

$$(B_\psi f)(b,a) = h_\mu\{(h_\mu f)(y)\overline{(h_\mu\psi)(ay)}\}(b). \tag{11.25}$$

Proof From [6], we have

$$\psi\left(\frac{b}{a},\frac{x}{a}\right)=\int_0^\infty \psi(z)D\Big(\frac{b}{a},\frac{x}{a},z\Big)d\sigma(z).$$

Using (11.11), we get

$$\psi\left(\frac{b}{a},\frac{x}{a}\right)=\int_0^\infty \psi(z)\int_0^\infty j_\mu\Big(\frac{b}{a}u\Big)j_\mu\Big(\frac{x}{a}u\Big)j_\mu(zu)d\sigma(u)d\sigma(z).$$

Substituting $\frac{u}{a}=y$, we find

$$\begin{aligned}\psi\left(\frac{b}{a},\frac{x}{a}\right)&=\int_0^\infty \psi(z)\int_0^\infty j_\mu(by)j_\mu(xy)j_\mu(zay)a^{2\mu+2}d\sigma(y)d\sigma(z)\\ &=a^{2\mu+2}\int_0^\infty j_\mu(by)j_\mu(xy)\int_0^\infty \psi(z)j_\mu(zay)d\sigma(z)d\sigma(y)\\ &=a^{2\mu+2}\int_0^\infty j_\mu(by)j_\mu(xy)(h_\mu\psi)(ay)d\sigma(y)\\ &=a^{2\mu+2}h_\mu\{j_\mu(xy)(h_\mu\psi)(ay)\}(b). \qquad [\because\ j_\mu(z)(h_\mu\psi)(z)\in L_{\mu,2}]\end{aligned}$$

Therefore,

$$\psi_{b,a}(x)=a^{-2\mu-2}\psi\left(\frac{b}{a},\frac{x}{a}\right)=h_\mu\{j_\mu(xy)(h_\mu\psi)(ay)\}(b).$$

And in view of [6, Theorem 3, p. 245], we have

$$(B_\psi f)(b,a)=h_\mu\{(h_\mu f)(y)\overline{(h_\mu\psi)(ay)}\}(b).$$

Theorem 11.1 *Let $\psi\in H_{\mu,2}$ be the Bessel wavelet. Then for $f\in H'_{\mu,2}$, the continuous Bessel wavelet transform $B_\psi f(b,a)$ of f with respect to kernel $\psi_{b,a}$ is a continuous function of b,a in a compact neighborhood of the point (b,a), $b\ge 0$, $a>0$.*

Proof For $f\in H'_{\mu,2}$ and $\psi\in H_{\mu,2}$, we have

$$(B_\psi f)(b,a)=c_\mu^{-1}\langle f(t),\psi_{b,a}(t)\rangle=c_\mu^{-1}\Big\langle f(t),a^{-2\mu-2}\psi\Big(\frac{b}{a},\frac{t}{a}\Big)\Big\rangle, \tag{11.26}$$

where $c_\mu=2^\mu\Gamma(\mu+1)$.

To check the continuity of $(B_\psi f)(b,a)$, we can write

$$\begin{aligned}
&(B_\psi f)(b+\Delta b, a+\Delta a) - (B_\psi f)(b,a) \\
&\quad = c_\mu^{-1}\left\langle f(t), (a+\Delta a)^{-2\mu-2}\psi\Big(\frac{b+\Delta b}{a+\Delta a}, \frac{t}{a+\Delta a}\Big)\right\rangle \\
&\quad = c_\mu^{-1}\left\langle f(t), (a+\Delta a)^{-2\mu-2}\psi\Big(\frac{b+\Delta b}{a+\Delta a}, \frac{t}{a+\Delta a}\Big) - a^{-2\mu-2}\psi\Big(\frac{b}{a}, \frac{t}{a}\Big)\right\rangle.
\end{aligned}$$

Now, we need to show that

$$(a+\Delta a)^{-2\mu-2}\psi\Big(\frac{b+\Delta b}{a+\Delta a}, \frac{t}{a+\Delta a}\Big) - a^{-2\mu-2}\psi\Big(\frac{b}{a}, \frac{t}{a}\Big) \to 0$$

in the topology of $H_{\mu,2}$ as $\Delta a, \Delta b \to 0$ independently of each other.

In view of Lemma 11.1, we get

$$\begin{aligned}
&\Delta_\mu^k\left[(a+\Delta a)^{-2\mu-2}\psi\Big(\frac{b+\Delta b}{a+\Delta a}, \frac{t}{a+\Delta a}\Big) - a^{-2\mu-2}\psi\Big(\frac{b}{a}, \frac{t}{a}\Big)\right] \\
&= \Delta_\mu^k\big[h_\mu\left\{j_\mu((b+\Delta b)y)(h_\mu\psi)((a+\Delta a)y)\right\}(t) - h_\mu\left\{j_\mu(by)(h_\mu\psi)(ay)\right\}(t)\big].
\end{aligned}$$

Using (11.21) and (11.22), we obtain

$$\begin{aligned}
&\Delta_\mu^k\left[(a+\Delta a)^{-2\mu-2}\psi\Big(\frac{b+\Delta b}{a+\Delta a}, \frac{t}{a+\Delta a}\Big) - a^{-2\mu-2}\psi\Big(\frac{b}{a}, \frac{t}{a}\Big)\right] \\
&= h_\mu\left[j_\mu((b+\Delta b)y)(-y^2)^k(h_\mu\psi)((a+\Delta a)y)\right](t) \\
&\quad - h_\mu\left[j_\mu(by)(-y^2)^k h_\mu(\psi)(ay)\right](t) \\
&= h_\mu\left[j_\mu((b+\Delta b)y)\{(a+\Delta a)^{-2k}h_\mu(\Delta_\mu^k\psi)((a+\Delta a)y)\}\right](t) \\
&\quad - h_\mu\left[j_\mu(by)\{a^{-2k}h_\mu(\Delta_\mu^k\psi)(ay)\}\right](t) \\
&= h_\mu\left[j_\mu((b+\Delta b)y)\{(a+\Delta a)^{-2k}h_\mu(\Delta_\mu^k\psi)((a+\Delta a)y)\}\right. \\
&\quad \left. - j_\mu(by)\{a^{-2k}h_\mu(\Delta_\mu^k\psi)(ay)\}\right](t).
\end{aligned}$$

From the definition of $L_{\mu,2}$–norm and (11.3), we have

$$\begin{aligned}
&\left\| \Delta_\mu^k\left[(a+\Delta a)^{-2\mu-2}\psi\Big(\frac{b+\Delta b}{a+\Delta a}, \frac{t}{a+\Delta a}\Big) - a^{-2\mu-2}\psi\Big(\frac{b}{a}, \frac{t}{a}\Big)\right]\right\|_{L_{\mu,2}} \\
&= \|h_\mu\left[j_\mu((b+\Delta b)y)\{(a+\Delta a)^{-2k}h_\mu(\Delta_\mu^k\psi)((a+\Delta a)y)\}\right. \\
&\quad \left. - j_\mu(by)\{a^{-2k}h_\mu(\Delta_\mu^k\psi)(ay)\}\right](t)\|_{L_{\mu,2}} \\
&= \|j_\mu((b+\Delta b)y)\{(a+\Delta a)^{-2k}h_\mu(\Delta_\mu^k\psi)((a+\Delta a)y)\} \\
&\quad - j_\mu(by)\{a^{-2k}h_\mu(\Delta_\mu^k\psi)(ay)\}\|_{L_{\mu,2}}.
\end{aligned}$$

In view of the continuity of $j_\mu(z)h_\mu\{\Delta_\mu^k\psi\}(z)a^{-2k}$ and Dominated Convergence Theorem in $L_{\mu,2}$, we find that

$$\| j_\mu((b+\triangle b)y)h_\mu(\triangle_\mu^k\psi)((a+\triangle a)y)(a+\triangle a)^{-2k} - j_\mu(by)h_\mu(\triangle_\mu^k\psi)(ay)a^{-2k} \|_{L_{\mu,2}}$$

$\rightarrow 0$ as $\triangle a, \triangle b \rightarrow 0$.

Thus,

$$(a+\triangle a)^{-2\mu-2}\psi\Big(\frac{b+\triangle b}{a+\triangle a}, \frac{t}{a+\triangle a}\Big) - a^{-2\mu-2}\psi\Big(\frac{b}{a}, \frac{t}{a}\Big) \rightarrow 0$$

in the topology of $H_{\mu,2}$ as $\triangle a, \triangle b \rightarrow 0$. □

Lemma 11.2 *If $D(x, y, z)$ is basic function, then we obtain*

$$\int_0^\infty (-z^2)^k D(x, y, z)d\sigma(z) = P(x, y), \quad x, y, z \in I \tag{11.27}$$

where $P(x, y)$ is an even polynomial.

Proof From [6] and using the Bessel operator $\triangle_{\mu,t}^k = t^{-2\mu-1}D_t t^{2\mu+1}D_t$ on both sides, we find

$$\int_0^\infty D(x, y, z)\{\triangle_{\mu,t}^k j_\mu(tz)\}d\sigma(z) = \triangle_{\mu,t}^k\{j_\mu(tx)j_\mu(ty)\}.$$

From above we find that

$$\int_0^\infty (-z^2)^k D(x, y, z)j_\mu(tz)d\sigma(z) = \triangle_{\mu,t}^k\{j_\mu(tx)j_\mu(ty)\}. \tag{11.28}$$

From Betancor et al. [12], we have

$$\triangle_{\mu,t}^k = \sum_{r=k}^{2k} p_{r,k}(t)(t^{-1}D_t)^r, \tag{11.29}$$

where $p_{r,k}, r = k, ..., 2k$ is an even polynomial.

Moreover, for each $r \epsilon \mathbb{N}$ and using Leibnitz formula, we get

$$\begin{aligned}
&(t^{-1}D_t)^r\{j_\mu(tx)j_\mu(ty)\} \\
&= c_\mu^2(t^{-1}D_t)^r\{(tx)^{-\mu}J_\mu(tx)(ty)^{-\mu}J_\mu(ty)\} \\
&= c_\mu^2\sum_{l=0}^r \binom{r}{l}(t^{-1}D_t)^l\{(tx)^{-\mu}J_\mu(tx)\}(t^{-1}D_t)^{r-l}\{(ty)^{-\mu}J_\mu(ty)\} \\
&= c_\mu^2\sum_{l=0}^r \binom{r}{l}(-x^2)^l(tx)^{-\mu-l}J_{\mu+l}(tx)(-y^2)^{r-l}(ty)^{-\mu-r+l}J_{\mu+r-l}(ty).
\end{aligned}$$

This implies that

$$\begin{aligned}&\Delta^k_{\mu,t}\{j_\mu(tx)j_\mu(ty)\}\\&=\sum_{r=k}^{2k}p_{r,k}(t)c_\mu^2\sum_{l=0}^{r}\binom{r}{l}(-x^2)^l(tx)^{-\mu-l}J_{\mu+l}(tx)(-y^2)^{r-l}(ty)^{-\mu-r+l}J_{\mu+r-l}(ty).\end{aligned}$$

At $t=0$

$$\Delta^k_{\mu}\{j_\mu(tx)j_\mu(ty)\}=P(x,y), \tag{11.30}$$

where $P(x,y)$ is an even polynomial.

Hence, putting (11.30) in (11.28), we obtain (11.27). □

Lemma 11.3 *Let ψ be a Bessel wavelet whose all even moments weighted by $x^{2\mu+1}$ are zero and f_1 and f_2 be distributions in $H'_{\mu,2}$ such that $f_1=f$, $f_2=f+x^{2m}$, then the Bessel wavelet transform of f_1 and f_2 will be equal.*

Proof From (11.23), we take $f_1, f_2\in H'_{\mu,2}$ and ψ is a Bessel wavelet, we have

$$(B_\psi f_1)(b,a)=c_\mu^{-1}\langle f_1,\psi_{b,a}\rangle=c_\mu^{-1}\langle f,\psi_{b,a}\rangle \tag{11.31}$$

and

$$\begin{aligned}(B_\psi f_2)(b,a)=c_\mu^{-1}\langle f_2,\psi_{b,a}\rangle&=c_\mu^{-1}\langle f+x^{2m},\psi_{b,a}\rangle\\&=c_\mu^{-1}\langle f,\psi_{b,a}\rangle+c_\mu^{-1}\langle x^{2m},\psi_{b,a}\rangle.\end{aligned} \tag{11.32}$$

Now, the 2nd term of (11.32) be

$$\begin{aligned}c_\mu^{-1}\langle x^{2m},\psi_{b,a}\rangle&=c_\mu^{-1}\left\langle x^{2m},a^{-2\mu-2}\psi\left(\frac{b}{a},\frac{x}{a}\right)\right\rangle\\&=c_\mu^{-1}\int_0^\infty x^{2m}a^{-2\mu-2}\psi\left(\frac{b}{a},\frac{x}{a}\right)x^{2\mu+1}dx\\&=a^{-2\mu-2}\int_0^\infty x^{2m}\left\{\int_0^\infty\psi(z)D\left(\frac{b}{a},\frac{x}{a},z\right)d\sigma(z)\right\}d\sigma(x)\\&=a^{-2\mu-2}\int_0^\infty\psi(z)\int_0^\infty x^{2m}D\left(\frac{b}{a},\frac{x}{a},z\right)d\sigma(x)d\sigma(z).\end{aligned}$$

Taking $\frac{x}{a}=u$ and in view of the Lemma 11.2, we obtain

$$
\begin{aligned}
c_\mu^{-1}\langle x^{2m}, \psi_{b,a}\rangle &= a^{-2\mu-2}\int_0^\infty \psi(z)\int_0^\infty a^{2m+2\mu+2}u^{2m} D\Big(\frac{b}{a}, u, z\Big)d\sigma(u)d\sigma(z)\\
&= a^{2m}\int_0^\infty \psi(z)\left\{\int_0^\infty u^{2m} D\Big(\frac{b}{a}, u, z\Big)d\sigma(u)\right\}d\sigma(z)\\
&= a^{2m}\int_0^\infty P\Big(\frac{b}{a}, z\Big)\psi(z)d\sigma(z)\\
&= 0.
\end{aligned}
$$

So, all the even moments weighted by $x^{2\mu+1}$ of basic wavelet $\psi(x)$ are zero.

To discuss the inversion formula of the continuous Bessel wavelet transform of distributions in $H'_{\mu,2}$, we consider only those basic Bessel wavelet kernels whose all even moments weighted by $x^{2\mu+1}$ are non-zero. □

Theorem 11.2 *Let $\psi \in H_{\mu,2}$ be a Bessel wavelet and $f \in L_{\mu,2}$. Then the following inversion formula in classic sense holds:*

$$
f(x) = \frac{1}{A_\psi}\int_0^\infty\int_0^\infty \left(B_\psi f\right)(b,a)a^{-2\mu-2}\psi\left(\frac{b}{a},\frac{x}{a}\right)\frac{d\sigma(b)d\sigma(a)}{a^{2\mu+2}},
$$

where $\left(B_\psi f\right)(b,a)$ is the integral Bessel wavelet transform of $f \in L_{\mu,2}$ which is defined by

$$
\left(B_\psi f\right)(b,a) = \int_0^\infty f(x)a^{-2\mu-2}\overline{\psi\left(\frac{b}{a},\frac{x}{a}\right)}d\sigma(x),
$$

where

$$
A_\psi = \int_0^\infty \frac{\left|\left(h_\mu\psi\right)(y)\right|^2}{y^{2\mu+2}}d\sigma(y) < \infty.
$$

Proof Let us consider

$$
F(x) = \frac{1}{A_\psi}\int_0^\infty\int_0^\infty \left(B_\psi f\right)(b,a)\psi_{b,a}(x)\frac{d\sigma(b)d\sigma(a)}{a^{2\mu+2}}.
$$

In view of Lemma 11.1, the above expression can be written as

$$
F(x) = \frac{1}{A_\psi}\int_0^\infty\int_0^\infty [h_\mu\{(h_\mu f)(y)\overline{(h_\mu\psi)}(ay)\}(b)h_\mu\{j_\mu(xy)(h_\mu\psi)(ay)\}(b)]\frac{d\sigma(b)d\sigma(a)}{a^{2\mu+2}}.
$$

Now using Parseval formula of Hankel transform with respect to variable b, we get

$$
\begin{aligned}
F(x) &= \frac{1}{A_\psi}\int_0^\infty \left[\int_0^\infty (h_\mu f)(y)\overline{(h_\mu \psi)}(ay) j_\mu(xy)\left(h_\mu \psi\right)(ay) d\sigma(y)\right]\frac{d\sigma(a)}{a^{2\mu+2}} \\
&= \frac{1}{A_\psi}\int_0^\infty j_\mu(xy)\left(h_\mu f\right)(y)\left[\int_0^\infty \frac{\left|\left(h_\mu \psi\right)(ay)\right|^2}{a^{2\mu+2}} d\sigma(a)\right] d\sigma(y) \\
&= \frac{A_\psi}{A_\psi}\int_0^\infty j_\mu(xy)\left(h_\mu f\right)(y) d\sigma(y) \\
&= \int_0^\infty j_\mu(xy)\left(h_\mu f\right)(y) d\sigma(y) \\
&= f(x).
\end{aligned}
$$

Here convergence is in $L_{\mu,2}$. □

11.3 Inversion of the Bessel Wavelet Transform of Distributions

In this section, the inversion formula and its properties of the Bessel wavelet transform of distributions in $H'_{\mu,2}$ are obtained by exploiting the theory of the Hankel transformation.

Lemma 11.4 *Let $\mu \geq -\frac{1}{2}$ and $\psi_{b,a}(x) = a^{-2\mu-2}\psi\left(\frac{b}{a}, \frac{x}{a}\right)$ be Hankel translation and dialation of $\psi \in H_{\mu,2}$, then*

$$
\Delta_{\mu,x}\,\psi\left(\frac{b}{a}, \frac{x}{a}\right) = \Delta_{\mu,b}\psi\left(\frac{b}{a}, \frac{x}{a}\right).
$$

Proof The proof of the lemma can be obtained from Lemma 10.3. □

Lemma 11.5 *Let $\psi \in H_{\mu,2}$ be a Bessel wavelet and $\phi \in H_{\mu,2}$, then*

$$
\frac{1}{A_\psi}\int_0^\infty \int_0^\infty (B_\psi(\Delta_\mu^k \phi))(b, a)\psi_{b,a}(x)\frac{d\sigma(b)d\sigma(a)}{a^{2\mu+2}}
$$

converges uniformly to $\Delta_\mu^k \phi(x)$ for every $x \in I$.

Proof For $\psi, \phi \in H_{\mu,2}$, using Theorem 11.2, we have

$$
\begin{aligned}
F(x) &= \frac{1}{A_\psi}\int_0^\infty \int_0^\infty (B_\psi(\Delta_\mu^k \phi))(b, a)\psi_{b,a}(x)\frac{d\sigma(b)d\sigma(a)}{a^{2\mu+2}} \\
&= \int_0^\infty \{h_\mu(\Delta_\mu^k \phi)(t)\} j_\mu(xt) d\sigma(t) \\
&= \Delta_\mu^k \phi(x).
\end{aligned}
$$

By Weierstrass M-test, we have

$$\begin{aligned}
|F(x)| &= \left| \int_0^\infty \{h_\mu(\Delta_\mu^k \phi)(t)\} j_\mu(xt) d\sigma(t) \right| \\
&\le B_\mu \int_0^\infty \left| \{h_\mu(\Delta_\mu^k \phi)(t)\} \right| d\sigma(t) \\
&\le B_\mu \int_0^\infty \frac{1}{\sqrt{(1+t^2)} t^{\mu+\frac{1}{2}}} \sqrt{(1+t^2)} t^{\mu+\frac{1}{2}} \left| \{h_\mu(\Delta_\mu^k \phi)(t)\} \right| d\sigma(t) \\
&\le B_\mu \left(\int_0^\infty \frac{1}{(1+t^2) t^{2\mu+1}} d\sigma(t) \right)^{\frac{1}{2}} \left(\int_0^\infty (1+t^2) t^{2\mu+1} |\{h_\mu(\Delta_\mu^k \phi)(t)\}|^2 d\sigma(t) \right)^{\frac{1}{2}} \\
&\le B_\mu C \left(\int_0^\infty (1+t^2)^{\mu+\frac{3}{2}} |\{h_\mu(\Delta_\mu^k \phi)(t)\}|^2 d\sigma(t) \right)^{\frac{1}{2}} \\
&\le B_\mu C \left(\int_0^\infty (1+t^2)^{2\rho} |\{h_\mu(\Delta_\mu^k \phi)(t)\}|^2 d\sigma(t) \right)^{\frac{1}{2}} < \infty,
\end{aligned}$$

where C is a positive constant depending on μ, $2\rho \ge \mu + \frac{3}{2}$, $\rho \in \mathbb{N}$ and $(1+t^2)^\rho \{h_\mu(\Delta_\mu^k \phi)(t)\} \in L_{\mu,2}$ by [5, Proposition 2.3, p. 223].

Therefore,

$$\frac{1}{A_\psi} \int_0^\infty \int_0^\infty (B_\psi(\Delta_\mu^k \phi))(b,a) \psi_{b,a}(x) \frac{d\sigma(b) d\sigma(a)}{a^{2\mu+2}}$$

converges uniformly to $\Delta_\mu^k \phi(x)$ for every $x \in I$. □

Theorem 11.3 *Let $f \in H'_{\mu,2}$ and $\psi \in H_{\mu,2}$ be a Bessel wavelet. Define the Bessel wavelet transform of f with respect to the Bessel wavelet ψ by*

$$\left(B_\psi f\right)(b,a) = c_\mu^{-1} \left\langle f(t), a^{-2\mu-2} \psi\left(\frac{b}{a}, \frac{t}{a}\right) \right\rangle, \tag{11.33}$$

where $\langle , \rangle$ is functional notation.

Then the inversion formula of the Bessel wavelet transform is given by

$$\lim_{\substack{A,B\to\infty \\ \epsilon\to 0+}} \left\langle \frac{1}{A_\psi} \int_\epsilon^A \int_0^B \left(B_\psi f\right)(b,a) \psi_{b,a}(x) \frac{d\sigma(b) d\sigma(a)}{a^{2\mu+2}}, \phi \right\rangle = \langle f, \phi \rangle, \quad \forall\, \phi \in H_{\mu,2}. \tag{11.34}$$

Proof From Betancor [5, Proposition 2.2, p. 222], we have

$$f = \sum_{k=0}^{r} \Delta_\mu^k f_k\,, \tag{11.35}$$

where $f_k \in L_{\mu,2}$.

Then,

$$\left(B_\psi f\right)(b,a) = c_\mu^{-1}\left\langle f(t), a^{-2\mu-2}\psi\left(\frac{b}{a},\frac{t}{a}\right)\right\rangle.$$

Therefore, using (11.35), we get

$$\left(B_\psi f\right)(b,a) = \sum_{k=0}^{r} c_\mu^{-1}\left\langle \triangle_{\mu,t}^k f_k(t), a^{-2\mu-2}\psi\left(\frac{b}{a},\frac{t}{a}\right)\right\rangle.$$

By distributional differentiation, we find

$$\begin{aligned}\left(B_\psi f\right)(b,a) &= \sum_{k=0}^{r} c_\mu^{-1}\left\langle f_k(t), \triangle_{\mu,t}^k a^{-2\mu-2}\psi\left(\frac{b}{a},\frac{t}{a}\right)\right\rangle \\ &= \sum_{k=0}^{r} c_\mu^{-1}\int_0^\infty f_k(t)a^{-2\mu-2}\,\triangle_{\mu,t}^k\,\psi\left(\frac{b}{a},\frac{t}{a}\right)t^{2\mu+1}dt \\ &= \sum_{k=0}^{r}\int_0^\infty f_k(t)a^{-2\mu-2}\,\triangle_{\mu,t}^k\,\psi\left(\frac{b}{a},\frac{t}{a}\right)d\sigma(t). \end{aligned} \tag{11.36}$$

Consider

$$F(x) = \frac{1}{A_\psi}\int_\epsilon^A\int_0^B \left(B_\psi f\right)(b,a)a^{-2\mu-2}\psi\left(\frac{b}{a},\frac{x}{a}\right)\frac{d\sigma(b)d\sigma(a)}{a^{2\mu+2}}. \tag{11.37}$$

Therefore,

$$\begin{aligned}&\lim_{\substack{A,B\to\infty\\ \epsilon\to 0+}}\langle F(x),\phi(x)\rangle \\ &= \lim_{\substack{A,B\to\infty\\ \epsilon\to 0+}}\left\langle\frac{1}{A_\psi}\int_\epsilon^A\int_0^B \left(B_\psi f\right)(b,a)a^{-2\mu-2}\psi\left(\frac{b}{a},\frac{x}{a}\right)\frac{d\sigma(b)d\sigma(a)}{a^{2\mu+2}},\phi(x)\right\rangle.\end{aligned} \tag{11.38}$$

Using (11.35), (11.38) will be turned into a classical one. Taking lower limit $\epsilon\to 0+$ and upper limits $A, B\to\infty$, then using (11.36) we obtain

$$
\begin{aligned}
&\lim_{\substack{A,B\to\infty\\ \epsilon\to 0+}} \langle F(x), \phi(x)\rangle \\
&= \Big\langle \frac{1}{A_\psi}\int_0^\infty \int_0^\infty \Big\{ \sum_{k=0}^{r} \int_0^\infty f_k(t) a^{-2\mu-2}\, \Delta_{\mu,t}^k\, \psi\left(\frac{b}{a},\frac{t}{a}\right) d\sigma(t)\Big\} \\
&\quad \times a^{-2\mu-2}\psi\left(\frac{b}{a},\frac{x}{a}\right)\frac{d\sigma(b)d\sigma(a)}{a^{2\mu+2}}, \phi(x)\Big\rangle \\
&= \sum_{k=0}^{r}\Big\langle \frac{1}{A_\psi}\int_0^\infty \int_0^\infty \Big\{ \int_0^\infty f_k(t) a^{-2\mu-2}\, \Delta_{\mu,t}^k\, \psi\left(\frac{b}{a},\frac{t}{a}\right) d\sigma(t)\Big\} \\
&\quad \times a^{-2\mu-2}\psi\left(\frac{b}{a},\frac{x}{a}\right)\frac{d\sigma(b)d\sigma(a)}{a^{2\mu+2}}, \phi(x)\Big\rangle \\
&= \sum_{k=0}^{r}\Big\langle \frac{1}{A_\psi}\int_0^\infty \Big[\int_0^\infty \Big\{ \int_0^\infty f_k(t) a^{-2\mu-2}\, \Delta_{\mu,b}^k\, \psi\left(\frac{b}{a},\frac{t}{a}\right) d\sigma(t)\Big\} \\
&\quad \times a^{-2\mu-2}\psi\left(\frac{b}{a},\frac{x}{a}\right) d\sigma(b)\Big]\frac{d\sigma(a)}{a^{2\mu+2}}, \phi(x)\Big\rangle.
\end{aligned}
$$

Making use of Lemma 11.4, and using integration by parts, we get

$$
\begin{aligned}
&\lim_{\substack{A,B\to\infty\\ \epsilon\to 0+}} \langle F(x), \phi(x)\rangle \\
&= \sum_{k=0}^{r}\Big\langle \frac{1}{A_\psi}\int_0^\infty \Big[\int_0^\infty \Big\{ \int_0^\infty f_k(t) a^{-2\mu-2}\psi\left(\frac{b}{a},\frac{t}{a}\right) d\sigma(t)\Big\} \\
&\quad \times a^{-2\mu-2}\, \Delta_{\mu,b}^k\, \psi\left(\frac{b}{a},\frac{x}{a}\right) d\sigma(b)\Big]\frac{d\sigma(a)}{a^{2\mu+2}}, \phi(x)\Big\rangle \\
&= \sum_{k=0}^{r}\Big\langle \frac{1}{A_\psi}\int_0^\infty \Big[\int_0^\infty \Big\{ \int_0^\infty f_k(t) a^{-2\mu-2}\psi\left(\frac{b}{a},\frac{t}{a}\right) d\sigma(t)\Big\} \\
&\quad \times a^{-2\mu-2}\, \Delta_{\mu,x}^k\, \psi\left(\frac{b}{a},\frac{x}{a}\right) d\sigma(b)\Big]\frac{d\sigma(a)}{a^{2\mu+2}}, \phi(x)\Big\rangle,
\end{aligned}
$$

as $\Delta_{\mu,b}^k\psi\left(\frac{b}{a},\frac{t}{a}\right) = \Delta_{\mu,x}^k\psi\left(\frac{b}{a},\frac{t}{a}\right)$. Exploiting distributional derivative, we get

$$\begin{aligned}
&\lim_{\substack{A,B\to\infty\\ \epsilon\to 0+}} \langle F(x), \phi(x)\rangle \\
&= \sum_{k=0}^{r} \Big\langle \frac{1}{A_\psi}\int_0^\infty \Big[\int_0^\infty \Big\{\int_0^\infty f_k(t) a^{-2\mu-2}\psi\left(\frac{b}{a},\frac{t}{a}\right) d\sigma(t)\Big\} \\
&\quad \times a^{-2\mu-2}\psi\left(\frac{b}{a},\frac{x}{a}\right) d\sigma(b)\Big] \frac{d\sigma(a)}{a^{2\mu+2}}, \triangle^k_{\mu,x}\phi(x)\Big\rangle \\
&= \sum_{k=0}^{r} \frac{c_\mu}{A_\psi}\int_0^\infty \Big[\int_0^\infty \int_0^\infty \int_0^\infty \{\triangle^k_{\mu,x}\phi(x)\}\, a^{-2\mu-2}\psi\left(\frac{b}{a},\frac{t}{a}\right) \\
&\quad \times a^{-2\mu-2}\psi\left(\frac{b}{a},\frac{x}{a}\right) \frac{d\sigma(x)d\sigma(b)d\sigma(a)}{a^{2\mu+2}}\Big] f_k(t)d\sigma(t).
\end{aligned}$$

Therefore,

$$\begin{aligned}
\lim_{\substack{A,B\to\infty\\ \epsilon\to 0+}} \langle F(x), \phi(x)\rangle &= \sum_{k=0}^{r} \frac{c_\mu}{A_\psi}\int_0^\infty \Big[\int_0^\infty \int_0^\infty \int_0^\infty \Big\{\triangle^k_{\mu,x}\phi(x)\Big\}\, a^{-2\mu-2}\psi\left(\frac{b}{a},\frac{t}{a}\right) \\
&\quad \times a^{-2\mu-2}\psi\left(\frac{b}{a},\frac{x}{a}\right) \frac{d\sigma(x)d\sigma(b)d\sigma(a)}{a^{2\mu+2}}\Big] f_k(t)d\sigma(t).
\end{aligned} \tag{11.39}$$

Applying Lemma 11.5, the bracket of the above Eq. (11.39)

$$\frac{1}{A_\psi}\int_0^\infty \int_0^\infty \int_0^\infty \Big\{\triangle^k_{\mu,x}\phi(x)\Big\}\, a^{-2\mu-2}\psi\left(\frac{b}{a},\frac{t}{a}\right) a^{-2\mu-2}\psi\left(\frac{b}{a},\frac{x}{a}\right) \frac{d\sigma(x)d\sigma(b)d\sigma(a)}{a^{2\mu+2}}$$

converges to $\triangle^k_{\mu,t}\phi(t)$

(i) in $L^2(I)$.
(ii) uniformly $\forall\, t \in I$.

Therefore,

$$\begin{aligned}
\lim_{\substack{A,B\to\infty\\ \epsilon\to 0+}} \langle F(x), \phi(x)\rangle &= \sum_{k=0}^{r} c_\mu \int_0^\infty \{\triangle^k_{\mu,t}\phi(t)\}\, f_k(t)d\sigma(t) \\
&= \sum_{k=0}^{r} \big\langle f_k(t), \triangle^k_{\mu,t}\phi(t)\big\rangle \\
&= \sum_{k=0}^{r} \big\langle \triangle^k_{\mu,t} f_k(t), \phi(t)\big\rangle \\
&= \Big\langle \sum_{k=0}^{r} \triangle^k_{\mu,t} f_k(t), \phi(t)\Big\rangle \\
&= \langle f(x), \phi(x)\rangle, \quad \forall \phi(x) \in H_{\mu,2} \text{ and } f \in H'_{\mu,2}
\end{aligned}$$

using (11.35) and [5, Proposition 2.2, p. 222].

Thus

$$\lim_{\substack{A,B\to\infty\\ \epsilon\to 0+}} \left\langle \frac{1}{A_\psi} \int_\epsilon^A \int_0^B \left(B_\psi f\right)(b,a) a^{-2\mu-2} \psi\left(\frac{b}{a}, \frac{x}{a}\right) \frac{d\sigma(b) d\sigma(a)}{a^{2\mu+2}}, \phi \right\rangle = \langle f, \phi\rangle \tag{11.40}$$

for all $\phi \in H_{\mu,2}$, and $f \in H'_{\mu,2}$. □

References

1. Pandey, J.N.: Continuous wavelet transform of Schwartz distributions. Rocky Mountain J. Math. **49**(6), 2005–2028 (2019)
2. Pandey, J.N.: Continuous wavelet transform of Schwartz distributions in $D'_{L^2}(\mathbb{R}^n)$. Symmetry **13**(7), 1106 (2021)
3. Pandey, J.N., Maurya, J.S., Upadhyay, S.K., Srivastava, H.M.: Continuous wavelet transform of Schwartz tempered distributions in $S'(\mathbb{R}^n)$. Symmetry **11**(2), 235 (2019)
4. Pandey, J.N., Upadhyay, S.K.: Continuous wavelet transform of Schwartz tempered distributions. Cogent Math. Stat. **6**(1), 1623647 (2019)
5. Betancor, J., González, B.: Spaces of $\mathscr{D}_{L^p}$-type and the Hankel convolution. Proceed. American Math. Soc. **129**(1), 219–228 (2001)
6. Pathak, R.S., Dixit, M.M.: Continuous and discrete Bessel wavelet transforms. J. Comput. Appl. Math. **160**(1–2), 241–250 (2003)
7. Schwartz, A.L.: An inversion theorem for Hankel transforms. Proceed. American Math. Soc. **22**(3), 713–717 (1969)
8. Betancor, J.J.: Hypoellipticity of Hankel convolution equations in $\mathscr{D}_{L^1}$-Type spaces. Zeitschrift f*ü*r Analysis und ihre Anwendungen **24**(3), 561–580 (2005)
9. Altenburg, G.: Bessel transforms in spaces of test functions on the interval $\Omega = (0, \infty)$ and related dual spaces. Math. Nachr. **108**(1), 197–218 (1982)
10. Zemanian, A.H.: Generalized integral transformations. Pure and applied mathematics XVIII. Interscience Publishers, New York (1968)
11. Koh, E.L.: The Hankel transformation of negative order for distributions of rapid growth. SIAM J. Math. Anal. **1**(3), 322–327 (1970)
12. Betancor, J.J., Rodríguez-Mesa, L.: On Besov spaces in the Hankel setting. Acta Math. Hungar. **111**(3), 237–262 (2006)

Index

S. K. Upadhyay and J. S. Maurya, *The Bessel Wavelet Transform*, Industrial and Applied Mathematics,
https://doi.org/10.1007/978-981-96-9938-4

MIX
Papier aus verantwortungsvollen Quellen
Paper from responsible sources
FSC® C105338

If you have any concerns about our products,
you can contact us on
ProductSafety@springernature.com

In case Publisher is established outside the EU,
the EU authorized representative is:
Springer Nature Customer Service Center GmbH
Europaplatz 3, 69115 Heidelberg, Germany

Printed by Libri Plureos GmbH
in Hamburg, Germany